Furnace Operations

Third Edition

Third Edition

Furnace Operations

Robert D. Reed

Gulf Publishing Company
Book Division
Houston, London, Paris, Tokyo

DEDICATED TO
JOHN STEEL ZINK

For more than three decades of association a completely priceless experience has been mine because of his loyalty, leadership and trust, which has allowed creation of a career which I would not exchange for that of any man who ever lived.

FURNACE OPERATIONS
THIRD EDITION

Library of Congress
Catalog Card Number   75-15240

Library of Congress Cataloging in Publication Data

Reed, Robert D.   1905-
    Furnace operations.
    Bibliography: p.
    Includes index.
      1. Furnaces.   2. Oil burners.   3. Gas-burners.
I. Title.
TJ320.R44   1981   621.402'5   80-26274
ISBN 0-87201-301-4

First Edition, May 1973
Second Edition, January 1976
  Second Printing, May 1978
Third Edition, February 1981
  Second Printing, November 1981

Preface

It might be said of handbooks that their prime reason for existing is to offer engineers solutions to the many problems they must contend with in the execution of daily tasks.

It might also be said that the excellence with which the engineer functions is in direct proportion to his comprehension of handbook information. It is a rare person who has an encyclopedic mind capable of data retention, formulaic approach, and mathematical techniques imparted to him in the course of formal education if, indeed, the formal education provided information pertinent to the problem at hand. Engineering progress is irrevocably correlated with handbooks and the information they provide.

In engineering, requirements for precision vary. There is one state which is defined as ''within the limits of engineering tolerance'' and there is another state in which utmost exactness is necessary despite the fact that safety factors—or more literally—ignorance factors are applied.

If requirements for exactness exist, the ponderous mathematical meanderings typical of the average handbook would seem to be justified. But here a fact of life enters that at least 95% of practicing engineers are not capable of deriving a solution if calculus is involved in the absence of adequate explanation and simplification. Experience over the past 40 years has clearly shown this to be true as a result of countless conversations with the engineers involved.

Since information to be derived from this volume falls within the category of engineering tolerance, there is emphasis on discourse. The mathematics presented are simple algebra, geometry and arithmetic to permit complete understanding by not only the typical engineer but also by the typical bright high school graduate in a minimum of time and with minimal difficulty.

ROBERT D. REED

Contents

Acknowledgment

As is true of men who fashion careers, many people have been sources of comfort and encouragement during the years and in times of stress. It is impossible to name them all, but some cannot be omitted:

Miss Marie Jett, secretary to Mr. Zink, has softened many of the bumps common to the engineering profession and has literally gone out of her way many times to aid, encourage and assist me.

Dr. R. L. Huntington, Research Professor of Chemical Engineering, Emeritus, the University of Oklahoma, has urged completion of the monumental task of writing this handbook and has been the source of academic favor.

Last but far from least is my wife, Iva, who as a long-suffering process-widow never once complained of her lot and has been the safe port no matter what the circumstance might have been. Without her steadfast devotion, my career in engineering would not have been possible.

1

Noise

Any form of pollution is a source of concern and concern is certainly merited if the pollution can, in any way, cause ecological damage or discomfort. It is unfortunate that pollution, instead of spurring scientific and engineering communities to work toward better living conditions has become something of a witch-hunt. Poorly informed people use the news media to keep the nation in a state of perpetual alarm. However, as is often the case, some of the alarm cries are justified and one of these regards serious noise pollution. Noise may be serious as a source of annoyance or it may be serious as a source of actual physical damage.

Noise — A Pollution Source

An annoyance syndrome can be quite genuine, even if the annoynace is due to an individual's psychological factors and are not characteristic of people generally. A noisy condition may be said to exist when there is unwanted sound of any intensity such as the drip-drip-drip of a leaky faucet or a squeaky car or the howling of a dog. Such noise is not necessarily intense but must be stopped. This is equally true of more intense noises in industrial areas where noise is a part of the industrial way of life. Burner noise, fan noise, turbine noise or engine noise, if unchecked or unattenuated, can be deafening in areas where men must spend appreciable time in the course of their work.

Because of the enactment of laws relating to noise in industrial areas, deafening conditions must no longer be tolerated and steps toward reduction in sound level are demanded for many reasons. But sound reduction is not easy nor inexpensive; thus noise pollution becomes an important element in the cost of industrial operation. But, surprisingly enough, it is not unusual to find that the improved employee morale causes improved working efficiency, which can more than amortize the sound abatement equipment cost.

Literature is rich in references to noise, noise measurement, nature of noise and means for noise abatement, but the *Handbook of Noise Measurement* by A.P.G. Peterson and Ervin E. Gross, Jr., Sixth Edition, General Radio Company, West Concord, Massachusetts, has proven to be an excellent reference for both noise and vibration factors and is recommended for such technical data as may be required.

Sound is produced by rhythmic variation in atmospheric pressure. These rhythmic variations are detected by the ear, which creates the sensation of sound; the pitch of the sound is based on the pressure variation frequency. Sound is rarely at a single frequency and is usually a complex mixture of frequencies ranging from 30 cps to 10,000 cps. For convenience the frequencies are broken up into octave bands with 30 cps very low in the bass range and 10,000 cps high in the treble range. With some exceptions, the normal person of 45 or older cannot hear more than about 9,000 cps. Greater power is a characteristic of low frequencies but the higher frequencies are most damaging to the ear. Therefore, allowable sound power levels in the low frequencies are greater than in the high frequencies.

Sound Measurement

Sound is measured in terms of *decibels,* which is a term borrowed from the electrical industry where 1 decibel (db) is defined as the weakest sound that can be heard by a person with very good hearing in an extremely quiet environment such as an anechoic chamber or other base reference condition. As sound becomes stronger the reference level is greater and is expressed numerically in dbs, but an increase of 3 db represents doubling and an increase of 6 db is four-times the power. Instruments which are commercially available measure sound power in dbs and the instruments use microphones which have the widest possible frequency response in connection with electronic circuitry which converts the sound-power sensed by the microphone to dbs in very sensitive metering but as a part of the circuitry are "weighting" R/C networks which cause controlled response to specific frequencies of sound at the meter. These weighting networks are the *A*; the *B* and the *C*. The *A* network has peak response from 1,000 cps to 5,000 cps. The *B* network peak-responds from about 450 cps to 4,000 cps and the *C* network provides essentially "flat" response to all frequencies of interest in sound measurement. These networks permit reasonable checks of sound frequency characteristics without the use of sepa-

Table 1-1
Typical Environment Noise Levels
As Observed in Use of the C Weighting
Scale

50 db	Quiet private business office
70 db	Voice at conversational level
75 db	Open field in country with 15-mph breeze
79 db	Noisy office with business machines
89 db	Inside a sedan at 60 mph on highway
94 db	Inside a bus in city traffic
97 db	Inside a subway train
103 db	Inside 707 jet airliner in normal flight
106 db	Ventilating fan - 10 ft.
110 db	Inside a sedan at 70 mph
121 db	Auto horn - 5 ft.
138 db	Large orchestra—fifth row of seats
159 db	Jet engine—50 ft.
168 db	Jet engine with after-burner—300 ft.

Typical Petrochemical Process Area
With Natural Draft Burners Firing

84 db	After addition of both primary and secondary muffling
93 db	After addition of primary muffling only
107 db	Before any muffling means added

Note: The dramatic reduction in sound level through addition of primary muffling and the reduced effectiveness of secondary muffling in use of partial-premix gas burners with methane as fuel.

rate octave-band analysis for quick checking, but octave-band analysis is demanded for dbA calculation. Sound-power in relation to db is as the curve of Figure 1-1; Table 1-1 shows typical environmental noise levels.

Process areas provide many sources of noise in quantity such as engines, turbines, fans, compressors, pumps and burners with the noise in all frequency ranges. In some areas it is common to find

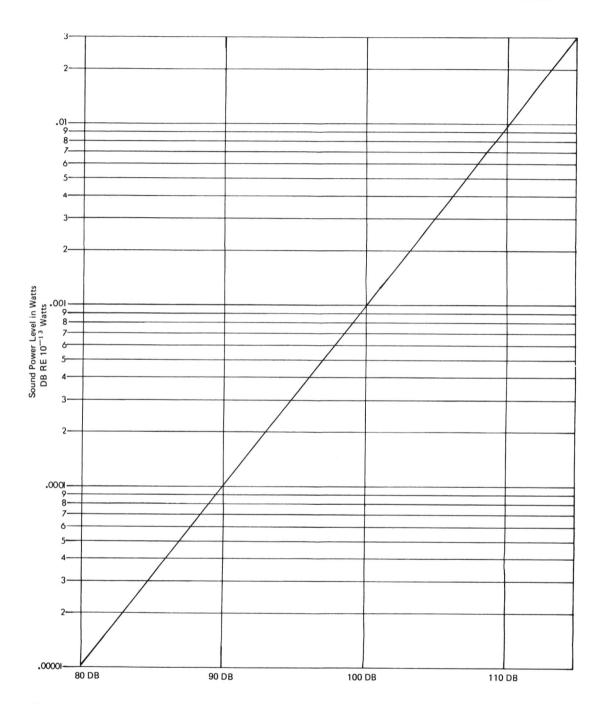

Figure 1-1. Sound level measurement expressed in decibels (db). When a sound power measured as 80 db is added to a second sound power also measured as 80 db, the new sound level is not expressed as 80 + 80 = 160 db but as a total of the added sound powers in watts—in this case, 83 db (0.0001 + 0.00001 = 0.00002). From the Handbook of Noise Measurement, *General Radio Company.*

noise levels considerably greater than 115 db as observed in particular areas when 85 db is specified as the maximum allowable by law. It is difficult to determine the source of greatest sound as a typical thing but it is necessary to run-down and correct all sources. As an example, when two sound sources which are closely adjacent are treated to produce 85 db each, the area sound level will be 88 db, which is too great. A further source of difficulty is found when separate sounds at identical frequencies reach the microphone "in phase" or "out of phase" according to the microphone location, and error in observation may result with the minimal error as 3 db.

Sound Sources

There are many sources of sound but our concern here is noise resulting from burner operation. All fuels burn at speeds directly related to the condition of turbulence. The noise produced by burning is also related to turbulence, but at a fixed condition of turbulence noise production is governed by the nature of the fuel. In the burning of hydrocarbons, noise production is partially governed by the autoignition temperature of the fuel. A high ignition temperature produces greater noise than a lower temperature. However, the addition of free hydrogen to a hydrocarbon fuel adds to its noise potential for reasons which are not clear, but the presence of 50 mol-percent or more of free hydrogen to hydrocarbons can add up to 10 db to the noise level produced in burning. Chemical engineers have been able to make great forward strides because burner designers have produced burners to greatly speed the burning of fuels. But something of an impasse has been created since noise levels in operation of heaters have also increased very markedly. It is fundamental that more rapid burning of fuel accounts for many processes which would be otherwise impossible, but chemical engineering progress has created a noise problem which demands solution.

Years of research to discover burner design factors which will lower noise levels while retaining rapid burning of fuels have not been too fruitful. However, some design modifications have been modestly successful but the goal of relatively silent burning where there is also demand for extremely rapid burning has not been reached. As a prime example, as late as 1940 furnaces for chemical process functions were constructed on the basis of 8,000 Btu/cu. ft. of furnace volume, whereas current design for such furnaces is approaching 60,000 Btu/cu. ft. or more.

Synthesis of valuable products from hydrocarbons, which is the basis for the huge petrochemical industry, has made great progress because the more rapid burning of fuels with accompanying very high heat densities and high heat transfer rates now available have literally made the impossible commonplace in today's technology.

There are many products synthesized in this manner, but some of the most significant are ethylene, propylene, butadiene and ammonia—all of which are vital to the nation and the world.

It is now in order to ask why all this progress has resulted in a noise problem of magnificent proportions.

The first factor is that unabated research in the burning of fuels has made the progress possible. Manufacturers of burners have, through research, learned how to better use the physical and chemical factors which govern burning. These factors are the classic *"Three T's"* of combustion: time, temperature and turbulence.

As there was progress in burning speed because of research, the designers of fired heaters were quick to take advantage by immediately reducing furnace volume and increasing furnace temperatures. The burner designer thus finds that two of his precious Three T's have been preempted and he has only the final T of turbulence with which to work.

Therefore, to compete in manufacturing suitable burners, the burner designer must use every energy available to him for the promotion of turbulence. Energy sources are the pressure from which the fuel is discharged for mixture with air in preparation for burning, and pressure drop in the air supply for mixture with the fuel.

Turbulence is demanded both in the zone where the fuel and air are mixed and in the zone where the fuel is burning. A state of turbulence as the fuel is discharged and mixed with air prior to burning produces noise. This is understandable because in gas burning, for example, gas pressures are from 15-30 psig, which establishes the gas-fuel discharge at sonic velocity. Higher pressures are typical of oil burning. Energy is proportional to the square of the velocity ($MV^2/2$). Energy is demanded for turbulence. Therefore, sonic velocity of fuel at discharge and a maximum of turbulence are demanded for rapid burning of fuel.

Combustion Noise

Because of these factors, there is an inescapable production of certain noise in the burning of fuels as demanded by today's technology—but this source of noise is not of greatest significance because as the fuel burns there is combustion noise which can, at times, be literally overpowering.

It is quickly said that if the fuel can be burned in conditions of laminar flow or in a state of minimal turbulence, noise production largely disappears, but the state of burning is so slow and the heat density as produced is so low that such operation is completely unacceptable today. Fuel/air noise and combustion noise seldom exceeds 3-5 db above background noise in laminar or minor turbulent burning.

Research shows clearly that the fuel/air noise is toward the higher frequency end of the audio spectrum and the combustion noise falls within the 30-300 cps range, but combustion noise will vary greatly as the fuel characteristics change.

It is to be noted that the fundamental economics of process plant operation require burning of such residual fuels as may be available and as they become available.

Wasting valuable fuel components in favor of noise reduction is obviously unwise. In a relatively small plant, where the total heat release is 200,000,000 Btu/hr. LHV, the annual fuel cost is more than $525,000 based on fuel cost at 30¢/MM

Btu. Fuel costs are perhaps the greatest single element in operational cost.

As noise production is at the point of fuel burning, it may be concluded that the greatest single factor is, therefore, combustion noise. In this respect, there is certain relief from noise to be expected if the burner design as chosen for the service confines combustion noise to the internal areas of the furnace. Further relief from combustion noise can be expected if many small burners are used instead of fewer large burners, for a specific total release of heat. But here again economics severely limit the degree to which this procedure can be followed, since the burner cost is largely in proportion to the number of burners used and such costs are capital costs.

Confining combustion noise to the internal areas of the furnace is not as effective as might be thought because the internal noise "telegraphs" through the furnace structure. Thus, it continues to be a factor in the environmental noise level in operating areas adjacent to the furnace, but with from 3-6 db attenuation in most instances, according to the particular structural features of the furnace.

Burner Design

Burner noise, which is always a serious problem, will vary according to the available or most economical fuels used. The greatest variation is found in gaseous fuels. As a general condition, decreased gas molecular weight creates an increased noise level in a burner. Gas that contains high mol percentages of free hydrogen is the noisiest of all. Burner noise from liquid fuels does not follow the gas fuel pattern to the same degree; however, the burning of liquid fuels is considered a noisy course regardless of the burner design.

Typically, gas burners operate at 15 lbs or more gauge pressure. Therefore, the critical (sonic) velocity with which a gas is discharged provides the basis for the generated noise level. Critical velocity for gases will vary according to two factors: molecular weight and temperature. As molecular weight decreases, the critical velocity increases; as temperature rises, the critical velocity increases.

Gas discharge velocity creates noisy turbulence that is a product of the energy with which gas is discharged for mixture with air. Gas discharge energy will vary as the square of the velocity with which the gas flows. Thus, the lighter the gas fuel, the greater the noise level; the hotter the discharged gas, the greater the noise level. Noise level data taken on a cold day will always be exceeded by noise level data taken on a hot day.

It will be evident that to avoid excessive noise levels in the operating areas adjacent to the fired heater, there is small relief through burner design selection if the fired heater is to perform in keeping with process requirements.

If the heater is to perform its required service with any burner design as chosen, reducing environmental noise to a level at 85 db is considered as extremely difficult in the 30-300 cps range and higher, whether this level is taken as a broadband measurement or as any particular octave-band indication.

This is to say that any attenuation due to burner choice per se cannot provide adequate reduction of environmental noise level to comply with an 85-db requirement. And if this specification is to be met, additional attenuation means will be demanded if the heat release within the furnace exceeds 1,000,000 Btu/hr. LHV.

There are numerous theories as to how the additional attenuation is to be obtained and there are names for the attenuation devices such as dampeners, mufflers and mutes according to the supplier.

Attenuation

Attenuation devices are required, for such noise sources as may exist, to meet the noise level specification in burner operation. Essentially, the sources are combustion noise and the sound produced by the discharge of fuel and air flow prior to combustion. Sound attenuation is required for both (and separately) according to conditions of application in the magnitude of separately produced noise levels.

Low frequency sound is characteristic of combustion and higher frequencies are typical of air and fuel flow sources with significant octave-band levels as high as 6,000 cps or higher.

Studies of attenuation show clearly that combustion noise is more intense unless the burner structure is completely enclosed in acoustic structures such as wind-boxes which are suitably lined and where the combustion air supply is from fans or from some source at pressures greater than the pressure within the furnace.

Where so-called natural draft within the furnace is used as motive power for the air supply and where pressure drop functions preempt attenuator design considerations, there is difficulty in securing suitable attenuation because air flow areas must be left open, which allows the escape of significant portions of the noise. Such attenuation is generally designated as secondary.

Muffling of air-fuel sound is generally designated as primary, and while such attenuation can also be burdened with pressure drop functions, the problem is usually much less difficult at sound frequencies of 1,000 cps or more. In fact, such primary attenuation is frequently productive of dramatic reduction of environmental noise to the ears of listeners.

It is, then, to be considered that within the limitations of suitable fuel burning for chemical process functions, and after exhaustive research toward reduction of noise in fuel burning, there is no escape from the use of additional means for sound attenuation if the tolerable limit is set at 85 db. This is not to say that research toward significant reduction in burner noise will not continue, but at this time, designers and operators of process plants are faced with a relatively severe problem in fundamental economics because of the 85-db sound level limitation.

As an example of continued research toward noise reduction in fuel burning to satisfy heat-density, heat-transfer conditions which are demanded, engineers associated with John Zink Pollution Research have examined flames typical of such burning conditions through the use of high-speed color movies of flames. Typical speeds are in the 500-1,000 frames per second range, which allows study of flame characteristics at time intervals ranging from 1/1,000th of a second to even greater speeds. Pictures in color permit the study of flame chemistry and flame physics.

The study of flames at these speeds and these conditions permits better understanding of the sources of combustion noise so that burner design considerations can eliminate this most significant noise source to a greater degree.

Costs

The first consideration must be given to tax factors as the installation or operation of a process facility is studied. Costs and justification must take into account the required capitalization. As capital costs rise, there is greater and greater reluctance to either install a facility or to continue to operate an existing facility.

Noise limitation can become an even more severely critical factor if proposals include installing a new facility in an area where the existing level is at or very close to 85 db; because if the new facility is designed for the same level, the cumulative level of the two units will exceed the prescribed level by close to 3 db.

Real estate or area availability within the process area is quite typically a problem in the location of a new facility. If there is a probability that a new facility added to an operating area will result in greater than 85 db in the overall area noise, the area must either be dropped from consideration or significantly greater cost for sound attenuation must be tolerated.

Burner Configurations

Fired heaters are constructed in either of three basic burner configurations. One is the horizontal firing of burners from either the side walls or the end walls. A second provides upward firing from the floor of the heater. The third configuration makes use of downward firing from the roof of the heater.

These three configurations present quite varying burner noise production characteristics in respect to the heater environmental areas. In all configurations, areas immediately adjacent to burners have noise levels based on the characteristics of the particular burner design as well as the fuels to be fired. However, noise level in the process area about the furnace can vary considerably according to burner location in the fired heater; in this respect there are judgment factors as to exposure time/noise level.

In upward firing from the floor of the heater, there must be a clear space under the heater for access to burners for control or inspection; the height of this space is usually 6 ft. or more. It is in this sub-floor area where reverberation effects add up to 10 db to the characteristic burner noise and maximum environmental sound level will be found. Sound levels can easily reach 120 db in this area; but operating personnel enter the area infrequently and usually for less than a minute at any particular time.

In horizontal firing there is very rapid decrement of sound in movement away from the burners. However, noise immediately adjacent to the burners will be typical of the burner design and will be much greater.

Since down-firing burners are installed atop the fired heater, the height of which is usually 15 ft. up to 75 ft., the noise level at grade is dictated by adjacent noise sources rather than by the burners, to a greater degree.

These data are interesting in point of noise suppression as a function of design, but here again economics can be the deciding factor since heater costs vary quite widely according to the manner in which the burners fire.

It is not the intent here to suggest that noise limitation in chemical process plants requires special consideration or leniency in any way. It is, rather, to point out factors which can limit the progress of chemical engineering in meeting noise limitation specification which is prescribed by competent authority.

It is perhaps, an understatement to point out that the practice of the art of chemical engineering in association with the process industries is already very heavily burdened with problems which must be met. As is typical of the industry the problems will be met but at untold added costs and in areas where specific knowledge is not widely held.

Noise and Personnel

Under consideration here will be matters associated with noise as such and its effects on personnel who will be required to endure the noise. First it is suggested that there is a subtle difference between noise and sound, even though both have identical sources. It is something of an oversimplification to say that noise is an unwanted or unpleasant sound. For example, at times during an orchestra concert the listener is subjected to sound levels which can be well in excess of 120 db for quite appreciable periods, but the experience is pleasant.

Because of this factor and also because there is ample evidence of hearing loss caused by prolonged exposure to high sound or noise levels, there has been considerable effort on the part of major companies engaged in process work to define sound levels which men can endure tolerably for 8 hrs. each working day without suffering hearing impairment.

A sound standard for measurement was required. In studies of acoustical functions the term *decibel* (db) was borrowed from the electrical industry. The sound level at 1 db is that level which can just be detected by a person with acute hearing in a very quiet environment. Sound is an expression of power; sound power level can be conveniently measured in watts, and since sound is heard because of cyclic variation in atmospheric pressure beginning at 0.0002 microbars, with the microbar defined as substantially one millionth of a standard atmosphere, it is convenient to measure sound power in watts.

Figure 1-1 gives sound power expressed as watts versus decibels re 10^{-13} power level, with sound power delivered by cyclic variation in pressure due to incidence of the sound and with the pitch of the sound thus produced according to the frequency of the cyclic pressure variation. Thus, the tone or the sound of the standard musical note A is produced at a frequency of 440 cps, and an A at the next higher octave is 880 cps. Each octave is either twice or half of a reference sound frequency according to whether the sound is higher or lower in pitch.

While decibels can be correlated with sound power in watts, the relative loudness of a sound will vary with frequency. The term used to denote loudness is *phon*. Loudness characteristics of sound are based on the condition at 1,000 cps and typically from 0-120 phons at 1,000 cps in research.

At 1,000 cps a loudness factor of 60 phons corresponds to 60 db, but at 100 cps, 60 phons is equal to 72 db. At 3,500 cps 60 phons is equal to 57 db. Thus, loudness of sound and decibels do not directly correlate. If a sound specification is made in phons, there must be reference to phons at a specific frequency; since the basis for establishing phons is 1,000 cps, at other measured frequencies the number of phons will vary.

Sound, as commonly considered, is composed of many frequencies which are coincidentally delivered to the ear or to a microphone. The lowest frequency encountered is approximately 30 cps or very deep in the bass range, as A at the low end of the piano keyboard. The highest C of the piano keyboard has a frequency of 4,186.01 cps. High C is a shrill note, but frequency measurements as high as or higher than 10,000 cps are also made in sound studies and by octave-band measurements of sound in an area. Ability to hear or sense high-pitched or high-frequency sound will vary with individuals of the same age. As a particular individual ages he is less and less able to hear or perceive high-frequency sound. There is certain evidence that hearing loss is due, in greater degree, to the high-pitched sounds than to low-pitched sounds at identical db levels.

Annoyance at noise incidence is readily detectable, but as yet no suitable calibration means for annoyance levels in respect to noise or sound has been devised. There has been wide investigation, but because reaction to noise is so much a matter of individual tolerance, the psychological problems become almost infinite. As an example of problems in this regard it is to be said that reaction to or annoyance with sound will vary widely in the same individual according to what he is trying to do at the time the sound is heard. Presumption that annoyance level will vary as the sound loudness level varys is not completely correct but is rather a good yardstick for estimation. However, high-frequency or shrill noises are usually far more annoying, probably because they are so very difficult to disregard.

When there is dependance on the hearing characteristics of people, noise analysis tends to be confusing. It is common to find one sound almost completely masking another. The 60-cycle hum of light fixtures is completely unnoticed in ordinary working conditions because of other environmental sounds. When the other sounds are not factors, the 60-cycle hum can be clearly heard. Here, relative loudness effects become significant in sound perception.

Since relative loudness will vary with sound frequencies and since it is very rare for sound to be at a single frequency, except in a closely controlled laboratory experiment, there is further difficulty in evaluating sound effects in the typical industrial area as people and their idiosyncracies are studied.

Operators of industrial facilities must be aware that the noise produced during their operations can no longer be disregarded because of an obligation to be not only good neighbors but also to respect the comfort and welfare of the employees who serve the facility. Public relations demand the good-neighbor policy but—and more forcibly—labor relations as well as laws make noise suppression a cardinal responsiblity of industrial operation.

Because of these facts, the lack of authoritative reference data and the lack of agreement by authorities as to what constitutes a healthy environmental noise level in the various octave-band frequencies, a state of high confusion exists in noise level specification.

A table of typical environmental noise levels as measured on the broadband C scale of sound measurement instruments is shown in Table 1-1. A noise level found in an open field with a 15 mph breeze blowing is 75 db. A typical office in which business machines are operating has a mean noise level of 79 db. Yet, engineering and operating groups are issuing environmental noise specifications for industrial areas at 75 db for a particular operating facility equipped with burners. A check of the existing noise level in industrial areas before erecting a new facility will produce noise levels more than 85 db. Thus, there is a specification for noise in operation of the new facility which is completely impossible to meet. The background noise level exceeds the specified level.

Noise Specs

Such a state of affairs is far from rare as noise specifications for new facilities are issued. There is an obvious lesson—existing equipment should be closely checked to determine if there is reason to work toward attenuation of existing noise by muffling, eliminating vibration, shielding and other procedures calculated to reduce noise emission. Noise specification for new equipment should always include firm data for noise levels in all octave-bands as maximum figures against which or combined with which noise production characteristics of the new facility are to be measured.

At this time it would appear that a broadband noise level (a mean of all frequencies) at 85 db is to become a strongly favored optimum environmental level which is required by such laws and ordinances. There are few existing industrial facilities which can continue to operate without a very thorough program of noise elimination which will be quite expensive as well as extensive. Costs which will accrue as a result of noise level requirements are in the same category as costs of efforts to avoid air and stream pollution. The normal man exposed to excessive noise levels for prolonged periods experiences hearing loss to a greater or lesser degree and, at times, even more serious symptoms. However, industry is at times burdened with nuisance-type complaints of excessive noise which cannot be justified on any reasonable basis; but because noise complaints by citizens prompts response by elected officials when, in all justice, no action should be taken, certain injustices are to be expected.

Noise is a function of industry because industrial installations by their nature use equipment which is the source of noise. It is becoming increasingly evident that an essential portion of a site study for the erection of an industrial facility include a very thorough understanding of tolerable noise limits at the time of erection as well as for following years. And it is further indicated that the 85-db limit be kept firmly in mind as the study progresses.

If portions of the facility must be erected fairly close to the borders of the tract, particular care should be taken. If, however, the equipment can be located at some distance from the border there is relief to a degree because the power of a sound varies inversely as the square of the distance. Distance and noise measurement are distinctly related and should be considered (see Figure 1-1).

Two areas are of interest to process facility operators. One pertains to in-the-plant noise levels to which the operating personnel will be exposed for varying periods. The second pertains to edge-of-plant levels and the effect such levels may have on neighbors. Both are important. Levels which are considered as intolerable in the plant will demand relief according to exposure time. Levels at the plant boundary are equally critical if they are excessive.

There is presently and will continue to be certain confusion as to how individual groups are to determine necessity for work toward sound attenuation. A good starting point is preliminary survey both in the plant and at the plant borders with a portable sound meter in which there are fresh batteries and which has been checked for accuracy. As an excessively noisy area is found there is reason to use octave-band analysis of the noise as a means for identifying the noise source and the procedure for attenuation.

When the noisy areas are discovered and octave-bands analysis determines whether the noise is in the low or the high frequencies (to the greatest degree) it is possible to track sound back to its source. However, this procedure allows only a fairly rough estimate since all frequencies will be discovered as present in most instances and the sources of both frequency ranges will require exploration to their sources.

Generally speaking, it will be discovered that noise from fan or turbine operation is rich in high frequencies. Burner noise will vary according to the burner design, the condition of operation, the orientation and the fuel as burned. It is difficult if not impossible to suggest potential frequency ranges. The wind direction at the time of sound measurement should be noted since sound carries much better in the down-wind direction than in the up-wind direction. It is probably better to make sound measurement on a still and fairly warm day.

Study of sound and sound problems should probably be referred to someone who is qualified by experience and education for solutions to avoid expensive error. However, there are certain fundamentals which may be of value such as knowledge that high frequencies respond best to acoustic treatment and there is therefore greater tolerance for error here, but low frequencies can be quite difficult to attenuate to a required degree. Reverberatory or echoic sound can be difficult. In muffling devices (attenuator devices) there must be care in design since a relatively tiny leak can destroy the effectiveness of the devices.

Acoustic Treatment

Materials for acoustic treatment vary in their effectiveness to a very great degree according to the manner in which they are applied. The greatest effectiveness will be evident when an acoustic lining of adequate thickness for the particular material is used in a structure which completely encloses the noise source such as a lined wind box over burners and with air for combustion coming from a lined duct but at the expense of fan noise unless there is adequate natural draft. Such procedure is hardly possible for much equipment and a solution may lie in the use of acoustic sound barriers or the like.

It would be difficult to make a greater public relations error than to disregard noise complaint since, by its nature, noise and reaction to it is a psychological function which defies either analysis or reason. Correction of noise can be expected to be expensive and difficult, but there is every evidence that, bitter as the pill may be, it must be taken. Annoyance results from failure to do anything but if complainants see that something is being done they will tend to be far more friendly and cooperative even if the efforts are not completely successful.

There are so many psychological factors involved in response to sound, as is shown by Table 1-1, where sound level is reduced from 107 db to 93 db to produce a dramatic reduction in ear-response which is pleasing but still considerably more than the required 85 db. Legal matters are one thing but public relations are still another and public relations are utterly important to continued operation. There must be compliance with the law but plant management can buy time for compliance and in the meantime have peace of mind if there is effort toward sound reduction.

A frequently missed source of noise is vibration if the vibration period equals or exceeds 15 beats per second and distressing sound power can result. The techniques for vibration reduction are many and if vibration is found to be a significant noise source, dampening in any of the many manners is required. Fans and ducts are prime sources of such noise because a particular structure is frequently discovered to be resonant at the fundamental vibration frequency or one of its harmonics. Hot air ducts are common offenders and in this case any alteration of hot air flow characteristics will provide correction through flow diversion or through change in flow quantity or flowing temperature as well as flow pressure, but the condition of pressure is not usually a fruitful source of correction.

In the firing of furnaces a source of noise exists when a furnace becomes resonant to make a most annoying humming or howling sound at a specific frequency which usually is low. This phenomenon occurs when flow temperature and velocity of gases as well as the mass flow of gases are at a state which causes the furnace to become resonant. Such conditions of resonance are not too frequent but they can be a source of embarrassment to both heater suppliers and burner suppliers because it is virtually impossible to predict resonance in advance of operation and to design against it because specific velocity and temperature contours at all conditions of operation are far from predictable. The resonant sound may come and go as operating conditions change. The resonance can be stopped in particular heaters through any significant change in gas flow contours or gas temperatures. At times the noise can be stopped by change in operating gas pressure; by judicious placement of firebrick or by change in operating excess air; or through burner modification. The resonant noise will demand correction not only because it is so annoying but also because the vibration which is the source of the noise can severely damage the heater structure.

2

Flaring and Disposal

No single element involved in safe and satisfactory operation of a process plant is more critical than the design and operation of flares and flare systems for operational or emergency relief of quantitites of flammable substances in either the liquid or the gaseous phase or both.

The flare system must deliver the relieved products to the flare with rapidity and in such manner as to permit safe burning of the products at the flare. As these factors are studied elements of complexity enter. When there is need for pressure relief in portions of an operating process facility, the need is immediate and urgent. Since pressure relief valves are provided for the state of immediate relief required, it then becomes the function of the flare system to deliver the relieved products to the flare without impedance or interference.

If products as relieved are in the gaseous phase or are at temperature levels that cause immediate flashing of liquid to vapor, the problem is much less severe than when the relieved products occur in a two-phase condition, because pressure drop calculation in two-phase flow is extremely difficult as temperature levels change.

Knock-Out Pots

It has been found expedient to provide a means for the separation of the two-phase flow as quickly as possible after the relief through the use of knock-out pots for separate entrapment of the liquid and continued flow of the gases to the flare through the system (see Figure 2-1).

In the study of knock-out pots, there should be an understanding of the severe limitation of the ability of a simple enlargement of the line to remove liquid. Unless the pot is properly designed, a portion (even a major portion) of the liquid can carry through and continue toward the flare because of the great state of turbulence and inertias within the pot with the inertias in this instance being those of movement. There are recorded cases where the entire flare system has filled with liquid to pour, as burning liquid, from the flare.

If the pot is well designed for the removal of liquid but there is not adequate storage space for removed liquid or if the pot is not properly designed, there can be discharge of burning liquid from the flare with great hazard resulting.

Dew Point

Surprising quantities of liquids can accumulate in flare systems because of the dew-point characteristics of the flared products as complex mixtures of gases at released temperatures as high as 400° F. There is a sharp drop in the temperature of flared gases as they move through the system enroute to the flare.

The temperature drop is due to sensible heat loss to the steel of the system as well as the loss of from 5-10 Btu/sq. ft. per degree of temperature difference between atmospheric temperature and the temperature of the steel per hour. A principle source of variation in loss is due to variation of wind action.

Significance of the dew-point factor is clearly shown in a recently completed study of the problem of flaring approximately 1,000,000 lbs./hr. of hydrocarbons where less than 600,000 lbs. of products finally reach the flare and burn. Facility for undisturbed storage of 400,000 lbs./hr. of liquid hydrocarbon is required within the flare system. This quantity of liquid is recovered rather than lost by burning at the flare.

As dew point occurs the liquids at dew point are present as micron-size droplets which, in flow, collect on the surfaces of the flare system elements. Liquid at the inner surface is moved along with the gas flow to either accumulate or be discharged from the flare.

For this reason, the base of the flare should contain a well-designed mist eliminator for satisfactory entrapment of dew-point liquids; and as a part of the flare, there should be a liquid trap to force the return of trapped liquid to grade. Such flares and mist eliminators are commercially available.

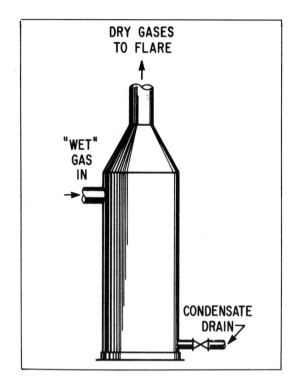

Figure 2-1. Mist-trap knock-out pot.

Because the liquid is carried by the flared gases in particles ranging from 10 microns to 200 microns, it is important that mist extraction occur at the base of the flare riser if the flare is to be capable of satisfactory smokeless operation. To burn with speed, hydrocarbons must be in vapor phase. If liquid hydrocarbon is present as burning of gases begins, the liquid must be vaporized by the burning heat. Burning is delayed, and the specific volume difference between a hydrocarbon as a gas and the same hydrocarbon as a liquid overloads the flare burning capacity. Another result of liquid presence in flared gases is excessive demand for steam as a smoke suppressant.

Flare Line Size

Opinions differ as to the sizing of flare system lines, which is typical of a proposition having various conditions. But if the system is to serve its purpose of quick relief of large volumes of flared products, flare line sizing should deliver the flared products to the flare with minimal pressure drop and at velocity in the order of 200 ft./sec. maximum at flowing pressure and temperature. Economic conditions should not be allowed to dictate flare line size.

While sprays of burning liquid from the flare are by no means rare, a state of much greater hazard exists when air in any significant quantity is allowed to enter the flare system at a time when the flare pilots are operating.

On entering the flare system, air mixes with the combustible gases within the system and usually in a most unhomogeneous way such that no matter what the air quantity may be and no matter what the combustible may be, at some point in the mixture of gas and air the state of mixture is within the explosive range.

Explosions and Detonations

Violence of the explosion or detonation will be in proportion to the air quantity and the degree with which it fills the system as well as in proportion to the characteristic of the fuel. It is well to distinguish between explosions and detonations.

An *explosion* is a state in which a mass of gas-air mixture expands abruptly but uniformly as the fuel burns uniformly and progressively throughout the mass of the fuel-air mixture. The result of such burning is simple thermal expansion which, if confined, can result in an instant increase in pressure which may or may not be destructive. Such a state is typical when burning of anti-knock fuel in an automobile engine.

Detonation occurs when there is instant burning of the entire fuel-air mixture to produce a detonation wave of greater or lesser magnitude according to the nature of the fuel. Damage in detonation is not necessarily caused by pressure increase alone but is probably due to detonation-wave impact, in addition to pressure increment. The knocking of an automobile engine with low octane fuel is typical of mild detonation.

In detonation, damage tends to occur in the immediate zone of the detonation because of the detonation wave, whereas in an explosion there is more even distribution and relief of pressure. Of the two evils, detonation or explosion, the latter is to be preferred, particularly if the confining space is capable of enduring the pressure.

As a mass of fuel and air is ignited in a confined space and as pressure rises in the space, there is greater tendency for detonation as distinguished from explosion. Some fuels such as hydrogen, acetylene, ethylene oxide and carbon disulfide detonate in any state of pressure, but hydrocarbons generally, become less detonative in movement toward lower pressure.

In a flare system which is operating normally, the greatest single hazard is the entry of air at any point within the flare system or the presence of air within the system.

Sources of Air Entry

There are numerous sources of entry of air into the flare system and all sources should be very carefully checked to avoid the hazard. When the flare system is fairly static and flow is either very small or nonexistent toward the flare and the system including the flare riser is filled with either low molecular weight gases or gases at high temperature, the draft or less than atmospheric pressure at the base of the flare may be 2 in. WC or more.

With this state of less than atmospheric pressure within the flare system, air will leak into the system if there is opportunity for it to do so. The flare system must be gas-tight at all points and, more importantly, it must not be opened for service while the pilots are burning.

A very serious explosion in a flare occurred in just such a condition when without extinguishing the pilots, a blind-flange was removed from the system. It was immediately observed that there was a great inrush of air as the flange was removed from the line leading to a very high stack. The explosion followed in a very short time interval.

It is to be noted that the pressure at the base of the flare riser will be less than atmospheric when the weight per cubic foot of the gas content

Table 2-1
Draft at the Base of a Flare
Due to Low Molecular Weight
Gases in the Flare Riser

Condition of draft at the base of a flare when the molecular weight of the gas content of the flare is less than 29 can be calculated as follows:

H = Height of flare riser in feet
MW = Molecular weight of gases in flare

$$\frac{(H \times 0.0763 \times 28) - (H \times 0.0763 \times MW/29 \times 28)}{144} = \text{Draft in inches WC}$$

To determine the pressure condition at the stack base as whether the pressure will be greater-than atmospheric or less than atmospheric the following:

MW = Molecular weight
T = Fahrenheit temperature

$$\frac{.0763 \times MW/29 \times [520/(T + 460)]}{.0763} \quad \begin{array}{l} = \text{Greater than atmospheric if} > 1 \\ \text{Less than atmospheric if} < 1 \end{array}$$

of the flare riser is less than the weight per cubic foot of atmospheric air, either by molecular weight difference or temperature difference. See Table 2-1.

Another source of air entry into the flare system, and particularly into the flare riser, is present when the vertical flare riser is filled with gases which are lighter than air because of molecular weight difference or temperature difference and a condition of no flow or very small flow exists within the flare system.

Purge Gases

The buoyant gases refuse to remain within the flare riser and are replaced with air in countercur-
rent flow as the gases emerge and the air enters. It is an industry practice to supply gases to the flare system constantly to avoid a static condition of flow. These gases are referred to as *purge* or *sweep* gases. Such purge or sweep gases represent a large annual cost.

Purge gases may be any gases which cannot go to dew point under any condition of flare operation. Natural gas, inert gases and nitrogen are commonly used; steam is not at all satisfactory as a purge gas. Calculated volumes of purge gas should enter the flare system at its very beginning so that there is assurance of sweeping the entire system and so that the volume of purge gases is increased by the heat content of the flare system and the gases which are within it.

There are two reasons why entry of purge, or "sweep gases," to the flare piping system is required to avoid entry of air to the system. Both reasons are related to the weight per cubic foot of gases within the system compared to the weight per cubic foot of air at any ambient meterological condition. If the flare-contained gases are at conditions that make them heavier than air, their weight causes them to be contained in the system so that air cannot enter. If, however, the molecular weight of the flare system gases is less than 28.966, the flare gases will be buoyant and will readily "decant" from the flare discharge point to be replaced by atmospheric air, causing an explosion hazard to exist. If the gas temperature within the flare is equal to atmospheric temperature, and if the molecular weight of the flare gases exceeds 28.966, the gases will be weight-contained within the flare so that air cannot enter.

However, flare gases are usually relieved to the flare system at a much greater temperature than ambient. For this reason, it is dangerous to rely on molecular weight for avoidance of air entry because, at high temperature, gas expansion over corrects for molecular weight difference, and dangerous air entry can occur until a temperature decrease brings about the weight difference that relative gas/air molecular weights will indicate.

Also, the temperature and gas volume decrease from changing absolute temperature ratios causes an added indraft of air because of contained volume decrease and a drop below atmospheric pressure within the flare system. In any case of "purge" or "no purge" a device such as a molecular seal should be located immediately below the burning zone of the flare. Many designers maintain that because relief valves to the flare system do not always close "bubble-tight" there will be enough leakage to make purging unnecessary. This assumption is dangerous and wasteful if leakage does occur.

The use of methane (natural gas) as flare purge gas is usually necessary but undesirable for two reasons. First, the cost of natural gas is very high. Second, the molecular weights of such gases seldom exceed 18, and the flare gas content is dangerously buoyant. Unless they are dehydrated, higher mol-weight inert gases are dangerous for cold climates because of condensation and freezing. Nitrogen is too expensive. If natural gases are used for purge, a proven device for avoidance of air entry is required.

There is divergent opinion as to the volume of purge gas which may be required. One researcher asserts that purge gas in sufficient volume to create a flow velocity of 0.10 ft./sec. in the flare riser is adequate. However, there is evidence that this research was based on gases at atmospheric temperature only and that higher temperature level would demand greater purge volume.

There is seeming contradiction of this theory as the result of one test of a 200-ft. high, 16-in. diameter flare riser filled with essentially pure methane in which a purge gas was admitted at a linear velocity at close to 3 ft./sec. In the test, there was a venting of flared gases which were also methane. At the base of the flare there was an oxygen analyzer operating continuously.

Repeated checks showed clearly that oxygen appeared at the base of the flare within less than a minute following shut-off of the flared volume, leaving only the purge gas flowing at approximately 3 ft./sec. It would appear then that in this test, purge volume in excess of 3 ft./sec. is required to avoid deep penetration of oxygen in flares in a stand-by condition.

In the research showing a need for a flow velocity of only 0.10 ft./sec., the state of wind action at the time of the tests was not reported. Research shows that the need for purge gas varies greatly with wind action because of the wind acceleration over the open end of the flare riser and the zone of low pressure thus established. The test on the 200-ft. flare as discussed was carried out in conditions of ground-level wind velocity at 20 mph.

Elementary mathematics will show that for a 24-in. flare riser with purge gas admitted at 3

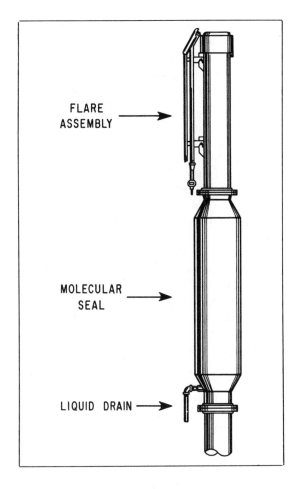

Figure 2-2. Molecular seal.

The constant purge gas cost with the molecular seal then becomes a maximum of $2,887 per year rather than approximately $60,000 per year for very interesting economy in the case of a 24-in. flare riser.

Further study of purge gas volume has shown that the temperature of the flare system (temperature of flared gases) does influence the calculated rate of purge gas admission. The rate of purge gas admission must be great enough to cause movement of gas toward the flare as the hot gases in the system cool off. Gases within the system are always at a lower temperature than that at which the gases are relieved because of heat loss to the steel in the system as well as a state of radiation from the system as its temperature rises. However in purge considerations we accept the temperature of the gases as relieved as a safety factor.

If we consider a 24-in. flare system which is 1,000 ft. long, the system has a volume of 3.14 (1,000) = 3,140 cu. ft. If we fill the system with gases at 400° F, the gases are expanded and will shrink as they cool.

In this instance, the gases would shrink from 3,140 cu. ft. at 400° F to 3,140 (520/860) = 1,898 cu. ft. at 60° F.

The difference in volume is 3,140 − 1,898 = 1,241 cu. ft. and unless the purge gas quantity is adequate, air will be drawn back into the flare system by the shrink of the gases.

In a 24-in. system as discussed, purge gas volume would be 1,130 scfh, which after heating by the heat storage in the system to 200° F, would expand to 1,434 cu. ft. This is greater than the volume of shrink due to cooling and would be considered adequate if the cooling period was 1 hour. The rate of cooling should be even over the cooling period. The cooling period is 15 minutes and the rate of cooling is exponential rather than linear. Thus, during the period when a static (flow) flare system cools from 400° F to 60° F, the volume of purge gas required is considerably more than four times greater than the volume required at 0.10 ft./sec. The fact that flare system explosions cannot be considered common is thought to

ft./sec. velocity, the annual cost for the purge gas based on natural gas at 20¢/Mcf approaches $60,000 per year.

It so happens that a commercially available molecular seal, Figure 2-2, installed immediately below the flare at the top of the riser will establish perfect safety from entry of air into the flare system. The seal is effective when the purge volume admitted is capable of line velocity at from 0.10-0.15 ft./sec. if the purge volume is admitted at the beginning of the flare system and for flared gas temperatures up to 150° F.

be failure of relief valves to close tightly in all cases. Also, static flare system temperatures at 400° F cannot be considered common, but such temperature is distinctly possible in many instances. Great hazard is possible here and much thought and experimentation have been directed toward corrective measures. Instrumentation for automatic addition to purge volume activated by a simple thermocouple in the flare line has not been satisfactory for the hot system condition, but the leading flare manufacturer has solved the problem with an instrumentation system known as the "Tempurge."

If the purge gas is admitted at the beginning of the flare system where the cool entering purge gas can absorb heat from the flare piping and contents, the sweep effect is increased in proportion to the temperature of the system and its contents.

Safety demands that purge gas be admitted to the flare system at least 24 hrs. in advance of pilot ignition and that the entire flare system be thus purged. The flare system does not become an explosion hazard until such time as the pilots are ignited. If the system is made safe through purging, it is then safe to light the pilots.

Flame Arrestors

There is a marked tendency to forego using flame arrestors as portions of flare systems because of some undesirable characteristics of the typical labyrinthine flame arrestor structures. In some services, particularly when the flared gases are capable of polymerization, there is tendency for the small passages through the flame arrestor element to plug and obstruct flow.

In other flared gases which are dirty, there is the same tendency for obstruction of the arrestor gas passages such that annual cleaning may or may not be adequate to permit discharge of the required quantity of flared gases at a reasonable pressure drop.

Typical flame arrestors are not capable of stopping a flame front in mixtures of air with hydrogen, acetylene, ethylene oxide and carbon disulfide; thus they are of no value. See Table 2-2.

Water Seals

If there is positive need for checking a flame front in mixtures of air with these gases, the checking must be done with a suitably designed water seal. Note that a typical dip-leg water seal is by no means satisfactory for this service because as the flow quantity through the seal increases, there is uninterrupted gas flow through the water. Experience with hydrogen-air mixtures shows clearly that a flame front will move countercurrent to velocities well in excess of 200 ft./sec. This speed of flame movement has been verified repeatedly despite published flame speeds in hydrogen-air mixtures of from 9-16 ft./sec.

For the water seal to be effective in checking a flame-front passage of gas through the water, there must be a series of separate and distinct bubbles with water intervals between the bubbles. Such water seals are commercially available.

A very undesirable operating characteristic of improperly designed water seals is their surging tendency in which there are relatively violent interruptions of flow to create rhythmic pressure surges both upstream and downstream of the water seal.

This characteristic can be observed in the operation of flares where there is rhythmic violent burning followed by extinction of the flame at the flare burning point with an annoying boom as the burning begins at each rhythmic cycle upon reignition. The use of weirs of various designs or serrated dip legs has no effect on this pulsation. Water seals which do not surge at all are commercially available. Surging makes stable pilot operation very difficult.

Note that where smoke suppression is required for the flare as it burns, the state of interrupted flow of flared gases caused by surging at the water seal makes it virtually impossible to secure suitable suppression of smoke as the flare operates.

Table 2-2
Flash-Back Probability in Premix Burners with Various Fuels
as They Compare with the Flash-Back Characteristics
of Methane (Natural Gas)

Fuel	Ratio Upper/Lower Explosive Limits	Probability of Flash-Back
Methane	3.00	1.00
Ethane	4.02	1.34
Propane	5.25	1.75
Butane	4.52	1.51
Ethylene	10.04	3.33
Propylene	5.55	1.85
Butylene	4.88	1.63
Butadiene	5.75	1.92
Acetylene*	32.00	Infinite
Hydrogen Sulphide	10.60	3.52
Ammonia	1.71	0.57
Cyanogen	6.45	2.15
Acrylonitrile	5.57	1.85
Methyl Chloride	2.26	0.75
Vinyl Chloride	5.42	1.80
Ethyl Chloride	3.70	1.23
Oil Gas	6.84	2.28
Gasoline (Mean)	5.06	1.68
Naphtha	5.45	1.81
Carbon Disulfide	40.00	Infinite
Ethylene Oxide	26.66	Infinite
Hydrogen	18.55	Infinite
Carbon Monoxide	5.93	1.97
Methyl Alcohol	5.43	1.81
Aromatics (Mean)	5.00	1.66
Acetone	5.01	1.67
Hydrocyanic Acid	7.14	2.38
Ethyl Alcohol	5.77	1.92

* = Self-Detonative (pyrophoric)

Note: These data, as based on UEL/LEL information as supplied by AGA and other literature references are useful for determining fuel characteristics. The data are also very useful for flare or disposal burning of gases in determining the effectiveness of typical labyrinthine flame arrestors. In any case where flash-back probability is shown as *Infinite*, a flame arrestor *must not* be relied upon and a bubble screen water seal *must* be used. In any case where the ratio of UEL/LEL exceeds 11.00 use of a flame arrestor is highly questionable. Presence of *any* O_2 is dangerous because of lack of homogeneity which is possible in mixture of gases.

Smokeless Flares

Because of increasingly stringent air pollution laws, smokeless flare operation in process plants has been made a must rather than a point of preference in the interest of good public relations. In the flaring of gases such as hydrocarbons, the tendency for smoke production as the gases burn is governed by the weight ratio of hydrogen to carbon in the gases (Figure 2-3) but is not directly proportional to the H/C ratio by weight.

As an example, the burning of methane (H/C = 0.33) produces no smoke at the flare while the burning of ethane (H/C = 0.25) produces comparatively faint smoke; but the burning of propane (H/C = 0.222) makes comparatively heavy smoke. As the H/C ratio by weight moves further in the downward direction the smoking intensity increases.

In the burning of a complex mixture of gases where the calculated H/C ratio by weight is greater than 0.25, there may be considerable smoke production at the flare because the flared gases are not homogeneously mixed as they burn and separate burning of the lower H/C gases is producing the smoke. This factor can become extremely critical in successful suppression of smoke at the flare. Thus it is required that flared gases be in a state of reasonably homogeneous mixture; but each flare system requires separate studies to assure reasonable homogeneity of mixtures of flared gases. It is to be noted that despite the widely held opinion that there is good mixture of gases in turbulent flow within a pipe line in short distance travel, experience shows clearly that there is very little or no mixture as the gases flow in the line.

There have been numerous approaches to the problem of smokeless burning of waste process gases. Since the principle means for suppressing smoke involves the various chemistries associated with reactions of water vapor with the components of the flared gas stream, there have been various schemes for delivering the water to the burning zone as either steam or as water spray in one form or another.

Smokeless Burning and Chemistries

Suppression of smoking in the flaring of gases is based on a number of fundamental chemical states or reactions, but essentially it depends on two main factors: (1) securing a combination of carbon with another element, and (2) significantly upgrading the H/C ratio by weight.

If carbon can be made to combine with oxygen as either CO or CO_2, the carbon cannot be seen and thus produces no smoke.. The burning of CO has an effect identical with that of hydrogen. Essential chemistries follow using methane as an exemplary hydrocarbon:

$$CH_4 + H_2O = CO + 3H_2$$
$$CH_4 + 2H_2O = CO_2 + 4H_2$$
$$C + 2H_2O = CO_2 + 2H_2$$

Chemistries of carbon with water vapor are typical water-gas-shift reactions, but dissociation of the hydrocarbon is required before the shift reactions can become significant. Direct chemistries of hydrocarbons to water vapor do not require dissociation and conversion of carbon to a combined form plus the release of hydrogen. Thus, these chemistries are quite significant in smoke suppression.

However, the chemistries of smokeless burning as shown are endothermic in that they are heat-demanding. Thus, there must be both prior burning plus great acceleration of burning to supply needed heat quantities which may be as great as 88,635 Btu/pound-mol of hydrocarbon or more.

There has been certain limited success with water injection for smoke suppression but the hazard of freezing makes use of this system in any area other than a sub-tropical zone questionable; in addition, there is the great nuisance of a spray of unvaporized water to grade in normal flare operation. It is for these reasons that steam is almost universally used for suppression of smoke in flare operation. Flares for suppression of smoke are commercially available in either design.

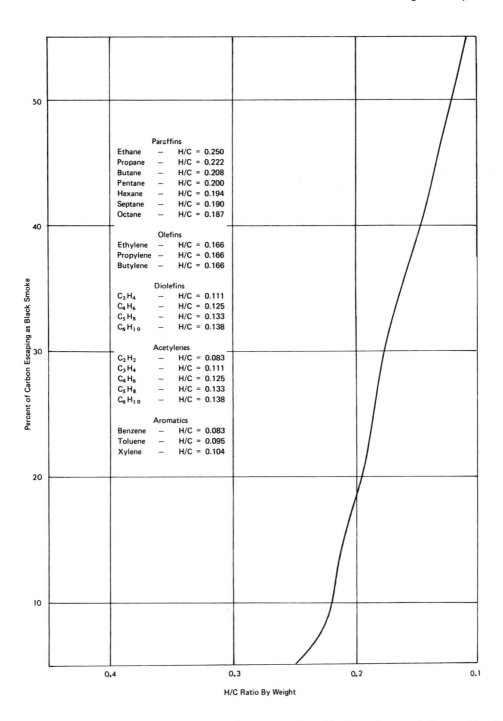

Figure 2-3. Tendency to produce black smoke in flare burning of hydrocarbons as influenced by the H/C ratio by weight of the flared gases where there is no suppression of smoking.

In the many cases where steam for smoke suppression is not available, and the gases for flaring are decidedly smoke-prone and at very low pressures (a few inches WC), it is possible to achieve smokeless burning at the flare for relatively small volumes of gases. Such flares suppress smoking through the flow effect of high-velocity air past the gas discharge point. The high-velocity air flow is from a blower that provides only a fraction of the theoretical air demand for the burning of fuel. The remainder of the required air for burning comes from the atmosphere surrounding the burning zone. The blowers for such flares are power-driven, and power must be available at, or near to, the site of the flare. Either turbines or electric motors can drive the blowers.

Ground Flares

Principally in foreign areas but also at times in the United States, there is interest in what are referred to as *ground flares* for smokeless burning of relatively small volumes of flared gases. Such flares are not the simple flare pit or burning pit which once were common but are somewhat complex structures to heights which are calculated as required for the service involved. The equipment or apparatus for smokeless burning in ground flares will vary widely because in most instances an essential purpose of the ground flare is complete concealment of the burning gases as well as smokeless burning, plus relatively complete abatement of noise due to burning. In these structures there is less emphasis on chemistries of water vapor to hydrocarbon/carbon content and greater emphasis on maintaining a temperature level or turbulence in the burning zone which will prevent the escape of unburned or uncombined carbon. Most ground flares use no steam or water and are quite successful.

A number of design approaches to ground-level flaring have been successfully adapted according to conditions for flaring which may be required for the particular service. Two factors govern design here. One is the lowest H/C ratio by weight of the flared or relieved gases. The other is the pressure from which the relieved gases may be discharged to atmospheric pressure.

Smokeless flaring of relieved hydrocarbons is an accomplished fact in the typical gasoline plant where the relieved gases are in the paraffin series of hydrocarbons, where the relief pressure may be 10# gauge or more and where the H/C ratio is in the order of 0.19 or more and where no adequate steam supply for smoke suppression is present.

Flare design here incorporates a manifold from which pressure-controlled burners receive flared gases according to flared volume, but one of the burners is not pressure controlled to permit safe discharge of small volumes of gas continuously. Burners consist of runners attached to the manifold where each runner is equipped with a plurality of burner heads from which flared gas is discharged for burning in a state of turbulence and temperature which prevents escape of unburned carbon as smoke. The flare is enclosed in a diked area with a suitably designed "wind-fence" atop the dike to avoid radiation from the burning and to conceal the burning except in conditions of extreme emergency flaring. Flaring noise is minimized but still present.

If the chosen flare site does not require noise and glare reduction, a patented, elevated flare design will provide smokeless burning for huge quantities of greatly smoke-prone gases if the gases, as flared, are at a pressure of at least 15 lb gauge. The design has been proven for the flare-burning of ethylene at rates in excess of 1,000,000 lb/hr of flaring at full load and at less than 1% of full load. Radiation to grade is controlled by calculated elevation of the burning area above grade. No additional smoke suppression by steam or water injection is required.

Where flaring relief pressure cannot greatly exceed 1# gauge and where the H/C ratio of the flared gases is less than 0.19 other design procedure is demanded. Because process plants are frequently located in urban areas there are two approaches to the problem of flaring to avoid legal and public-relations difficulty regarding noise and flare flame visibility. The simplest and least expensive approach is to use elevated flares in which steam suppresses smoke but at the expense of noise production and visible glare from the burning at the flare. The noise production can be minimized but not eliminated by suitable muffling which is standard and operation proven, but the state of burning is there for all to see.

Both the noise and the glare problems can be solved through use of the ZTOF System designed and under patent application by John Zink engineers. The system is one in which flared gases are burned within furnaces designed for the purpose where there is maintenance of temperature to assure complete burning as well as noiseless burning for 98% of the flare operation time. For conditions of extreme emergency relief such as in power failure or cooling water failure or the like, an auxilliary elevated and smokeless flare is provided for added relief. Steam is required only for the elevated flare in most cases and where the H/C ratio is 0.16 or lower. Through use of this system for flaring, urban location of process plants becomes possible at a time when ecological factors are so important because there is no visible emission and at a distance of 100 ft. it is difficult to determine by sound whether the system is or is not in operation.

Fundamental economics in the initial cost for furnace enclosed ground flares limit their use for more than a portion of the panic or emergency dump rates. Stand-by elevated smokeless flares are provided for venting flared gases in excess of the design condition for the ground flare through suitable instrumentation or diversionary devices. However, since the normal or day-to-day venting to the flare seldom exceeds 30% of the design condition for flaring, such installations are becoming more and more attractive.

Steam Control

For the suppression of smoke in elevated flares, as has been suggested, either steam or water can be injected in preferred manners. However, steam injection has been repeatedly shown to be superior for this service, probably becuase of two factors—loss of turbulence due to steam injection

from relatively high pressure and difficulty in securing suitable vaporization of liquid water as injected to the burning zone. Since steam is the preferred smoke suppressant and since steam is considerably more expensive than water, flare operating economics demand control of steam injection largely in proportion to the flaring rates. Also, in a flare designed for smokeless burning, simultaneous flaring and steam injection are demanded to avoid very severe heat attrition at the flare burning point.

Because manual steam control tends to result in excessive amounts of steam used and because of stringent air pollution laws, automatic control of steam injection is greatly preferred. Only recently has a device for such control which is satisfactory for the service been offered commercially. Known as a "Flow-Sensor," the device will sense the movement of 29 molecular-weight gas in the flare line at 1½ ft./sec. and will begin admitting steam for smoke suppression according to the state of flow of flared gases for satisfactory suppression of smoke in normal operation. It is impossible to obtain smoke suppression in the emergency flaring condition in elevated flares; however, there is retarding of smoking even in this condition.

It must be noted that even if the flare is completely smokeless as it operates, there may be accessory air pollution problems if the flared gases contain substances other than hydrocarbons which, as they burn, can produce serious pollutant material such as $SO_2 - SO_3$, HCL, HF and others. In addition to this consideration, there must be assured completeness of burning and the flare design must be such as to assure complete burning.

Complete burning is demanded for ammonia and for gases containing small or trace quantities of phosgene, hydrogen sulfide, hydrogen cyanide and other gases. Special flares for such service are commercially available.

Flare Height

Because air pollution laws now require that flare burning of gases shall not produce grade level concentrations of SO_2 greater than 0.10 ppm, and since the presence of sulfur in flared gases is typical rather than unusual, the height of the flare will, of necessity, be based on air pollution factors rather than on radiant heat factors derived from burning at the flare.

Today, there are two formulas to calculate flare height to avoid pollution. They are the Sutton-Lowery equation and the Bosanquet equation. These equations, derived from research, are widely used. The U.S. Public Health Service has added factors but there is general agreement in calculation. The reference for these formulas is *Air Pollution Handbook* by Magill, Holden and Ackley (McGraw-Hill).

Flame Radiation

A universally accepted figure for maximum radiant heat as produced by the burning of gases at the flare to include solar radiation is 1,000 Btu/sq. ft./hr. at grade. The solar factor is quite significant. At the latitude of Boston, solar radiation is in the order of 260 Btu/sq. ft./hr. In the U.S. Gulf Coast area, solar radiation approaches 300 Btu/sq. ft./hr. Thus, since solar radiation must be taken into account, the allowable figure for flare radiation at Boston is 1,000–260 = 740 Btu/sq. ft./hr. on the Gulf Coast the allowable radiation from the flare is 1,000 − 300 = 700 Btu/sq. ft./hr. based on 1,000 Btu/sq. ft./hr.

At 1,000 Btu/sq. ft./hr., the escape time for personnel caught by a flare period in the area of the flare is 30 sec. if pain is to be avoided. These data are taken from the ASME paper 57-SA-20 by K.J.K. Buettner and have been found to be acceptable. With this radiant density and with a grade emissivity at 0.80, the maximum grade temperature at the end of 20 minutes exposure is approximately 375° F, but at the end of one minute the grade temperature can be as high as 195° F.

If the flare area is sufficiently remote and if vegetation can be controlled in the flare area, total radiant rates in excess of 2,000 Btu/sq. ft./hr. may be tolerated.

Radiation from the flare is minimal at grade when there is no wind and the flame is vertical. Maximum radiation from the flare occurs when the flame is wind-blown and in areas directly beneath the flame, as it is blown by the wind. Thus there is a radial area about the base of the flare which is sterile in point of potential heat flux. The radius of the area is the length of the flame from the flare plus approximately 10%.

Flame Length

Calculation of flame length is difficult and at best is an estimate based on the burning characteristics of the flared gases. A formula for estimating flame length (L, ft) is as follows:

$$L = Q / A (20) 400,000$$

where:

Q = Heat release based on higher heating value, Btu

A = Area of flare in sq. ft.

It should be understood that the flame length thus calculated may be in error by as much as 50% as the speed of burning of the flared gases is influenced by the separate characteristics of the flared gases.

Emissivity

There is much confusion as the literature is searched for information on flame emissivity. In fact, there is such a state of confusion that field observation of radiant characteristics of various flared gases has been required to determine what state of emission exists as fuels burn and as their burning characteristics vary.

Field observations confirm that when the H/C ratio-by-weight of the flared gases is greater than 0.50, the emissivity is close to 0.075. As the H/C ratio reaches 0.33, the emissivity is 0.110. The emissivity is maximum at 0.120 when the H/C ratio is approximately 0.250, and as the H/C ratio moves downward there is a decrease in emissivity to 0.07 at 0.170 H/C.

Emissivity moves downward after an H/C of 0.25 for two reasons. The first being that below H/C of 0.25 there is smoke production with the smoke being unburned carbon at 14,000 Btu/lb.; thus all of the fuel is not burning. The second is that the carbon forms a highly heat-absorptive mantle about the flame to obstruct radiation.

Flare Structures

As flare structures are erected and operated, there are two problems which must be considered. One involves the temperature of the gases as flared, while the second is one of wind resonance or vibration of a vertical structure.

Because flare structures expand as they become heated, they must be designed for expansion without damage. This is particularly critical in guyed flares (Figure 2-4). The manner of attachment of guys as well as the angle of approach and the amount of slack permitted in the guys must permit the required expansion. In self-supported structures the external piping arrangement must take this into account.

If the gases as flared can be within the cryogenic temperature range, the metallurgy of the flare structure must be suited to the minimum temperature range. Any temperature as low as −50° F or lower requires steel with improved impact resistance for the structure to be safe. Materials for such conditions are nickel-steels, any of the 300 series stainless steels or aluminum.

Wind resonance of a vertical structure occurs when the action of the wind sets up forces which cause the structure to become resonant or to oscillate rhythmically. In guyed structures, the attachment of the guys can cancel resonance. In self-sup-

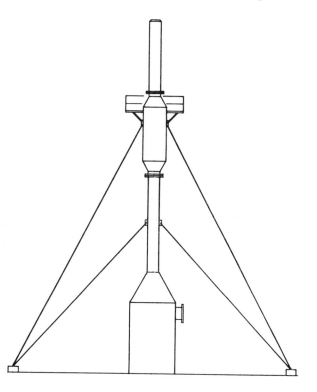

Figure 2-4. Guyed flares.

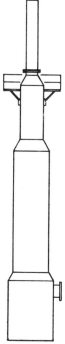

Figure 2-5. The resonance effect can be cancelled in self-supporting structures if they are composed of at least three different diameters in rising.

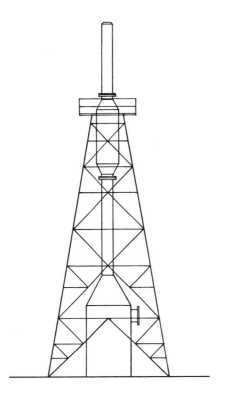

Figure 2-6. A tower or derrick structure provides flare support and stabilization.

ported structures if the structure is composed of at least three different diameters in rising (Figure 2-5), the resonance effect can be cancelled. In structures of identical diameter throughout the rise, resonance can be cancelled by welding spoilers at random (vertically and circumferentially) to alter the aerodynamic characteristics of the structure.

At times, a third approach to wind resonance, expansion and vertical support is used to combine relatively easy access to the flare with other required properties. This approach provides flare support and stabilization with some form of tower or derrick structure such as shown in Figure 2-6.

Because of preference there are, at times, reasons for erecting two flare structures to vent gases where the flares are to operate in parallel for capacity or for solutions to radiation problems. This design configuration is satisfactory only if one flare structure is isolated from the second flare structure, in the stand-by condition, by a well-designed water seal.

If the isolating water seal is not provided, because of varying wind action over the separate flares air will be drawn into one of the flares to create an explosion hazard within that structure. The entry of air is due to the fact that without the isolating seal and with two vertical flare structures which are connected by a common flare line fed from some source of flared gases, the configuration is that of a huge U-tube with the upper ends of the tube subjected to differential pressures caused by wind action. This causes bleed-out of gas at the stack where the pressure is lowest and entry of air at the other stack where there is higher pressure. There is no basis for a prediction of the differential pressures since wind action is hardly definite. The state of air entry will be present even though the heights of the two stacks are identical. It is again pointed out that the danger of air entry exists when the flares are in a stand-by condition and there is no flaring of gases, which is certainly true the great majority of the time. The molecular seal cannot protect against this condition, unless there is a very large purge volume.

Lower Heating Value

Flaring of waste gases is the best and least expensive means for disposal of such gases; however, flaring is not always possible because of the nature of the waste gases. A key factor in the decision to flare or not to flare is the calorific value of the fuel components in the waste gas stream based on the lower or net heating value of fuel components as they arrive at the flare mixed with inert gases such as nitrogen, water vapor, CO_2, argon and others.

As the lower heating value of the flared gas stream falls below 150 Btu/cu. ft., flaring design and technique become quite critical in securing complete burning of the waste gases. Calorific values as low as 60 Btu/cu. ft. are being flare burned in specifically designed and commercially available endothermic flares with perfect safety but at a significant fuel demand. The preferred fuels for endothermic flares are methane, ethane or propane.

Flare burning of waste gases in a refinery, where hydrocarbons alone are flared with very great calorific values, presents many elements of difficulty with the rich flared gases. The difficulty may be said to vary inversely as the calorific value.

Many lean gases can be quite successfully flared if there is a complete absence of the cooling effect of wind, but a flare cannot be designed for that utopian condition. The flare design must cause the flared gases to burn in any meteorological condition. Design of the flare must be based on complex studies of kinetics, heat potential, wind action at 80 mph in the presence of driving and torrential rain as well as varying volumes of flared gases. Flare designs for such conditions are commercially available.

Temperature Level versus Reaction Rate

In studies of waste disposal through heat application and in the design stage, the equations of Arrhenius are applicable if enough data for the particular waste matter (matters) are available.

But this procedure is cumbersome as well as fraught with error potential because of unresolvable operational functions which are numerous. Therefore, experimental disposal on a semicommercial scale has been found necessary in establishment of design parameters for successful disposal.

In such experimentation it may be discovered that a specific temperature level in operation is not adequate and it will be obvious that a higher temperature level is demanded. But higher temperature levels translate to greater auxilliary fuel cost. Therefore, it becomes advantageous for the specific temperature increase demanded to be known to avoid fuel waste and excessive cost.

We are taught (*Chemical Engineers' Handbook,* Perry, 3rd Edition) that if a reaction is occurring at 520° A (60° F) and if the temperature is increased to 538° A (78° F) the reaction rate doubles. The ratio of 538/520 = 1.03461.

Thus we can assume 1.035 with tiny error. We are also taught that at higher initial temperatures greater temperature increase is demanded for reaction-rate doubling.

The following data have been repeatedly verified in applied research at the John Zink Research Installation.

If a state of reaction at T_1 (Observed Temperature °F) is not adequate and a higher temperature (T_2 °F) is required, the higher temperature may be determined as follows:

$$(T_1 + 460) \ [\ (0.035 \ \times \ N\ ) + 1] - 460 = T_2$$

where:

T_1 = Initial observed temperature °F

T_2 = Temperature required for increased reaction °F

N = Reaction rate increase

If, for example, a test is running at 1,200°F and it is required that the reaction rate be trebled ($N = 3$), the calculation would be:

$$(1200 \ + \ 460) \ [(0.035 \ \times \ 3) \ + \ 1] \ - \ 460$$
$$= 1374.3°F$$

Capital Expense

Uncontrolled venting of waste gases and liquids to the atmosphere and to the waterways of the world, which once was an accepted way of life in industry, is no longer to be tolerated and is rapidly becoming illegal.

Cost for means to avoid air and stream pollution is, at time, awing according to the nature of the materials for disposal. In fact, the necessity to avoid pollution in any respect may well be the determining factor in the choice of a plant location, according to local ordinances or pollution regulations.

Fuel demand for satisfactory disposal is entirely governed by the nature of the substance for disposal. If no means for heat recovery are to be provided, the fuel cost represents a complete loss except for the fact that the cost is an operating expense and presents a means for some tax relief.

The capital expense of means for waste disposal is significant, in any event. The total capital expenditure is also governed by the nature of the products for disposal as well as local regulations to avoid pollution. Separate studies of disposal problems should be made in each case with the study to take into careful consideration minimum acceptable standards for the service as required.

Separate and careful studies are suggested because there is ample history of under-designed facilities causing great financial loss as well as embarrassment when lack of knowledge of the many problem details as well as reluctance to make a suitable capital expenditure may be considered as causes.

Oxidation

Where endo-exothermic oxidation is the waste disposal process, the end products required are those of complete oxidation. Any waste containing elements which oxidize on exposure to adequate heat for a great enough time can be disposed of by oxidation whether they are in the liquid, solid or gaseous phase.

Requirements for such disposal methods must be based on the design temperature level, great enough residence at the design temperature level, a suitable condition of controlled turbulence and the presence of adequate amounts of oxygen. It is, perhaps, a bit disconcerting to consider that carbon tetrachloride ($C\ CL_4$) held at $1,800°F$ ($982.22°C$) for a period of 5 sec., in the presence of oxygen, is converted to $CO_2 + 2\ CL_2$ in a series of reactions which terminate in an exothermic state.

Thus the factors time, temperature and turbulence which are classic for the burning of fuels become factors in disposal by oxidation. However, there are equally important supplementary factors which also must be considered.

Experience shows clearly that the autoignition temperatures of disposal products are of small concern. Experience shows equally clearly that the deciding factor of the design temperature level for

speed of oxidation with any fuel can best be stated as one of molecular proximity. In this sense, the proximity of fuel molecules to oxygen molecules governs.

In the case of a stoichiometric mixture of air and methane (CH_4) where both methane and air are dry, there will be approximately 18.92% oxygen, 9.46% CH_4 and 71.62% nitrogen. Under normal conditions, this mixture will burn in approximately 10 msec at $1,200°F$. This speed of burning is established by the molecular proximity of oxygen to methane, typical of this mixture, or the readiness of combination as based on typical molecular dispersion in a homogeneous mixture such as this.

If, however, the methane should be diluted with nitrogen so that there is only 2% methane in the methane-nitrogen fuel and if this fuel should be mixed homogeneously with air in a stoichiometric mixture, the burning time would be very greatly increased because of a reduction in the proximity of oxygen to CH_4 in the mixture. The burning time would now be approximately 0.32 sec. *after* the time required to elevate the temperature of the fuel-air mixture to autoignition temperature to produce an observed burning time very close to 1 sec. at an environmental temperature of $1,200°F$.

If the dilution of the fuel with inert matter is carried further, burning times at $1,500°F$ begin to be tremendous; and the cost of a structure for disposal to provide the required time at $1,500°F$ goes far beyond economic limits. Fortunately, the equations of Arrhenius for the effect of temperature on reaction velocities provide a very suitable solution for this problem but at the expense of greater fuel demand.

Where there is 1% or less of burnable, toxic or noxious matter in a stream of otherwise inert material, experience shows clearly that a design temperature greater than $1,200°F$ will be required to secure complete oxidation in the presence of not less than 25% excess air in 1 sec.

At this point, a more comprehensive definition of the term *complete combustion* or oxidation of fuel is necessary. In the typical practice of burning fuels for production of useful heat, combustion is considered complete when the Orsat or the electrical flue gas analyzer shows an absence of combustibles in the gases following burning. However, these devices are seldom capable of an accuracy better than 0.05%. With accuracy at 0.05%, there could be as much as 500 ppm of toxic or noxious material in the flue gases following the burning period. Complete combustion, as we define it, does not exist in this instance.

Concentration at Grade

It is true that thermal rise and exit velocity effects will produce dilution of the stack gases. As the gases reach grade downwind of the stack, the concentration of toxic materials may be reduced to tolerable limits, for most toxic or noxious materials, with dilution obtained through a selection of the proper stack height. There are standard calculation methods for the determination of stack height to obtain the required dilution. However, the formulation contains both empirical and judgment factors which may introduce errors to a greater or lesser degree.

An average target concentration at grade, downwind of the stack, is in the order of 0.10 ppm or perhaps less. For most toxic or noxious substances, this concentration is satisfactory; however, there are many substances where this small concentration is far too great and a severe odor or health nuisance is created. A further hazard is the tendency for products not present in the disposal stream to be synthesized in the course of passage through the furnace. These products can be alcohols, aldehydes, organic-sulphur compounds and others.

It is interesting to note that according to Volume 2 of the *Manual of Disposal of Refinery Wastes, Waste Gases and Particulate Matter,* published by the American Petroleum Institute, the following substances will cause odor nuisance in concentrations as shown:

Isobutyl Alcohol	0.003 ppm
Isoamyl Alcohol	0.0026 ppm
Methyl Mercaptan	0.041 ppm
Ethyl Mercaptan	0.0028 ppm
nPropyl Mercaptan	0.0016 ppm
nButyl Mercaptan	0.001 ppm
Isoamyl Mercaptan	0.00043 ppm
pThiocresol	0.0027 ppm
Methyl Sulfide	0.0037 ppm
Ethyl Sulfide	0.000056 ppm
Propyl Sulfide	0.011 ppm
nButyl Sulfide	0.015 ppm

It is in order to question the absolute measurement accuracy of such tiny concentrations; however, if the accuracy is only 50%, odor nuisance will still exist. In the blowing of hot asphalt to improve its characteristics through partial oxidation, the gases contain odorants. While there is no definition of odor perception levels for these compounds in the literature, there is mounting evidence that concentrations in the order of 0.01 ppm are capable of creating an odor nuisance.

Smoke

Various research not reported in the literature has shown that in the burning of compounds containing sulphur, from 1%-5% by weight of the sulphur will appear in the stack gases as SO_3 when the burning has been carried out normally. The remainder of the sulphur is SO_2. The influence of SO_3 on the dew-point characteristics of combustion gases is such that the dew point occurs immediately after departure from the stack producing a light grey-blue smoke of submicron-size H_2SO_4 particles. The particles are small enough to be air colloids. Such smoke diffuses very poorly. From an airplane, the smoke has been observed in travel over more than 75 mi. from the point of origin, disappearing in the distant haze. This phenomenon was observed in a very dry climate, at a mean ground altitude of 4,000 ft. with ground wind velocity at approximately 20 mph. (See "Stack Pluming Factors," NPRA WR-70-63.)

Liquid Streams

In disposing of liquid streams, the residence time factor must provide for the time interval required to convert the liquid to the gaseous state. This can be quite appreciable. Also, in disposing of liquid streams, when mineral salts are present, it has been repeatedly shown that the salts exit from the furnace in the form of oxide or carbonate submicron-size particles, which also are air colloids. These particles are emitted from the stack with the appearance of smoke.

In one particular instance where there was approximately 5% weight of sodium acetate in the liquid stream for disposal at 1,800°F, there was very little accumulation of mineral residue within the furnace after a period of approximately six months. In this case, the waste stream flow rate was approximately 5 gpm continuously for the period of operation. Also in this case, there was no report of hazard or damage due to the gas-carried particles. Operation has continued safely and without incident for a number of years. Furnace operation at excess air rates in the order of 175% completely suppresses any tendency for the mineral matter to appear as smoke.

Smoke, as just discussed, is characteristically white or greyish in color. In the present state of emphasis on air pollution abatement, the presence of a visible plume of smoke at the stack is an alarm flag which is virtually certain to promote pollution complaints which, while not necessarily justified, are the source of much bad publicity. The end result is that while the smoke may be completely harmless it cannot be tolerated. A prime example of air pollution emphasis and the virtual certainty of complaints because of visible plumes at any point in the plant is seen in the following example. A West Coast refinery was nearly compelled to make a $250,000 capital investment and spend $50,000 per year to superheat a cloud of water vapor rising from the cooling tower.

Plumes of mineral material at the stack are produced through ionization functions within the furnace. At high temperatures mineral oxides are initially produced which may later be converted to either the carbonates or the bicarbonates of the mineral which is oxidized but in the submicron-size range. These particles, being so very small, tend to behave as molecules which bear a negative charge. It is this condition which makes it almost impossible to entrap the particles in a water spray because the droplets of spray are also negatively charged. Like charges repulse each other, which allows the mineral particles to travel through the spray and emerge, untouched, at the stack. Specially designed scrubbers are used where velocity energy greater than the energy of repulsion permits the water droplets to wet and entrap the submicron particles so that they no longer appear in the stack gases after the scrubber.

In many instances there will be halogens present in the waste matter. The halogens appear as halogenic acids such as HCL and HF in the stack gases along with tiny concentrations of the halogen alone. Air pollution requirements are such that these products must not be vented to the atmosphere. Here again there is a demand for suitable scrubbing equipment which must be designed to avoid damage caused by the extremely corrosive conditions which will be certain to exist due to the halogenic acids, as such, but with particular reference to a potential for wet chlorine to be present. There are few alloys which, at a reasonable cost, are capable of resisting the attack of wet chlorine. Present techniques in scrubber design make use of glass fiber linings impregnated with various organic-derived compounds which are capable of polymerization to solid materials. Some scrubber designs incorporate titanium in critical areas.

Slurry

Where the waste matter is a liquid slurry with solids such as diatomaceous earth or other filter-aid matter and where the particle size in the slurry is great enough, the solid matter can be removed from the gas stream with suitably designed cyclones. There is limited use of such techniques in disposal of the waste matter which permits recovery of the filtering materials such as clays.

Fuel Cost

A very serious factor for consideration in any disposal process is that of fuel cost, which can be many thousands of dollars per year according to the nature of the waste matter as well as the quantity of waste. There is much study of waste-heat recovery as an adjunct to the business of disposal of wastes; but it must be made quite clear that if the waste disposal is properly carried out there must be a very careful study of waste-heat recovery so that it will not interfere with satisfactory disposal. Neither must the waste-heat recovery apparatus be subject to improper operation when there is solid matter present in the gases following disposal by burning. Corrosive matter in the gases must be anticipated in the design of the heat recovery apparatus lest there be undue destruction of it.

There is some relief from the tax standpoint for fuel cost in disposal; since the fuel cost is an operating cost and thus deductible, it is perhaps small comfort as a disposal problem is studied. But because of increasingly stricter laws governing air pollution, the fuel costs must be paid if the plant operation is to continue. One chemical plant spends more than $1,000,000 per year for disposal of a highly toxic waste stream. It is a wise group which, in the study of a new process facility, will carefully enter potential disposal costs in the economic portion of the study. The study should not neglect consideration of site space for the disposal facility, as the process area is allotted to equipment, because this factor can be quite significant according to the design of the disposal unit.

Space Requirements

In a study of the space required for the unit, it should be understood that a unit designed in a self-supporting, vertical cylindrical configuration is the most economical in terms of space, but it also costs more than a unit held vertical with guys—however, the space requirement for the guys and the required dead-men for guy anchoring may be prohibitive. An arrangement which will require less space than the guyed configuration is one in which a horizontal furnace is breeched into a vertical stack. This arrangement costs more and unless the stack can be designed for self-support, this can require as much space as if the entire unit were erected vertically.

A typical vertical cylindrical unit with an integral stack entirely lined with refractory has been shown to be a superior design in the disposal of chemical wastes because the entire structure including the stack provides volume for residence time at a calculated mean temperature level. It is possible to provide ample time for the required oxidation reactions without construction of a very large furnace for the residence time factor.

Stack Height

Stack height for the disposal unit serves two purposes which are quite important. The first is that the stack is capable of creating ample natural draft to eliminate the need for forced-draft fans. The second purpose is that the height of the stack is vital to air pollution elimination through diffusion of toxic or harmful products such as sulfur oxides carried by the stack gases. At this time, according to individual state laws, the allowable concentration of SO_2 at grade can be in the range of 0.10-0.20 ppm. In the burning of process fuels which contain sulfur or in the operation of a sulfur recovery plant where incineration of the waste gases is required, allowable SO_2 concentration can be the actual basis for establishing stack height rather than the draft factor. Acceptable calculation methods for stack height are the Sutton-Lowery procedure or the Bosanquet procedure. Both procedures may be found in the *Air Pollution Handbook* (McGraw-Hill). These procedures provide a means for determining height for satisfactory diffusion of stack gases which are not acceptable in the sense of air pollution. All stack heights should be carefully checked prior to start-up. Checking should be directed toward potential air pollution difficulty rather than the ability to produce a required state of draft. This is particularly true if there is any appreciable quantity of sulfur in the burned fuels, for any service.

Oxidations

As a study is made of materials for disposal and a means for handling them, thinking may well be based on a well-proven thesis. If the material can be either directly oxidized or if it can be first dissociated then oxidized there will be a satisfactory means for pollution-free handling of the material through the application of heat at a calculated level for a calculated time in the presence of adequate quantities of oxygen.

There is a very long list of waste matters which have been safely charged for thermal oxidation in reactions which may be endothermic or exothermic to units specifically designed for the service to be performed. Some of these wastes are as follows:

Water laden with HCN
Mineral salts in water solution
Asphalt blow-fumes
Plastics as solids
Various sludges
Phosgene in moist air
Sulfur plant off-gases
Toxic insecticide wastes
Hydrogen cyanide
Carbon disulfide-air mixtures
Water laden with H_2S
Organic salts in many solutions
Fullers earth-oil slurries
Rubber as a solid
Mercaptan-laden water
Materials bearing phenols
Amine wastes as gases and liquids
Hydrogen sulfide
Organic chlorides
Acrylo and Acetonitriles

The above list clearly shows that there are few waste materials, which cannot be handled safely and properly through thermal oxidation. However, the manner of handling and the equipment for handling must be specific. There is no genuine basis for advance prediction of the method or equipment to use. Procedures and equipment for proper action in waste disposal must be the products of careful and individual studies.

Residence Time

As an example, a combustion volume which is entirely adequate in residence time, assuming the gases produced in burning are properly directed at entry to the combustion volume, can become completely inadequate if the gases are misdirected causing them to make a direct-line traverse of the space rather than to flow gently to all areas of the volume. In the case of the direct traverse, the residence time is the actual time for the direct traverse, which may well be a small fraction of a second rather than a time calculated for the volume of gases to pass through the entire combustion volume.

Test Required

Because of the true residence time factor in the provided combustion space, a study of chemical kinetics at the calculated temperature level becomes distinctly hazardous unless there is a semi-commercial scale test of the material for disposal at calculated conditions to verify complete combustion where complete combustion produces pollutant concentration in terms of ppm rather than in mol-percentage because 0.5% of pollutant in stack gases represents 5,000 ppm and diffusion after exit from the stack cannot dilute to 0.01 ppm as the stack gases return to grade without a very high stack. The grade concentration for SO_2 required can be 0.10 ppm and 0.01 ppm is well above many tiny concentrations which can cause odor nuisance. Calculation of time and temperature must be based on certain assumptions. If there is not prior experience with the disposal product the basis for assumption may be incorrect and unsatisfactory disposal may result.

3

Efficiency
and Fuel
Conservation

"Heat" is a convenient term that is improperly used to denote the product of burning fuels. People should make use of the term "heat-energy" because heat-energy is, literally, the source of the lifestyle and customs of the twentieth century. Clean-burning fuels, all of fossil origin, are expensive to find and in short supply. Thus, we have what the news media describes as an "energy crisis" because of the tremendous hunger for clean-burning fuels to preserve what is considered an essential lifestyle.

Why heat-energy rather than, simply, heat? Heat-energy is measured as temperature, and absolute temperature will vary as the square of the average molecular motion. Since molecules are in constant motion at temperatures greater than absolute zero, and since molecules have mass, the energy can be measured by $MV^2/2$ as simple kinetic energy. It is thought-provoking to realize that every single effect caused by heat-energy application or withdrawal is because of an old friend—kinetic energy!

Fuel Loss

A most disconcerting but quite true statement is that of all the fuel burned in the world a most significant portion—perhaps as much as 5%—is lost or wasted. The simple reason for the waste is that the people who burn the fuel have inadequate understanding of what is required to burn fuel to the best advantage.

In view of the confusion and contradictions existing in the literature, in reference to fuels and their burning as well as the gross misunderstanding of factors pertaining to furnace and burner operation, the reasons for the loss or misuse of fuels is not difficult to understand.

Basis for Fuel Loss

Concisely stated, there is but one basis for establishing the efficiency of fuel use in any fixed installation such as a furnace and associated heat-use appurtenances, as the installation is studied without modification in any way. That basis is the quantity of excess air present in the various sections of the installation.

When a study is made of the burning of fuels using flue-gas analysis, however the analysis may be made, there is reason for understanding all factors which may be involved to avoid error which can be of considerable magnitude. It is pointed out that the calculation of air/fuel relationships for a specific, excess-air condition is made on the basis of *dry* air rather than the humid air which is typically used as a source of oxygen for the fuel.

Relative Humidity

Difficulty here is that relative humidity at any time, on any day, at any temperature, is not a fixed factor. A safe procedure is to presume, as a design condition, that relative humidity can be 100% at some period during which fuel is to be burned. And if the air temperature should be 100°F, the water vapor content of air is quite close to 6.50%, which will produce an error of notable magnitude unless air volume calculations take the water vapor factor into consideration.

Many times questions arise as to just what is excess air and how is it to be measured from flue-gas analysis. An answer can well be that excess air is the volume of air supplied for burning the fuel which is in excess of the quantity required for complete burning; however this reply leaves unanswered the question of measurement. The principal difficulty is that the term *air* has not yet been defined properly.

Air Defined

Within very narrow limits, air is 78.084% N_2, 20.946% O_2, 0.033% CO_2, and 0.934% A, with a few parts per million of Ne, He, Kr, Xe, H_2, CH_4 and N_2O. Using normal analytical techniques, air may be considered as 20.946% O_2 and 79.054% N_2. Thus, to get 1 mol of oxygen it is necessary that there be supplied 4.774 mols of air of which 3.774 mols are considered as nitrogen. But remember that this is the dry analysis. See Figures 3-1a and 3-1b.

In making a flue-gas analysis where carbon is present in the fuel, CO_2 will be present which is easily analyzed. But when the fuel contains H_2, and/or NH_3, which is typical of process fuels today, there is no CO_2 produced in burning. Thus, CO_2 is no longer a factor in process plant flue-gas analysis; but residual O_2 in these gases is the source of accurate determination of the amount of excess air in any fuel. When the fuel is laden with sulfur as H_2S, CH_3SH or others, the sulfur appears in the effluent flue gases as SO_2/SO_3 which, absorbed in analysis, will appear as CO_2. However, with any fuel, the accurate indicator of the amount of excess air is the volume (mol) percent of O_2 present in the flue gases which is typically measured on the *wet* basis. In other words, the flue-gas sample is saturated with water vapor at the analysis temperature and here quite another factor enters.

Combustion Gas Dew-Point

Typical fuels contain hydrogen which, as it burns, produces water vapor which tends to elevate the dew point of the effluent flue gases. As an example, gases produced in stoichiometric burning of CH_4 reach the dew point at 138°F; at 25% excess air, the dew point is 130°F; and at 100% excess air, the dew point is 113.5°F. Thus, if analysis is made on the basis of 60°F, there is a loss of much of the water vapor formed as the hydrogen burns. There is a decrease in the sample volume of flue gases according to the temperature at which the analysis is made. End effect of the loss is to increase the residual percentages of noncondensable gases, according to the state of condensation between the furnace temperature and the temperature at which the analysis is made.

Excess Air

Methane burned at 25% excess air, using dry air as the source of oxygen, produces the following reaction: $CH_4 + 2.5\ O_2 + 9.435\ N_2 = CO_2 + 2\ H_2O + 0.5\ O_2 + 9.435\ N_2$ or 12.935 mols of product/mol CH_4. It will be observed that 2.5 mols of O_2 are supplied and O_2 required for methane as theoretical air is 2.0 mols/mol. Therefore, the air quantity supplied is 2.5/2.0 = 1.25 or 25% excess air. The mol-percentages of the components at furnace temperature are as follows:

CO_2 – 7.74%
H_2O – 15.46%
O_2 – 3.86%
N_2 – 72.94%

This analysis takes into account the water vapor formed in the burning of the fuel.

Effect of Analysis Temperature

Note that such a mixture will have a dew point very close to 130°F. If, in the course of analysis, the temperature of the gases should fall below 130°F, there will be condensation of part of the water vapor which will alter the analysis made at the lower temperature. As the analytical temperature continues to fall, there is greater condensation and alteration of the analysis.

If, as an example, the gases produced in burning of methane should be analyzed at 60°F and 100°F, the analyses would be as follows:

CO_2 – 8.98%	CO_2 – 8.55%
O_2 – 4.49%	O_2 – 4.27%
N_2 – 84.79%	N_2 – 80.70%
H_2O – Remainder	H_2O – Remainder
60°F	100°F

Analyses for the two temperatures show clearly that temperature level distinctly influences analysis. Analytical data should be on the basis of standard conditions such as 60°F, if excess air indication is taken on the basis of O_2 percentage. As an example, consider the analysis at 40°F which would be:

CO_2 – 9.06%
O_2 – 4.53%
N_2 – 85.57%
H_2O - Remainder

In any fixed firing and heat conservation procedure excess air is the efficiency determinant. But the firing process and the heat conservation means chosen can greatly—if not tremendously—influence fired fuel economy because heat loss to the stack at any excess-air condition determines what portion of fuel-supplied heat is usefully absorbed and what portion is lost to temperature elevation of combustion gases as they make final departure from heat-transfer areas enroute to the stack. It is true that efficiency can be determined as heat absorbed/heat released as a simple procedure. The simple procedure, applied in the case of any typical natural-draft fired heater, will show that significant heat loss is a problem because stack temperature must be high enough to supply adequate furnace draft. The "high enough" temperature is usually 600°F (315.5°C) or higher.

Sensible heat, which is fuel-supplied, is demanded for stack gas temperature elevation. A "reasonable" amount of fuel-fired heat must be lost to stack temperature elevation as a fuel-fired structure such as a process heater or a steam generator operates, and natural-draft firing is difficult to reconcile with minimal fuel firing. The process industries, to reduce fuel quantities as fired to a minimum, are increasingly adopting "forced-draft preheated air" fuel-firing techniques. All of these techniques are more complex and more expensive at first but richly rewarding in reduced fuel cost as operation continues. They also improve firing and process conditions. These beneficial conditions exist in preheated air firing for a number of reasons.

Fuel demand for any firing service is set by the heat required for the service to be performed vs. the efficiency with which the fired structure makes use of such heat as provided through fuel burning. Competent designers, through the application of calculated and experienced-gained procedures, can and do supply means for heat transfer to fluids for heating which can be described as "adequate." But "adequate" is according to the manner is which fuel firing is carried out. A natural-draft firing-heat availability is based on fuel-supplied heat and is burdened by demand for high enough stack temperature for stack-draft maintenance, since stack draft is necessary for furnace draft to cause an inflow of enough air for fuel burning. This heat demand, even in the best natural-draft firing, is a dismaying portion of fuel-produced heat when all heat available for useful heat transfer *is* fuel-produced. In preheated forced-draft operation heat available for transfer and total use is a *total* of fuel-provided heat *plus* the sensible heat imparted to the air supply by heat-exchanged from stack-bound combustion gases. The final stack gas temperature is independent of draft requirement, since induced-draft fans supply all required furnace draft. Note, however, that the furnace-draft condition must be the same for either forced/induced-draft operation or for natural-draft operation. Furnace pressure must always be negative (less than atmospheric) to avoid serious furnace damage. Furnace arch draft (which is minimal) will increase approximately 0.01 inches WC for each foot of furnace height from arch to floor. Burner operation in forced draft is independent of furnace draft.

In a design stage there can be a design option as to whether natural or forced draft is to be used for air supply for combustion. But in retrofit of existing furnaces a decision as to air supply must be made according to a number of variables. The first can be the potential saving in fuel cost caused by stack temperature reduction, and will the saving justify (amortize) cost for the shift from natural to forced draft with preheated air in a reasonable time. This is particularly true when the fuel/fuels contain as much as one weight-percent surlfur where a consensus of capable operators sets 450°F (232°C) as the minimum stack gas temperature without danger of serious sulfuric corrosion. Air-heater corrosion also requires consideration if it is the tubular type.

A second factor worth sober consideration concerns total required heat versus net saving because a projected *gross* cannot be considered a *net* saving. Additional costs are characteristic of preheated forced-draft firing. These extra costs can be caused by greater capital investment, added labor, added maintenance requirements, added power costs where natural draft needs no use of power, and more complex and expensive control for forced draft than for natural draft whether there is or is not air preheat. At times, cost factors are responsible for net loss rather than net profit in conversion! It is wise to consider *all* the factors, but if the projected heat release is large enough, profitability is almost certain.

A most significant advantage in fuel burning is available through resort to forced-draft burner operation with appreciable windbox pressure because of a greater velocity at which air flows through the burner for combination with fuel. A suitable condition of turbulence for air-fuel mixture is demanded for any burner. Fuel injection to the burner is typically at 15 pounds gauge or more, and the fuel flow is, initially, at critical velocity or near to it to deliver maximum turbulence to the mixing zone for fuel-air. However, mixing zone turbulence is a total because of fuel flow and air flow as fuel and air come together. Turbulence supplied by either air or fuel varies as the square of each flowing velocity as they meet. In natural draft an average air-pressure drop across the burner is 0.25 inches WC, and the resulting 60°F (15.5°C) air-flow velocity is approximately 33.4 ft/sec. In forced draft a minimal air-pressure drop across the burner is 2.00 inches WC and, at the same temperature, air-flow velocity is 94.4 ft/sec. Air-flow turbulence is increased $94.4^2/33.4^2$, and fuel burning is greatly accelerated. Flame volume is reduced, and it is possible to increase heat input to a specific furnace. Since fuel loss is a serious problem in any fuel-firing operation, it is best to adopt the fuel (energy) system that is least wasteful if all factors indicate it should be used. At times it is not wise or possible to do so, but no stone should be left unturned as the problem is considered.

In the 40°F analysis, the O_2 concentration is greater than it would be at 60°F, and while the difference is not great it is significant particularly for critical service or in critical analysis because as the O_2 increases the excess air becomes greater. The O_2 indicated at 60°F is for 25% excess air, but the O_2 indicated at 40°F is for approximately 25.30% excess air with methane as fuel with its H/C ratio-by-weight of 0.33. Using typical No. 6 fuel oil (bunker-C) as the fuel, with the same O_2 analysis, the excess air at 60°F would be 26.40% and at 40°F it would be 26.60%. As has been stated these differences are not great but in a "go-or-no-go" situation they can be significant.

A set of curves (Figure 3-1) for methane (H/C = 0.33) fuel and No. 6 fuel oil (H/C = 0.11) is provided. It will be observed from the curves that there is a small effect due to the fuel H/C ratios-by-weight. This state occurs because 9.548 cu. ft. of dry air is quite close to the theoretical air required for 1,000 Btu HHV for any fuel which is hydrocarbon and saturated (paraffin) in its nature. There is greater deviation with olefins and other unsaturated compounds but the deviation is not significant.

Temperature Correction for Excess Air

This information applies only where analytical methods and techniques are capable of great accuracy such as with a properly maintained oxygen analyzer which has been checked against a standard sample; but it does not apply in typical Orsat analysis where analytical error can be of any magnitude according to reagent freshness, leaks within the Orsat circuits, and changes in sample temperature in the course of analysis. If the analytical technique and instrumentation for analysis will permit suitable accuracy the following temperature correction to O_2 indication can be made:

40°F – 0.9911
50°F – 0.9955
60°F – 1.0000
70°F – 1.0089
80°F – 1.0181
90°F – 1.0321
100°F – 1.0515

$$\frac{\text{Excess Air at Temperature}}{\text{Temperature Correction Factor}} = \text{Std. Excess Air.}$$

It is because of this analytical problem and because the point at which the excess air should be measured is not too definitely understood that there are many needless expenses in burner change to permit operation at less excess air in the process industries.

Indicated O_2 is currently *the* correct indicator for excess air in flue gas analysis, but the indicated O_2 will vary according to the immediate temperature at which the flue gas analysis is made. Temperature correction data as provided presumes analysis of the flue gas sample at ambient temperature such as would be the case if the sample cools to atmospheric temperature *before* the analysis is made. But an analyzer which operates at stack temperature (and directly at stack temperature) by insertion in the stack is now widely used. At stack temperature, all of the water formed as the fuel hydrogen burns is in vapor phase. The water vapor dilutes other gases, and incondensible gases result from fuel burning. Less O_2 content is analyzed than would be the case if the water vapor should reach dew point and drop out as water prior to analysis. It is axiomatic to say that "2% O_2 means 10% excess air" because, prior to the stack-inserted analytical device, all analysis was made at atmospheric temperature, and the water vapor had dropped out. With all water vapor remaining in vapor phase, and at 10% excess air, the combustion reaction with methane fuel is:

$$CH_4 + 2.2\,O_2 + 8.36\,N_2 = CO_2 + 2\,H_2O$$
$$+ 0.2\,O_2 + 8.36\,N_2$$

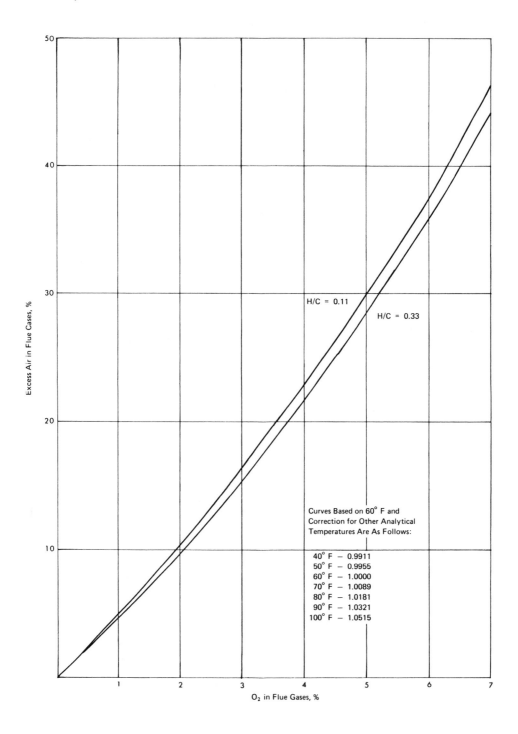

Figure 3-1a. Excess air indication by oxygen content of flue gases as based on the H/C ratio by weight of the fuel. H/C of 0.33 = methane; H/C of 0.11 = #6 (Bunker C) oil.

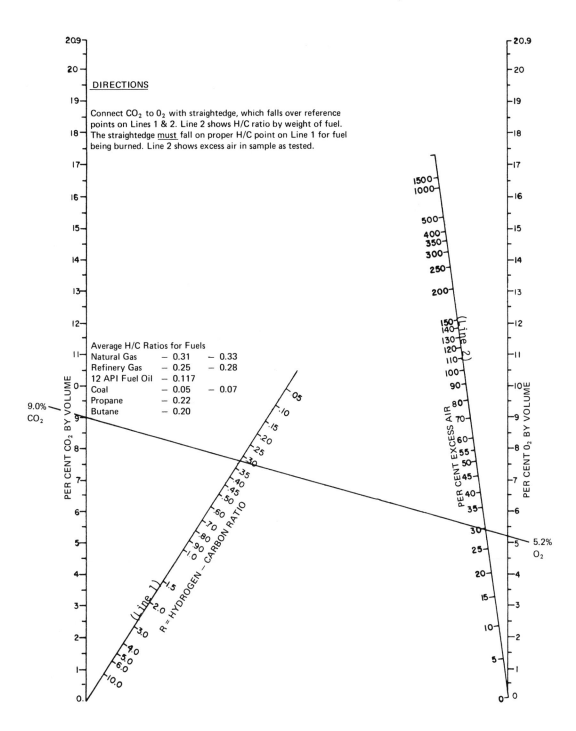

*Figure 3-1*b. *Properties of the products of combustion.*

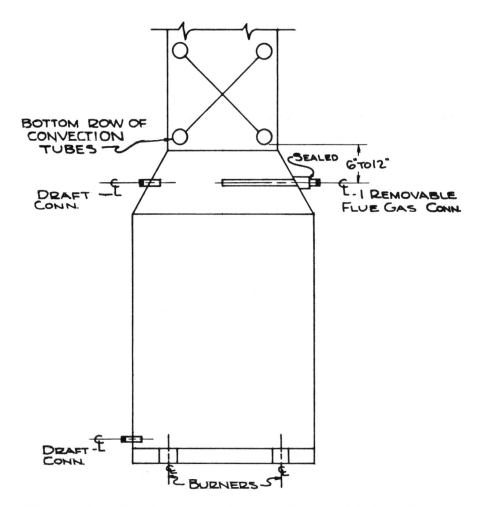

*Figure 3-2*a. *General elevation of recommended minimum flue gas and draft sampling connections.*

The oxygen mol percentage is $0.2/11.56 = 0.0173$ or 1.73% rather than 2%. The stack-inserted device will show less O_2 for a stated excess air condition. If the fuel contains significant quantities of CO or H_2, there must be correction for indicated excess air as based on balanced equation burning for other than hydrocarbon fuels vs. hydrocarbon fuel.

Burner Change for Fuel Ecomony

No reputable burner manufacturer will suggest burner changes in the interest of fuel economy without making his own checks of furnace conditions in detail prior to such recommendation. (See Figures 3-2a and 3-2b.) The burner manufacturer should be held closely to his predicted economy if

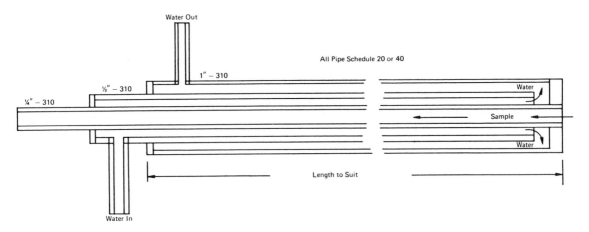

Figure 3-2b. Water-cooled sample tube.

he recommends a burner change after his checks. Any prediction of more than 1 or 2% fuel saving should be considered highly presumptious and probably impossible to achieve unless the burners which are to be removed are completely unsatisfactory because of excessive flame volume, because of flame impingement when the excess air factor is low for good fuel economy, and lack of ability to maintain good fuel economy at all conditions of firing and operation.

Firing Conditions

In many instances of unsatisfactory firing conditions, which cause the excess air factor to be too great, the burners are being operated at conditions which depart from the conditions for which the burners have been purchased. Correction of bad firing can be had from the original manufacturer at markedly less cost for burner parts and for lost process time. In any case, the original burner manufacturer should be consulted before his burners are removed. Also, it is the duty of the operator or his supervisor to be fully aware of particular furnace conditions far in advance of any call to people who are interested solely in burner sales without regard to what may occur as a result of the sale, as is too often true when a burner change is made.

If, as has been discussed, the operation of the burners leaves much to be desired, the serious problem is not fuel economy but is, instead, the state of process capability for the heater as well as the degree of aggravated attrition to the tubes and heat transfer surfaces which forces frequent heater shutdown and loss of its service.

The Role of Chemistries

As fuel is burned when using an oxygen source such as air, the burning processes are chemical in their nature since the burning of fuels is oxidation. Laws of chemistry state that if a chemical reaction is to be driven to completion in a reasonable time there must be an excess of one of the components for the reaction. Since efficiency of burning cannot tolerate an excess of fuel, the excess is taken as air; but because of the quantity of excess air there is certain heat loss because the excess air enters at atmospheric temperature and exits at stack temperature.

Thus, the laws of chemistry require that a certain heat loss must exist if the fuel is to be completely burned. The great error in fuel conservation occurs because the quantity of excess air is allowed to far exceed that quantity which would permit complete burning of the fuel. It would seem evident, then, that a procedure for drastic reduction in excess air in all furnaces is indicated.

Not necessarily so! There are important limitations which must be observed carefully to obtain genuine fuel economy and, more importantly, to obtain a state of satisfactory heat transfer based on specific burner and furnace conditions. As an example of the careful approach required, consider a heater supplied with fuel which varys widely in calorific value, where there is a considerable variation in heat demand, such that a state of comparatively high excess air is required to avoid air shortage and loss of fuel as conditions of firing vary.

This, then, points out that any approach to fuel economy through reduction of excess air in furnaces must take into account the type of fuel-burning equipment in use, the potential variations in fuel, the range of control required, the excellence of controls and the speed of control response to changes in heat demand. As suggested, it is unwise to go too far in the reduction of excess air if all factors do not lend themselves well to such reduction.

Heat Loss Evaluated

There is a general tendency to recognize the fact that excess air is expensive but to be concerned with other factors involved in the operation of a furnace. Better understanding of the magnitude of the loss can alter this attitude. With air temperature at 60°F the heat loss for each 380 cu. ft. of excess air (1 lb.-mol) at various stack temperatures is shown in Table 3-1.

Theoretical air per million Btu's LHV is approximately 10,540 scf. Therefore, at 10% excess air there would be 1,054 scf of excess air; at 20% excess air there would be 2,108 scf of excess air and at 30% there would be 3,162 scf of excess air.

Table 3-1
Heat Loss per Pound-Mol of Air
(Air Temperature, 60° F)

Stack Temperature (° F)	Heat Loss (Btu)
500	3,050
750	4,800
1,000	6,700
1,250	8,400

With the stack temperature at 1,000°F the heat loss at 10% excess air is 18,579 Btu; at 20% excess air the heat loss is 37,158 Btu and at 30% excess air the loss is 55,737 Btu.

Benefits from Excess Air Reduction

It is interesting to note that as excess air is reduced there are compound benefits which serve the operator of a process facility very well. There is improved heat transfer. Therefore for a stated service there is less fuel fired, and this appears in the plant operating balance at the end of the year as money saved because less fuel is burned per pound of product produced. This is tangible and pleasant to say the least, but there are further benefits.

When there is a decrease in fuel burned there is a decrease in total flue gases produced and a drop in stack temperature because a greater portion of the heat as fired is absorbed. As both the gas temperature and quantity drops, there is a very significant decrease in pressure drop across the heater; and while the reduced stack temperature reduces stack draft, the reduction in draft is less than the reduction in pressure drop, so that the end result is increased draft in the furnace. This is, at times, most beneficial in that it becomes possible to avoid furnace pressures greater than atmospheric as the excess air is reduced. The state of furnace draft is far more critical than is ordinarily thought to be the case because every operating heater is fired to its limit the greater portion of the time as standard practice. Unless the stack design has been very liberal, it is quite probable that the stack will not be capable of adequate draft to avoid furnace pressure.

Thus, in this case, if the excess air is reduced from 30% to 10%, the heat loss per million Btu's fired would be reduced by 37,158 Btu. There is no more fruitful means for reducing operating costs than maintaining the lowest possible condition of excess air in the firing of all fuels. Fuel cost varies quite widely according to geographical area and according to fuel availability, but it is a rare process facility which is supplied with fuel at less than 25¢ per million Btu's LHV. The cost can well be in the order of 50¢ per million Btu's to make the cost for fuel one of the largest if not the largest single portion of operating cost.

In a small plant consuming fuel at a rate of 200,000,000 Btu/hr., the annual fuel cost is $438,000 (based on 25¢ per MM Btu) and is $876,000 per year based on 50¢ fuel. This is a small plant. It would not be unusual for a plant to spend $5,000,000 per year for fuel alone, and in this instance, a reduction of only 1% in fuel cost can produce a return of $50,000 at a labor cost of not greater than $10,000 to produce the saving.

With these figures in mind, it is difficult to imagine why such a profitable procedure should not be followed closely, but there are reasons. The operator of a plant unit faces the continual burden of product production to specification. If he feels that pursuit of fuel economy will make it difficult to meet the required quantity of specification product, he will be reluctant to follow fuel economy closely. In justice, he is not due for censure for his attitude but is entitled to an explanation of why fuel economy can make it easier to produce his product.

It is quite easy, during times of difficulty with a unit, to open the burner air registers a little so that there is no necessity for close attention to furnace firing. When the difficulty is cleared up, there is a tendency to keep the added register opening providing higher excess air.

The true burden for proper activation of a fuel economy program lies with management and with supervisory employees who report to management. These people must explain to the operators and firemen why fuel conservation can help rather than hinder them in the performance of their duties. To obtain fuel economy, the burners, the controls and the furnaces must be in good operating order to automatically reduce the quantity of work required for operation. There should be an ample number of points for checking draft. There should be proper equipment and sampling points for flue gas samples. Thermocouples should be checked and maintained and close attention paid to their temperature indications because temperature variation is one of the first indications of trouble.

Management Responsibility

It is the responsibility of management to see that people who are to make checks for excess air are equipped with proper means for measurement. It is typical to make excess air measurements using the Orsat analyzer; however, it is to be noted that the portable Orsat analyzer is anything but reliable for this service because of its own limitations. If there is only a tiny leak in the valving between reagents for CO_2, O_2 and CO there can be an error in indication. If the temperature of the burette sample should change only $5°F$ there will be a 1% error in the flue gas data.

If the reagents for CO_2, O_2 and CO are not fresh, all the separate contents of the sample may not be absorbed. If all the CO_2 is not absorbed separately, the remaining CO_2 appears as O_2 in the analysis. If some of the KOH in the CO_2 reagent is accidentally drawn into the leveling water, some of the CO_2 is absorbed in the leveling water and does not appear in the analysis. The Orsat user will all too frequently be dismayed if he adds a few drops of phenolphthalein to the leveling water of his Orsat to find that the bright pink color following addition of phenolphthalein shows significant alkalinity in the leveling water.

It is not to be questioned that the Orsat as it is used in the laboratory, under closely controlled laboratory conditions, is a fine piece of equipment and is fully capable of delivering accurate analytical information; but field use of portable Orsats is to be highly questioned as to accuracy.

In one reliability test for Orsat data, five chemical engineers took five separate Orsats and without knowledge of what was going on made five separate analyses of the flue gases in a furnace where the firing rate was fixed and where air adjustment was unchanged. Five completely different analyses resulted, in which there was as much as 2% variation in CO_2, as much as 3% variation in O_2, and two analyses showed CO present. It is to be noted that each of the engineers performed his test faithfully and to the best of his ability such that the analytical data as taken erroneous due to leakage, alkaline leveling water, sample over-heating and spent reagents, among other things.

Flue Gas Analyzers

For cumbustion research to be valid, it is necessary for the volumetric accuracy with which oxygen and combustibles in flue gases are measured to be not only accurate but accurate to within 0.1% repeatably. The portable Orsat, even with faultless operation, did not approach this accuracy. Confronted with this situation, researchers set out to actively test each analyzer offered on the market for requisite accuracy. Many were vastly superior to the portable Orsat, but only two were found with an acceptable accuracy level.

The measurement of oxygen alone does not provide adequate data for fuel conservation because, according to a number of variables, both excess oxygen and combustibles can be present. If combustibles are present in the flue gases, there is a fuel loss. There is no need to know how much combustible matter is present; it should be eliminated if possible.

Because of the less-than-clear chemistry of combustion with any fuel, the combustibles may be carbon monoxide, or any of a number of aldehydes, alcohol, free hydrogen, or others. This phenomenon is particularly true with gas fuel, but with oil fuel there can be no smoking when there is incomplete burning; however, oil fuel is usually productive of black smoke (carbon) when burning conditions are incorrect—but not always! Non-portable flue gas analyzers that measure O_2 at stack temperature are not yet available for simultaneous combustibles measurement on the same continuous basis.

Flue Gas Sampling Techniques

Sampling techniques can be the source of considerable error in flue gas analysis. The sampling line must be tight and completely free from leaks. The sampling tube must be inserted far enough in the flue gas flow to avoid the effect of air leakage around the tube. If the gases as sampled are at high temperatures, the metallurgy of the sample tube must be adequate for the temperature or a water-cooled sampling tube must be used. In most cases, the use of a tube made of type 310 stainless-steel (25-20) will be satisfactory up to 1,800-2,000°F, but the sample should be drawn through the tube for at least 10 minutes to allow time for inner-surface oxidation which is going to occur. The oxygen comes from the sample gases being drawn through the tube. If the tube oxidation is not completed before the sample analysis is read, the analysis will show less O_2 than is actually present in the flue gases when there is excess air in the gases. If the flue gases are oxygen deficient, there can be a reduction of the oxide coating causing incorrect analytical data to be observed because the instrument will show a lower combustible content than may be present in the flue gases. Note that type 310 alloy tends to retain its oxide coating to a much greater degree than type 309 (25-12) or type 304 (18-8) and that while types 310 and 309 are adequate for temperatures at 1,800-2,000°F, type 304 alloy is not good for more than 1,500-1,600°F.

Sampling Errors

The metallurgy of the sampling tube in flue-gas analysis can be quite critical for still another reason if the temperature of the gas as drawn through the tube is in excess of 750°F. As has been noted, the tube is subject to oxidation at greater temperature levels with the oxygen coming from the sample as checked to show less O_2 in analysis than is actually present in the gases from which the sample is drawn. While faulty oxygen indication can be a serious error, there is an even more serious condition which can and often does occur. Water vapor in contact with iron oxide can cause hydrogen to appear in the sample as a combustible when the sampled gas temperature is high. This condition can and does occur when there is ample excess air present and there is no trace of hydrogen in the gases from which the sample is drawn.

As the gas sample is drawn through the sampling tube, when the temperature of the tube is high, the slow movement of the gases en route to analysis allows the following chemical reactions to occur according to the temperature of the tube's inner surface: $(Fe + H_2O) = FeO + H_2$ and $2 FeO + H_2O = Fe_2O_3 + H_2$.

Ferrous oxide is converted to ferric oxide and hydrogen is produced. Note that very high temperatures would be required for the direct reaction of water vapor with iron to produce ferrous oxide; but enough oxygen is present to combine with the iron, forming ferrous oxide, at much lower temperatures. In this discussion, the presumption is made that some oxygen is present in the gases from which the sample is drawn. If there should be an oxygen deficiency for the fuel and no oxygen is present in the sampled gases and if the inner surface of the sample tube is oxidized, the combustibles combine with the iron oxides to produce some very interesting results. For example, even though combustibles are present in the gases from which the sample is drawn there will be no or very little combustible matter in the analyzed sample.

In this instance, the ferric oxide may be reduced to ferrous oxide and if the condition continues for a great enough time, the ferrous oxide can be further reduced to metallic iron.

If it is presumed that the sample tube has oxidation resistance equal to type 310 stainless steel, no sample should be accepted as suitable for accurate analysis until the sampling gases have been drawn continuously through the sample tube for 10 minutes. This provision will ensure that equilibrium conditions within the tube have been reached at the sampling temperature with the further provision that there be no interruption in gas movement as the sample is taken for analysis. Continuous gas movement is very difficult to obtain with a portable Orsat but is quite characteristic of the analyzer where an electrically driven vacuum pump draws the sample continuously.

Excess air measurement is for the total air quantity—both the air entering through fuel burning equipment and air entering through furnace leaks are accounted for. Air leakage can be quite serious since air entering through random leakage points is present and is measured but it takes no part in the burning of the fuel. Therefore, there may be an excessive quantity of air present but there is no immediate means for controlling it. Air entering through the fuel burning euqipment must be adequate for the fuel quantity to avoid poor flame conditions, burning throughout the flue gas passages, and unsatisfactory heat-transfer conditions. Neither the burner design nor the burner manufacturer are to be censured when this condition exists.

Burning of the fuel must be in the zone immediately adjacent to the fuel-burning equipment, governed by the air supply in this zone as controlled by air registers and other air control means. There is no control of air leakage; therefore, the burning equipment has no control of conditions caused by air leakage. It is, indeed, a rare furnace in which there is no air leakage.

Furnace erection in which there is air leakage is not a factor of poor design; neither is it necessarily a factor of poor construction. Air leakage and furnaces are more or less inseparable; however, air leakage can be held in control to a very marked degree. An example is a 50,000 bpd topping heater. The heat release was in the order of 250,000,000 Btu/hr. After a maintenance crew spent less than a full day hunting down air leaks in the furnace wall, in the header boxes, and in various joints in the furnace structure, the heaters fuel demand dropped a full 5%. There was not a single change in draft or burner adjustment to produce the reduction in fuel demand. The fuel demand dropped because most of the air leaks in the furnace structure were found and sealed, at the cost of approximately 32 man-hours of labor and some material to produce an annual saving measured in thousands of dollars.

A furnace in which there are no header boxes is least subject to air leakage because a significant part of the leakage will occur in and around the header boxes. Unfortunately, a crack can exist in a header box and never be detected. The inner portion of the header box is under substantially the same draft as the furnace. When there is a crack just 1/16-in. wide and 10-feet long, it is the same as a hole in the furnace wall having an area of 7½ sq. in. or more than a 3-in. diameter hole. Such a hole would be immediately closed, but the 1/16-in. crack is seldom seen. Close inspection of the entire furnace will reveal some interesting evidence of air entry such as black streaks on the furnace wall. The streak is black because entering air chills it! Poorly closed peep doors are offenders.

With fuel cost at 35¢ per million Btu's, at a furnace draft at 0.25-in. WC and based strictly on the fuel loss due to elevation of 60°F air to stack temperature at 750°F, the annual cost per square inch of air leakage is $35.56. This loss does not take into account the heat-transfer loss due to the chilling effect of the cold air in the heater's radiant section, which alone could easily double the cost.

Annual loss due to an open 4-in. by 6-in. peep hole, under the same conditions, is $853.55. While it is not at all standard practice to leave peep holes open for a year, it is interesting to note that the cost for such an open peep hole for 24 hrs. is $2.33.

Air leakage is finite. It can be measured and its source can be found and the loss it causes can be controlled to a reasonable degree. Once this source of loss is pointed out, there is a marked tendency to avoid such unnecessary loss.

Air Leakage

There is a factor in the measurement of excess air and thermal efficiency which is not so easy to resolve. Despite many literature references advising the contrary, it is customary to locate a single flue gas sampling point in the heater stack with the thought in mind that this single sampling point will suffice for both measurement of excess air and thermal efficiency without further reference.

Excess air can be measured at this point, as is obvious. (See Figure 3-3.) Without question, overall thermal efficiency should be based on the heat content of the stack gases because at this point there is no further use of the heat; thus it is lost as it exits up the stack. But factors other than the air which is entering through the burning equipment influence both the excess air at this point and the thermal efficiency as measured at this point. Thus, if there is to be maximum use of fuel there must be additional measurement.

It is this practice of single measurement alone which accounts for the great majority of needlessly wasted fuel. It is common to find excess air in the furnace radiant section as low as 10%, while a simultaneous sample of stack gases may show as much as 100% excess air due to leakage between the furnace and the stack by either actual entry of this quantity of air or stratification of leak-admitted air to the sample point. It is again noteworthy that such a condition is common rather than rare.

Suppose that in this case management demanded a reduction in excess air to say 25% in the stack sample by the usual methods, which would

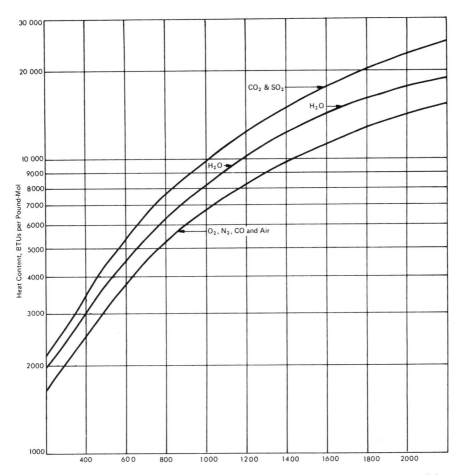

Figure 3-3. Sensible heat contents per pound-mol for various gases. Heat contents are sensible only and no latent heats are included in any case. (60°F base.)

be either adjustment of burner air dampers or closure of the stack damper. If there is only 10% excess air in the furnace at the time the reduction in air quantity is started while there is 100% excess air in the stack, it is quite obvious that within the furnace there will not be enough air for the fuel as the air quantity is reduced.

The results of such a state of reduction in air quantity are many. The first thing that will be observed is an abrupt drop in coil outlet tempera-

ture. This prompts the controls to admit more fuel to restore the temperature to the required level. Because of the lack of air response the control may open the fuel flow to the side-open condition. The entire furnace structure is filled with combustibles and the furnace will pant, puff or breathe.

If a furnace is puffing or panting, it is to be emphasized as strongly as possible that the proper corrective procedure is to immediately reduce the fuel to the furnace to approximately 25% of normal or less to stop the puffing and panting. This may take 15-20 sec. according to how seriously the furnace is flooded with fuel. Do not, under any circumstances, attempt to stop the puffing or breathing with increased draft or increased burner air-register opening. This procedure will cause the puffing or breathing to become so violent that serious furnace damage can occur. Because of violent flame expulsion and hot gases from openings in the furnace some very serious burns can be suffered by personnel in the area.

If the reduction in air quantity is not great enough to cause panting or puffing but is great enough to cause a lack of sufficient air for the burning equipment, there will be secondary combustion at each point where air is leaking into the furnace. A prime symptom of secondary burning is an abrupt rise in outlet temperature from the convection section. Fin tubes may rapidly lose their fins or marked fin attrition may be observed. Serious refractory damage can occur because a reducing atmosphere can lower the heat resistance of refractory very drastically and cause it to spall at what would be a normal temperature level in an oxidizing atmosphere.

Anyone who operates a gas-fired furnace for several years will note, at times, a condition that is best described as "a hazy furnace." The normal tendency is to be critical of the burners for what is seemingly a lack of short-flame capability as the furnace is operating. But the burners are improperly blamed! As a furnace operator manipulates draft in an effort to control stack excess air, the burners are actually short of air, and the gases rising from the burners are laden with combustibles. As the combustibles meet air which has leaked into the furnace from any of many sources, secondary combustion begins and is seen as "haze." Furnace air leakage (and an airtight process furnace can be considered a rarity) accounts for most of the 5% fuel waste that is a daily condition in process firing. Those engineers who are aware of the need for fuel conservation demand airtight furnaces as a design specification.

If excess air is to be closely controlled it must be done on the basis of the quantity of excess air immediately above the combustion zone or at the arch of the radiant section of the furnace. It is in the furnace proper that the fuel should burn and it is in this zone that the chemical laws require the presence of some measurable excess air.

The stack is relatively remote from the portion of the heater in which the fuel is to be burned and the possibilities for air leakage en route from the combustion area to the stack are more or less infinite. Such air leakage is not attributable to the burners and no burner adjustments can correct it; neither can a change of burners correct it. The leaks must be found and closed to the best of your ability with the firm understanding that complete closure of all leaks is seldom, if ever, obtained in practice.

Figure 3-2 shows a sampling arrangement which will allow the most economical use of fuel is one which provides two sampling connections for each heater. One connection should be in the combustion area, above all flames, for control of excess air; the second connection should be in the stack to determine the amount of air leakage which may exist between the combustion area and the point where there is no further use of heat.

When this sampling arrangement shows 10% excess air in the combustion area and 20% excess air in the stack, it may be presumed that further effort to reduce air leakage will provide a relatively small return. The higher indication in the stack can well be caused by channeling of air from a very small leak directly to the sample point. As the gap between the two readings begins to widen, there is reason for maintenance work to close the newly opened leaks or the new leaks which have caused the stack excess air to rise.

Following suggested procedure for sampling has, by actual experience in both large and small plants, produced annual fuel savings of more than 3%. This may be considered ample repayment for the cost of an additional sampling point, even if expensive alloy material is used.

Air leakage is not always confined to parts of the heater after the furnace proper, such as the convection section and the breeching to the stack. The furnace should be suspected and particularly if there are header boxes because these essential structures are very leak prone.

As they are designed, the header boxes will be equipped with hinged doors for access to the headers. Even with resilient gaskets, such a hinged door is very difficult to seal to a condition where the header box is reasonably airtight. After the door has been opened and closed a few times, there is simply no seal, and cracks with a width of 1/16-in. or wider exist. Checking the space between the gaskets and the steel with a knife blade will reveal the cracks.

As the tubes project between the furnace and the header box, they pass through the tubesheet or through the wall. Obviously, the opening for the tube must be larger than the tube to permit insertion. An average clearance is ¼-in. For a 4-in. OD tube, there are approximately 2.45 sq. in. around each tube for transmission of furnace draft to the header box. With 15 tubes, there are 36.75 sq. in. of open area between the furnace and the header box.

If the header box door is poorly sealed, the annual loss from air leakage can be $8,000.00 for a single header box. Fuel loss per year can easily exceed $75,000.00 because of general furnace air leakage.

The procedure for checking of furnace air leakage is simple if there is a combustion gas sampling point in the furnace proper, as has been discussed. The starting point is a sample of the gases in the furnace proper, then as leaks are found at the peep holes, in the header boxes, in the joints of the furnace wall and in other places, a second, third and perhaps fourth check of the combustion gases from the furnace sampling point should show decreased oxygen in the furnace gases. In one such procedure, after the leaks in just one header box were closed, it was necessary to open the air registers on the burners to keep the excess air as high as 10%. In this furnace, with further discovery of air

leakage, it was necessary to approximately double the air register opening to hold the excess air up to 10% as the test procedure was completed.

It is true that the furnace just discussed was not new, but it was a portion of a major oil refinery and had received maintenance typical of other heaters in the plant. Such incidents are not found every day but they are far from rare, and some very interesting results are found in such checks in any operating process facility. A draft gage applied to the header box to show significant draft provides a good basis for further searching.

Loss due to air leakage is not necessarily confined to fuel loss. In a vertical, cylindrical, steam-reforming furnace, continued loss of tubes at the floor line caused by extreme pitting of the tubes was traced to a leaky seal around the tube. The leak allowed infiltration of air around the tubes and in this case the tubes were made of very expensive alloy.

There is increasing evidence that tube failures at or near the ends of the tubes are caused by air infiltration due to both accelerated oxidation and thermal stresses in the tubes brought about by very abrupt chilling at high temperature levels.

A source of great error in the calculation of heat utilization factors is to be found in acceptance of temperature indications in the flow of gases from fixed thermocouples where the reading of the couple may be in error by as much as 150°F. (See Figure 3-4.) The error is caused by reradiation of heat from the thermowell to adjacent cold surfaces. It is only if the thermowell surroundings are at as great or greater temperature than the thermowell that the temperature indication of the thermocouple within the thermowell can be accepted as reasonably accurate.

Experience shows that bridge-wall thermocouples are usually reasonably accurate but may be in error by 25°F or more. Convection thermocouples may be in error by as much as 150°F and stack thermocouples may deviate from accuracy by as much as 100°F.

It is not a question of whether or not the thermocouple detects the temperature of the ther-

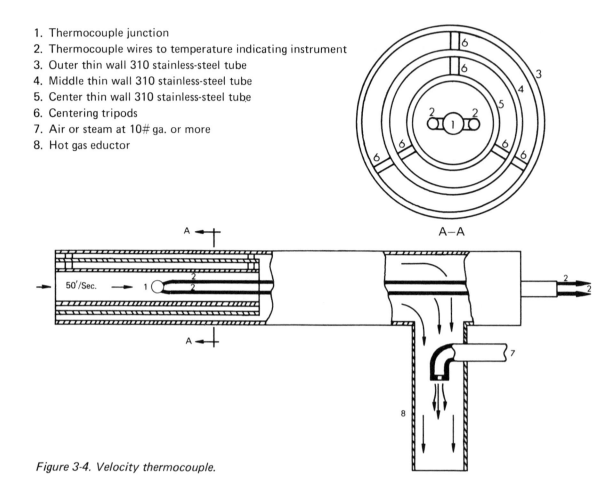

1. Thermocouple junction
2. Thermocouple wires to temperature indicating instrument
3. Outer thin wall 310 stainless-steel tube
4. Middle thin wall 310 stainless-steel tube
5. Center thin wall 310 stainless-steel tube
6. Centering tripods
7. Air or steam at 10# ga. or more
8. Hot gas eductor

Figure 3-4. Velocity thermocouple.

mowell within the limits of its own accuracy. However, the thermowell temperature is seldom as great as that of the gas flowing over it, principally because of reradiation from the thermowell but also because of poor scrubbing action of the gases over the thermowell versus heat conducted away from the area of the thermocouple by the thermowell metal. In the strict sense, the temperature indications of thermowells for gas temperature are yardsticks to a greater or lesser degree.

Velocity Thermocouples

Accurate gas temperature measurement should be made only through the use of a velocity thermocouple in which the gases are drawn briskly over a thoroughly shielded thermocouple junction and where the thermocouple shielding is also vigorously bathed in the flowing gases. The velocity thermocouple is made with concentric tubes where there is space between each tube. The center tube in which the thermocouple is inserted has a diameter not significantly greater than three times the diameter of the thermocouple junction. The thermocouple junction is located at the midpoint of the concentric tubes. The largest concentric tube is connected to an aspirator. Never less than three tubes should be used. The average space between tubes is 1/16-in. Gases are drawn over the tubes at approximately 50 ft./sec. until the inner tube reaches gas temperature. The assembly should be inserted for test of gas temperature, the aspirator turned on, and the rise in indicated temperature noted until there is no further increase in indicated temperature for five minutes. This temperature indication may be accepted as an accurate gas temperature measurement.

Experience shows that an attempt at heat balance where gas temperatures are taken from fixed thermocouples is largely a pointless exercise in calculation because of inaccuracy of gas temperature measurement and thus of gas heat content. The velocity thermocouple is commercially available to validate heat balances and to accurately determine thermal efficiency.

Where error exists in measuring gas temperatures with a thermocouple, the error is always toward the low side. The temperature indication of the thermocouple will be low according to the temperature at the point of measurement. Thus, temperature indication taken in this manner for calculating thermal efficiency will show less heat loss to the stack gases than is actually occurring. Such a procedure will thoroughly confuse an effort to match heat absorption with heat loss to the stack if a reasonable radiation loss figure is used as a factual rather than a flexible figure designed for compensation of calculation error.

Radiation Loss

Heat loss from furnaces by radiation can be rather a finite figure if the temperature of the exposed surfaces of the furnace walls, floor and roof are known rather than an estimated factor. Loss by radiation can vary considerably according to ambient temperature and wind velocity on exposed surfaces. In determining true thermal efficiency it is erroneous to assume that radiation loss from a heater is a fixed figure.

Generally speaking, the heat loss by radiation is least in the vertical cylindrical furnace because most of the wall surface is covered by the tubes and there is a minimum of bare refractory. In the so-called box or cabin heater, the radiation loss is greatest unless the bare end walls are covered by refractory and insulation to compensate for the lack of shielding by relatively cool tubes.

Surface heat loss in Btu/sq. ft. at various wall temperatures, various ambient temperatures and various wind velocities are given in Table 3-2.

It is clear from the table that the greatest variable is wind velocity, but atmospheric temperature also has an important bearing on heat loss from the wall. The entire wall surface will not be exposed to wind action but it is probably fair to presume that 60% of the wall surface will be exposed to the wind. Floor and roof heat loss should be based on zero wind velocity unless the floor is elevated significantly above grade and open on all four sides. In the latter case, estimate the heat loss through the floor based on 50% of the observed wind velocity. Using these variables, we depart from precision but it is possible to far more accurately determine radiation loss than would be true with any fixed figure for the loss. (See 3-5 and 3-6.)

Minimum Excess Air

If every effort has been made to stop air leakage in all portions of the furnace and if there is a

Table 3-2
Surface Heat Loss (in Btu/sq. ft.)

Wall Temperature 150° F

Wind Velocity, mph	0°F	40°F	70°F	100°F
0	290	195	153	100
10	795	530	445	280
20	1,300	970	715	445

Wall Temperature 250° F

Wind Velocity, mph	0°F	40°F	70°F	100°F
0	600	513	445	380
10	1,420	1,230	1,070	895
20	2,350	1,910	1,630	1,410

Wall Temperature 300° F

Wind Velocity, mph	0°F	40°F	70°F	100°F
0	790	715	640	565
10	1,775	1,570	1,410	1,220
20	3,000	2,600	2,100	1.900

point from which combustion area samples of gases can be taken, there is concern with what may be the proper minimum excess air factor in the furnace. Regretfully, there is no fixed excess air factor which is universally applicable because of heater design variables, burner variables and process variables. However, the figure for excess air should be the minimum which satisfies all conditions for heater operation.

The heater manufacturer states that with the specified fuel at a stated excess air condition, his heater will transfer the required heat quantity to the material being processed at a specified thermal efficiency and at a stated fuel consumption.

He bases his calculation for heat transfer on the radiant rates he can tolerate in the radiant sec-tion of the furnace. He must base his radiant trans-fer rates on a specific condition of excess air since this is the controlling medium for flame-gas tem-perature in the furnace. Fourth-power functions of absolute temperature differentials govern heat transfer rates to such an extent that a change of only 50°F in the flame-gas temperature can very sharply influence the quantity of heat transferred.

Excess air serves as a coolant or heat sink in the furnace. If there is too great a quantity of excess air the flame-gas temperature falls. If more fuel is not fired to compensate for reduced heat-transfer rates, the quantity of heat delivered to the material being processed is not adequate. Neither condition is preferred. Thus, it is desirable to keep the cooling effect of the excessive air volume out

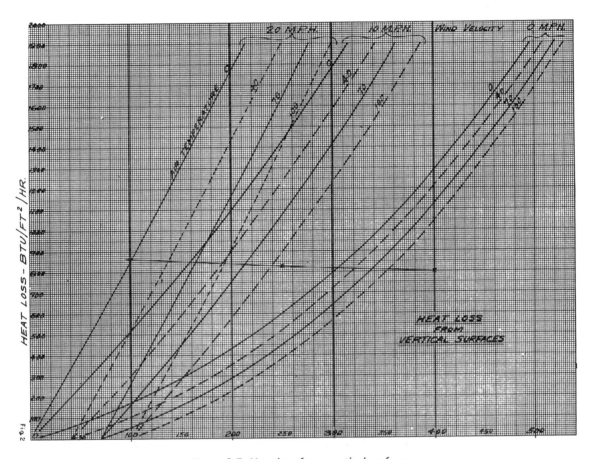

Figure 3-5. Heat loss from vertical surfaces.

of the furnace for the best processing conditions and the lowest fuel cost possible.

It is possible to go too far in a program of excess air reduction. Each furnace should be studied carefully to determine the minimum excess air rate which will permit entirely satisfactory operation at the least possible fuel cost. In some heaters, it is quite possible to operate at 5% excess air or less with excellent results for both the process and fuel economy. In other heaters, 20% excess air may be required for satisfactory operation. If it is necessary to operate at much more than 20% excess air to avoid process or heater damage, it is probable that corrective measures such as heater

modification or change in burners is indicated and should be carefully studied.

Heater damage usually takes the form of tube oxidation, tube scaling, or perhaps tube failure. Damage to other parts of the heater may occur because of localized overheating due to slow burning of fuel or erratic flow of the hot gases in the radiant section. The attack may occur in the shock-tube area which is generally the first row of tubes in the convection section.

Damage to the process may take the form of internal coking of the tubes, overheating of the material being processes to drive reactions past a preferred point, off-color product or excessive gas production. All these conditions fall outside the area of preference and are caused by excessive localized heat transfer in critical areas of the heater. Delayed coking and vacuum distillation are particularly prone to such process damage.

A ready cure for most of these difficulties is to increase the excess air factor to reduce the flame-gas temperature and to speed the burning of the fuel for shortening the flame. However, if it is necessary to increase the excess air factor to significantly more than 20%, the relief is obtained at undue fuel expense.

In most cases where the excess air is high in the heater's combustion area, check in this zone rather than the stack. To avoid damage to tubes, process, or furnace, the cause for the condition will be found in the burning of the fuel firing the heater.

Faulty Burners

This suggests that the fault lies with the burners alone, but this is not necessarily true. It might be the case if the burners were consuming fuels other than those for which they were designed and if the fuels were heavier. It is very true that a large number of burner designs may be capable of releasing the required quantity of heat for the furnace, but this is not to say that the heat as released will be satisfactory for the service expected of the heater. A commonly found fault in the firing of heaters lies in the use of too few large burners which are perfectly capable of adequate heat release but in a manner completely unsuited to the heater.

In the heater design stage, competent opinion should be sought as to the number of burners to be used and of the design and locations of the burners. After the heater is constructed and in operation, it is quite difficult to revise the firing in the interest of more satisfactory conditions of heat transfer. This is particularly true where there are too few large burners. Generally, the greater the number of burners the more likely the heater is to be completely satisfactory. This statement cannot be carried to infinity because of economic limits;

but if the choice is between X number of burners and X + 10% number of burners, the larger number can be considered as insurance for greater satisfaction and a better heater. Experience has shown this to be true with any type of burners which may be chosen.

Ideal Firing Conditions

If all heaters could be fired at fixed rates with perfectly constant fuel supplies and if the weather would cooperate by providing a constant atmospheric temperature along with wind at 5 mph, it would be quite easy to optimize the adjustment of burners for ultimate thermal efficiency. Such conditions are utopian since fuels do change, firing rates do change and wind and temperature vary. However, if the heater is to perform its function in the production of the specification product, heat delivery from burning equipment must follow the changes as demanded.

Meeting changes in heat demand makes preferred conditions of thermal efficiency somewhat difficult if all conditions are considered; the choice of fuel burning equipment to suit existing conditions can very greatly improve the thermal efficiency.

One quite excellent method, where gas alone is the fuel, is to use the kinetic energy of the gas at release from supply pressure for air induction necessary to burn the fuel. All combustion air is thus delivered to make the condition of excess air in the furnace very substantially linear in firing ranges from 100% of release to as little as 33% of release. However, to obtain this very desirable condition, the calorific value of the gas fuel cannot change more than 20% in the upward direction or there will not be enough air for burning the fuel and loss will result. This type of firing is with the typical sealed-port burner. If the burner is equipped with a means for entry of small amounts of secondary air, the fuel can change as much as 35% in the upward direction. Note that in this type of burner it is the highest calorific value which can exist that limits the use of such designs plus the requirement of approximately 35 psig gas pressure for the lowest calorific value operation.

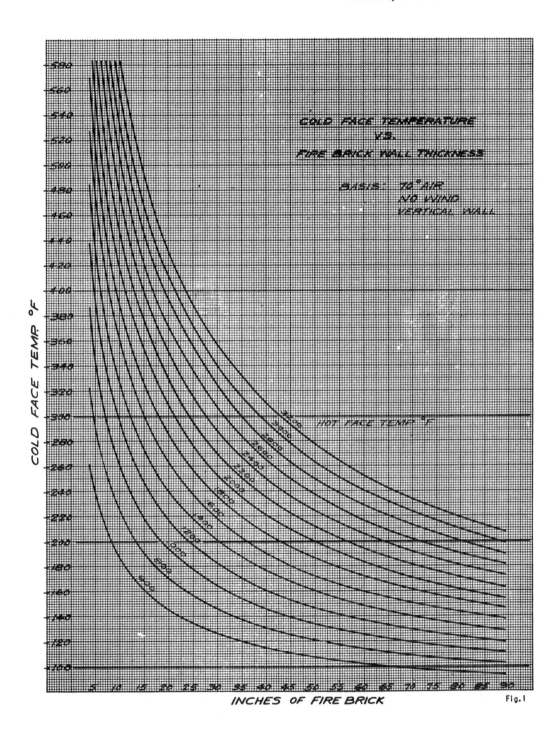

Figure 3-6. Cold face temperature vs. fire brick wall thickness. Basis: 70°F air, no wind, vertical wall.

If the swing in calorific value is greater than 1.35 to 1 but not greater than 1.75 to 1, greater use of secondary air (in combination with delivery of not less than 60% of theoretical air by gas energy) permits a fairly close approach to linearity of excess air in control ranges of from 100% of release to 75% of release. Again, gas pressure must be at 35 psig for the lowest calorific value.

Other burners which use still more secondary air can accept calorific value change of as much as 3 to 1 with good firing conditions. This is done at the expense of excess air linearity within the normal control range. That is, if the burners are properly adjusted for 100% heat release there will be a significant increase in excess air as the firing rate is decreased. These burners are generally of the so-called premix type for various primary air factors. There is still another basic gas burner design concept in which there is no premixture of air with gas prior to reaching the burning zone. This burner is generally referred to as the raw-gas design. In this design concept, all air is drawn through the burner as secondary air and is mixed with the fuel directly in the burning zone. Air delivery may be as in natural draft designs in which the draft or less than atmospheric pressure within the furnace induces air; or the air may be forced to the burner by forced draft at greater than atmospheric pressure.

When the raw-gas burner is operated in natural draft, there is no linearity of air delivery based on the quantity of fuel burned because the draft, which is the source of air pressure drop across the burner, remains substantially fixed in all normal ranges of firing control. Thus, the air quantity remains substantially fixed even though the fuel quantity changes and excess air tends to rise as the quantity of fuel burned decreases. However, the raw-gas burner has the great advantage of almost complete tolerance for change in fuel calorific value and the excess air at fixed firing rate tends to remain satisfactorily constant. Change in fuel calorific value does not require adjustment of the burner to compensate for the change in fuel.

In view of these burner characteristics, it is to be seen that any attempt to run very close on

excess air for maximum thermal efficiency must take into account the type of burner in use, the swing in calorific value potential for the fuel supply and the potential change in firing rate. If the burner is not at all capable of great linearity of air delivery with fuel delivery, it is a serious error to attempt to run very low excess air without constant supervision, control and testing.

If with the raw-gas burner the air is delivered by forced draft and if controls are adequate, the excess air may be trimmed to 5% or less in gas firing.

If fuel oil is fired, premixture of air with fuel is virtually impossible and all air for burning the fuel must enter as secondary air through either natural or forced draft. If forced draft is used and control is adequate, progress in burners for oil has been such that the excess air with oil may be held as low as 5% or even less. However, if natural draft is used, excess air will increase with a decrease in the firing rate. The minimum excess air condition in the furnace will be governed by the suitability of the heater-burner configuration to the high radiant-heat transfer rates to be expected with low excess air as much as, if not more than, the preference for maximum use of fuel heat values. In any event, flame impingement on heat transfer surfaces is not to be tolerated.

Forced Draft Factors

One of the advantages of forced draft is that in this system there is the possibility of, and energy for, the use of an air preheater which removes sensible heat from the stack gases and delivers it to the air en route to the burner. If the air temperature is thus caused to rise from 60°F to 450°F, the heat recovered from the stack gases which would otherwise be lost is 1,700 Btu/lb./mol of air or 51,700 Btu's per million Btu's fired at 10% excess air.

This represents a direct fuel saving of approximately 5.17%. However not all is net gain because of other factors such as the cost of power to drive the forced draft fans, the annual capital cost for equipment required for forced draft operation, maintenance on the forced draft equipment and loss of process time due to failure of any of the components.

In fact, because of these costs, there may actually be a loss using forced draft if the heat to be regained from the stack gases is not great enough to justify the risk. Opinion varies as to the lowest stack temperature which offers opportunity for fuel saving through the use of preheated air. It appears that the minimum stack temperature is in the order of 800°F.

Where there is any significant quantity of sulfur in the fuel, any final stack gas temperature of less than 500°F is an invitation to corrosion damage which may cancel a large portion of the potential saving. The final stack gas temperature is the temperature of the flue gases after passage through the air preheater, en route to the stack.

The final stack gas temperature after air-preheat versus the initial stack gas temperature establishes gross heat-energy saving where preheated forced draft is resorted to for fuel conservation. But the net saving may be a far cry from the gross saving because of cost factors such as required power, added labor costs, capital costs, and maintenance costs. Because these factors do not vary "in-phase" with fuel cost, there is no assurance that a projected "pay-out" will be correct. In fact, unless there is a large projected gross return, preheated combustion air has been known to be expensive rather than rewarding.

Where forced draft equipment has been added to a fired-furnace, a bad situation results when, for some reason, the preheated forced-draft becomes inoperative and the furnace operation must be stopped for repairs or the furnace operates at a very drastically reduced rate. It is fear of this condition which can lead to greatly over-sizing the burners to permit natural-draft burner operation for the repair period via windbox openings for burner air access. This over-sizing of burners to permit continued operaiton at reduced rate for a relatively short time has been repeatedly shown to be an error of some magnitude.

Burner performance is excellent or poor according to the velocity with which combustion air flows across (through) the burner throat for mixture with fuel. Greater air flow velocity greatly improves burner performance. Typical natural draft provides air flow velocity at approximately 44 ft/sec. Typical forced draft at 2.00″WC windbox pressure is 124 ft/sec. If the burner is sized for the full 2.00″WC pressure drop, its performance is greatly improved over the performance it might provide when it is over-sized to permit passage of the same quantity of air with a pressure drop of 0.25″WC which is a high natural draft figure. It has been repeatedly shown that when burners sized for natural draft are replaced with burners sized for full windbox pressure, the firing conditions go from very bad to very good—process conditions and process capacity improve, hot-spots on tubes disappear, long flames disappear, and the furnace can now be fired as designed.

Sulfur Bearing Fuels

Again, if there is sulfur in the fuel, the air preheater design must avoid the severe internal corrosion due to the SO_3 content of the flue gases, where the flue-gas dew point may be as low as 350-400°F producing very rapid sulfate corrosion. The tubular air preheater is particularly subject to such damage, but any preheater design may be subject to attack unless the preheater metallurgy takes sulfate corrosion into account. If the fuel being burned is oil with high ash content, the mineral residues tend to become entrapped in the air heater. Residues cause difficulty with maintenance and with continued delivery of the required air quantity at a reasonable pressure drop. (See Figure 3-7.)

Studies in the interest of fuel economy should take into account the results to be obtained through the installation of increased convection heat transfer surface to reduce stack losses along with careful consideraiton of possible lower temperature streams in convection sections. Such heat recovery means depend on natural functions for their operation and are therefore immune to mechanical failure and failure of energy for driving

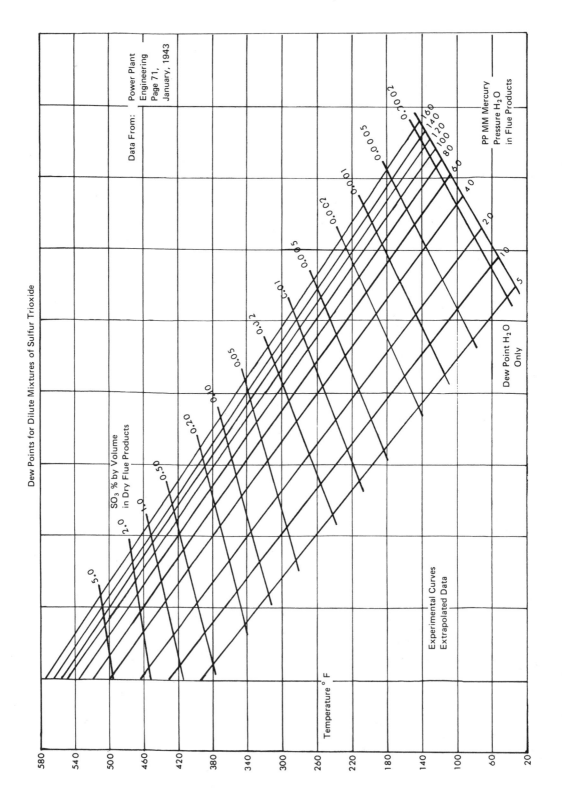

Figure 3-7. Dew points for dilute mixtures of sulfur trioxide. (Data from Power Plant Engineering, Jan. 1943, p. 71.)

the blowers which are required for forced draft operation. However, selection of the conditions requires caution. If the flue gases are the result of burning of sulfur-bearing fuels, the use of a charge temperature which is too low can cause severe corrosion if the SO_3 is allowed to reach the dew point (See Figure 3-4). If extended surface or fin tubes are considered to increase convection heat transfer, and if oil is the fuel it is characteristic of such tubes to so thoroughly trap mineral matter resulting from the burning of oil as to become rather well insulated. If oil is the fuel, the extended surface may be as studs with much better results but at greater expense. Also, using studs, there will be fouling of the tubes by mineral matter but not to the same degree as with fins. The metallurgy of the extended surfaces must be suitable for the maximum flue-gas temperature in normal operation and should be suitable for flue-gas temperatures which can exist if there is a tube rupture in the furnace. Experience shows that in fin tubes nearest the furnace and behind a row or two of shock tubes, the maximum gas temperature (caused by channeling) can be within $200°F$ of the bridge-wall temperature. Severe fin attrition occurs unless the metallurgy of the fins is suited to the actual temperature which exists as shown by the use of a velocity thermocouple for gas-temperature measurement rather than the indication of a fixed thermocouple. This is due to the tendency of the fixed thermocouple to show a lower gas temperature than actually exists. When the velocity thermocouple is used, it should be moved about to a number of places in the gas stream to find the maximum temperature to which the fins or extended surface will be subjected.

The tendency for fin tubes to foul with mineral matter is quite often the reason for failure of the fins to serve their purpose of added heat recovery. Even in gas-only firing, clean air always contains minor quantities of mineral matter in suspension. This mineral matter tends to accumulate in eddy areas of the tube fins to insulate them and block heat transfer.

Use of Fin Tubes

When the fins added to the tubes are too closely spaced, they tend to form their own eddy areas which promote entrapment of the insulating mineral matter. If the fins are too close together, there is very marked restriction of flow of hot gases to and over the fins so that there is not adequate delivery of heat to the fin surface. There is quite limited flow of gases in the spaces between the fins, and without ample gas flow over the fins and between the fins, all the way to the tube surface, the fins cannot absorb the design heat quantity and accordingly cannot be a suitable source of heat recovery from the gases. If the gases do not tend to penetrate the fin areas all the way to the tube at significant velocity, there is a tendency for drop out of mineral matter in the restricted flow area.

The author's intention is not to create the impression that fins used as extended surfaces for the tubes to promote added heat transfer are undesirable. Properly applied, such surface adds very significantly to effective heat transfer and is, indeed, highly desirable, if the metallurgy of the fin surface is suitable for the temperature level which must be endured.

There is reason to believe that for long service, ideal spacing of fins is a distance equal to the height of the fin. With this fin configuration, there is very good access of hot gas all the way to the tube surface along the fin and there is minimal eddy area for the promotion of mineral matter drop out at the surface of the tube and along the fins. However, the improvement in heat transfer in this configuration is due to still another significant factor which is associated with radiation rather than convection. The outer ends of the fins deliver their heat to the tube by conduction, which requires the portion of the fin farthest from the tube to be at a considerably higher temperature than the surface of the tube to which it is attached. There is a significant temperature difference between the end of the fin and the surface of the tube. With the fin at the highest temperature, there is radiation from the fin to the tube surface at an appreciable rate despite relatively small temperature differences because the distance for radiation is very small. If the fins are spaced a distance equal to the height of the fin, the conditions for radiation are very good. If the fins are spaced more closely, there is less radiation potential because the area for receipt of radiant energy is restricted by the shadowing effect of the fins. The radiant effect adds to normal conduction delivery of heat to the tube producing most interesting benefits.

Use of Soot Blowers

There has been considerable experimentation with the use of soot blowers in connection with heat transfer through convection and almost uniformly the results are good. In one case where the soot blowers were operated on 8-hr. cycles, there was a rise of 15-20°F in the convection outlet fluid temperature after each blowing cycle to reflect the added heat transfer caused by the removal of insulating matter. In such operation, the presence of fins on the tubes prevents removal of the fouling during the blow but the staggered stud arrangement permits fairly ready scouring of tube surfaces for removal of accumulated insulating material on the down stream tube surfaces.

Air pollution laws may have a very great bearing on any decision to install soot blowers in an operating heater. Removed accumulated material from the tubes is carried up and out of the stack, usually as a quite dark cloud of particulate matter. This cloud may be the source of annoyance to various neighbors and may result in nuisance citations from an air pollution authority.

One source of relief for this nuisance potential may be found in more frequent blowing cycles within the limits of economics. The cost of steam for the blowing operation must be considered versus the benefit to be expected in improved heat transfer. If there is less time for material to accumulate, there is less material in the stack gases. Thus, the cloud of particulate matter is reduced.

The particles of matter will be in all size ranges from 0.13 micron up. Particles in this size range do not fall out of the cloud but larger particles can and do fall out. The particles are derived from the oxides of the mineral matter present, with some tendency for formation of carbonates if there is hydration. The greater portion of the oxides will be sodium, calcium, magnesium and iron with sodium predominant in most instances. Soot may also be present.

One of the serious results of mineral accumulation on the surface of convection tubes is draft interference in the furnace from blockage of the inter-tube gas passage area. This blockage results in a progressive decrease in furnace draft. The blockage condition is equally undesirable for natural draft, induced draft, or forced draft. Various mineral removal techniques have been employed in the past, but none have been successful when attempted during shutdown periods. One Eastern refiner, reasoning that temperature shock was required for mineral removal, installed stainless steel nozzles for hot convection water flood (during reduced firing operation) of the tubes. He found that this process produced effective mineral removal and a significant increase in furnace draft. The mineral matter falls to the furnace floor. Consequently, there cannot be burners directly under the convection section. A number of refineries now make successful use of this technique, and no significant refractory damage has been reported. Reduction in firing from water-wash of convection tubes ranges from 20% to 100%.

There has been considerable effort toward improved scrubbing of tubes through the addition of water to the steam used for blowing. In some areas, there has been an addition of alkaline matter to the water in an effort to stop some of the sulfate corrosion but neither of the procedures have been considered successful because of accessory problems.

There is little doubt of the effectiveness of blowing soot and accumulated mineral matter from the passages of heat transfer structures, even when gas is the fuel fired. But there are certain accessory problems which should have due consideration before soot-blowing equipment is considered seriously in an effort to improve heat transfer.

SO₃ and Sulfidic Corrosion

Any procedure to recover additional heat from the fuel as fired should always be based on calculations of the minimum metal temperature which will be exposed to the gases because of the condition of severe corrosion which can exist if the minimum temperature is too low when sulfur in any form is present in the fuel.

From 5 to 10 weight percent of the sulfur can occur in the stack gases as SO_3 which is the anhydride of sulfuric acid. The SO_3 very drastically influences the temperature at which the flue gases will reach the dew point. If they do reach the dew point and SO_3 is present, the tubes and metal surfaces are subjected to the corrosive action of sulfuric acid. (See Figure 3-7.)

A good example of the need to calculate SO_3 percentage is as follows:

Fuel burned = 100 mols at 10% excess air
Methane = 98 mols
H_2S = 2 mols
90% H_2S to SO_2
10% H_2S to SO_3
Total mols of combustion products = 1149.878
SO_3 produced = 0.2 mols
Percentage of SO_3 = 0.00017
Dew Point = Approximately 308°F

In the example, if fuel should be fired in a process heater so that the flue-gas temperature drops below 308°F, there will be a direct invitation to corrosion. The same corrosion invitation would exist if the temperature of the fluid charged to the convection tubes should be at a temperature less than the same 308°F. Thus, the heat to be recovered from these gases is quite limited because of potential corrosion, whether heat recovery is by air preheat or through added heat recovery in the convection section. To avoid stack and breeching

corrosion, the minimum actual stack gas temperature in the example should be greater than 500°F.

It is in such examples that the goal of added heat recovery can produce equipment loss by corrosion that greatly exceeds the gain in added heat recovery.

Increasing Heat Recovery

The goal of reduced operating cost through the recovery of a great quantity of heat from the fuel fired is most interesting. In all fairness, the goal is distinctly worthwhile if at minimum excess air throughout the fired heater the stack gas temperature exceeds 800°F. As has been suggested, there are two courses to follow in adding heat recovery to an existing unit. One course would recover additional heat through preheat of combustion air. The other course would add a means for greater convected transfer which could be through addition of extended surface on the same number of tubes or through adding tubes to an existing installation for increased heat-transfer surface.

Each procedure has advantages and disadvantages. It is a wise group which will make a very complete study of the plus and minus factors of both approaches before electing a procedure. Capital costs for the two approaches vary in particular circumstances, and there is no fixed basis for estimating this cost factor. A factor which is all too often missed or not considered properly is the significant cost for power to drive the fans, which are usually required for preheated air operation. The potential cost for equipment maintenance including the blowers and the drive for them is another factor. Last but far from least is the potential cost in loss of production through down time due to mechanical failure. Loss of production through just one day's down time can cancel many day's saving in fuel.

One of the very great advantages of added convection transfer is that natural functions of draft still supply energy for air induction. Such heat recovery means do not operate under the hazard of mechanical failure and thus are always present and available for normal operation. In forced draft operation, if a fan fails there is either complete loss of firing or drastically reduced firing. However, a careful study must be made of the draft availability before natural draft operation is adopted. If induced draft fans must be used, there is the same hazard of mechanical failure as with forced draft; thus draft is an important factor in the decision.

When there is an addition of convection surface in the interest of better heat recovery, draft availability studies must take into account that the stack temperature will be reduced to decrease the draft available from an existing stack and that there will be less heat fired for production of a specific quantity of product. The effect of less draft may be largely cancelled because there is less stack gas but this factor should be carefully checked through the use of curves and formula procedures as discussed elsewhere. As these studies are made, the possiblity of adding height to the stack should not be neglected. A taller stack will produce greater draft energy if the stack structure will permit added height and if difficult problems in stack support do not develop.

A factor in heat conservation which should not be disregarded as studies are made is that of superheating the steam to be used in operating any facility for the manufacture of useful products.

Any increase in the heat content of the steam enables it to work to better advantage. In most instances, the increase in steam temperature is not harmful where the steam is used for partial pressure control in processing, fractionation or distillation. The fact that through superheating there is an absence of water, as a liquid, provides further advantages—All the water is in the vapor phase after the superheater.

Turbine Exhaust Gases

Costs and operating difficulty with waste-heat steam-generating equipment make use of this means for added heat recovery of limited interest unless the heat recovery potential is very large and will justify the expense and operating cost.

There is currently a great deal of emphasis on heat recovery from gas turbine exhaust gases. Here, waste-heat recovery becomes a genuine interest in an economic sense because there is a large volume of exhaust gas at temperatures ranging from 700-1,100°F. Most interesting is the fact that to control the maximum temperature level through the turbine very great quantities of excess air are admitted with the turbine fuel as it burns so the stream of exhaust gases can serve as the source of oxygen for burning more fuel within the stream.

When the heat from burning additional fuel is added to the initial heat content of the turbine exhaust-gases the total of the two heats provides a means for waste-heat recovery in conventional boilers at very low cost for the steam produced so far as fuel is concerned. Such steam-generating facilities can be set up to use forced draft air as the source of oxygen for burning fuels during the time the turbine is not operating so that there is no interruption in steam generation in any condition of plant operation.

In the past it has been the practice to burn gaseous fuels in the turbine exhaust gas stream because of difficulty in providing a suitable arrangement for burners handling liquid fuels such as fuel oil. The problem is the removal of the oil guns for cleaning or inspection as required during operation. This design difficulty has been overcome and installations are now running successfully using oil as fuel for burners installed in the duct leading from the turbine to the boiler.

When special furnaces are added to the boiler to permit installation and operation of oil burning equipment in a conventional manner there is little difficulty in the burning of either gas or oil for heat production as required. Narrowing limits of economics make it preferable to burn the fuels in the turbine exhaust duct to avoid the expense of large and separate furnaces. The special furnace provides a more flexible installation, but there has been considerable success in eliminating its cost for highly operable and satisfactory units used for steam generation.

In the insertion of burners for adding heat to the turbine exhaust gas stream, one of the very critical problems is the matter of pressure drop across the burners. Gas velocity past the burners must be in the order of 100 ft./sec. or more if the burners are to perform well, with a reasonably short flame as the fuels burn. Each application of burners for firing into these oxygen-rich gases must be made following a study of the duct which brings the gases from the turbine to the boiler so that the velocity past the burners is great enough and the flow of gas is, reasonably, properly distributed over the entire cross section of the duct at the point where the burners are installed.

If the duct design provides a velocity which is too low or, if due to turns in the duct, it is evident that the gas distribution in the duct is not satisfactory, baffling must be added to the duct at the point where the burners are installed and possibly in the upstream direction from the point at which the burners are to be installed.

Because the addition of back pressure very seriously influences the horse power capability of the turbine, the pressure drop caused by the baffling must be kept as low as possible. Pressure drops to secure 100 ft./sec. velocities at varying exhaust-gas temperatures are $250°F = 1.90$ in., $500°F = 1.23$ in., $750°F = 0.99$ in., $1,000°F = 0.89$ in., $1,250°F = 0.70$ in.

If the steam generating unit must continue to operate when the turbine is not in operation, provision must be made for the application of blowers to the duct between the turbine and the boiler and upstream from the burners supplying air to replace the oxygen content of the exhaust gases. The manner in which the air is delivered to the duct must be very carefully studied to avoid an upset in air distribution up to the burners and also to avoid reversal of airflow back through the turbine. The reversal of air flow usually requires some sort of damper in the duct between the air entry point and the turbine or other means for blocking reversal of flow if delivery of air up to the burners is uniform. Air entry to the duct causes a pressure

rise greater than atmospheric. While the inertia of the entering air stream from the blower can be used to certain advantage, other means for avoiding flow reversal will in all probability be required if the pressure within the duct exceeds atmospheric pressure.

Design of steam generating equipment for heat recovery from the turbine exhaust plus added heat from the burning of fuel should be based on as low a stack temperature as possible. A large portion of the heat to be recovered is based on the heat content of the gases entering at from $700-1,100°F$ and exiting to the stack at lower temperatures. Because the fuels for turbines are usually quite low in sulfur, there is little SO_3 to cause a reduced dew-point temperature for the flue gases (at very low stack temperatures) which are possible at exhaust from the waste-heat boiler.

The stack temperature will depend on the pressure at which steam is being generated. The steam temperature rises as the pressure rises and the stack temperature should always be significantly greater than the steam temperature. The temperature difference will vary with boiler design. However, it is necessary to keep the pressure drop through the boiler as low as possible. Added boiler surface is purchased at the expense of added pressure drop, unless final heat recovery is attained with an economizer. Relatively low feed-water temperature at entry to the economizer permits lower flue-gas exit temperature through greater temperature differential and improved heat transfer. Here again, clean fuels permit the use of fin tubes or other extended surface tubes for the economizer. In this case, heat recovery through the use of some sort of air pre-heater is not justifiable.

Cat-Cracker Off-Gases

In the typical refinery there is a further and interesting source of waste-heat recovery in the cat-cracker off-gases. The gases exiting from the regenerator section are at high temperature and also carry quite appreciable mol-percentages of CO and other gaseous constituents which have appreciable calorific value. The stream of off-gases is interesting from the standpoint of sensible heat alone, since the gas temperature ranges upward to 1,100-1,200°F. Considerable steam generation or heat recovery is possible for this reason alone. But the point of greatest interest lies in the potential heat value of the combustibles present in the off-gas. There is usually a very large volume of gases and the calorific value of the combustibles often provides as much as 30 Btu/cu. ft. of off-gas or even more if the gas is burned properly rather than vented to atmosphere as is usually the case.

The cost for equipment to use this source of heat is quite great since the gases must be returned to grade or close to grade and conducted through internally insulated ducts to the point where the waste-heat recovery equipment is located. Since the calorific value of the off-gas is very low, special burning equipment is required. The common practice is to separately fire standard fuel to maintain high furnace temperature, forcing the complete burning of the off-gas in the presence of an adequate supply of oxygen within the furnace. Because the fuel-gas content of the off-gas is quite low due to dilution with N_2 CO_2 H_2O and argon, the burning is quite slow unless the furnace temperature is 2,000°F or more.

General practice, in the past, required a separate refractory-lined combustion chamber, in which no heat was removed, to keep temperatures high before gases entered that portion where heat was to be absorbed, such as in a boiler. There has been significant success in eliminating refractory-lined furnaces, permitting direct firing into the furnaces of standard package boilers. A certain amount of refractory surface is added to the package boiler furnace to provide the required temperature level. The addition of the refractory to the furnace does not interfere with steam generation as has been clearly shown in the operation of such steam-generating facilities.

In the operation of steam-generating installations using cat-cracker off-gas because of the very large volume of gases exhausting to the stack, it is greatly preferred that the design of the installation provide as low a stack temperature as possible. However, there must be careful consideration of the off-gas sulfur content to avoid very severe SO_3 corrosion caused by dew-point temperature within the structure of the steam-generating facility. The stack temperature must be at least 100°F higher than the calculated dew-point temperature. This temperature margin can be dangerous at reduced generation of steam or in operation of the unit at reduced rating. To further avoid corrosion caused by the presence of SO_3, the saturation temperature of the steam as generated should also be well above the calculated dew-point temperature of the SO_3. Since firing of auxiliary fuel is required to maintain the furnace temperature and since the air supply for both the auxiliary fuel and the cat-cracker off-gas must be blower supplied, it is possible to use preheated air for further heat conservation improvement, in such installations. However, a certain amount of corrosion is to be expected if the concentration of SO_3 is great enough and if the stack temperature is driven too low in the interest of fuel economy.

A factor which must be considered when studying the burning of cat-cracker off-gas is the fact that certain quantities of catalyst fines will tend to be present as the gases come from the regenerator. These fines are abrasive. If they accumulate in quantity, they can interfere with the flow of combustion gases through the steam-generator unit. Means for removing the accumulated fines should be provided. An operating hazard exists in the use of off-gases in that as the cat-cracker regenerator section is upset, considerable quantities of oil vapor can be delivered to the furnace during the period of upset. The furnace floods with fuel, which may cause it to puff quite violently during the upset. The supplier of equipment for burning the off-gas should be consulted as to his procedure for this condition.

The use of such a supply of waste heat is not limited to steam generation. A number of such systems have been applied to process heaters in which quite satisfactory operation is reported for less critical process service. Because of the relatively large volume of gases per million Btu's, the convection sections of such heaters are usually quite large, allowing convection transfer of heat to permit a satisfactory state of heat recovery. Tubes with extended surface are quite typical of such convection sections.

Boilers and Steam Generators

The facility for steam generation in the usual process plant is a major consumer of fuel. Because the equipment suppliers for steam generation are extremely fuel conscious, steam-generating units will have been designed to run at very low excess air and at a quite high thermal efficiency which is closely monitored in the routine operation of the plant.

The generation of steam is conducted at assured conditions of high thermal efficiency. Since steam is accepted as a requisite tool in the plant operation, there is a marked tendency among people who use it to forget that unless there is proper steam conservation there can be quite serious loss of funds. These costs occur despite the endless efforts toward good fuel economy on the part of the people who make the steam.

In the usual process plant, there is a near chronic shortage of steam regardless of the care with which the estimated steam demand for the plant was determined by competent engineering forces plus a reasonable "ignorance factor." Steam shortage has frequently been found within six months of initial plant operation without additional steam load points over and above those originally considered.

There are reasons for the steam shortage. These are to be found in unanticipated steam leakage at valve stems, packing glands, improperly operating steam traps, flanged joints, in needless use of steam hoses or failure to shut off the steam to the hose promptly when it has served its purpose; failure of insulation on steam lines, leaky valves and fittings, and faulty instrumentation are additions to the other loss factors.

It is probable that the cost of steam, as an average figure, is reasonably close to 80¢/1,000 lbs. The economics of the steam-generating plant

as well as scheduled steam use can be based on such a figure in estimating plant operating costs. This becomes decidedly interesting as loss of steam is considered as an operational cost factor and as efficient operation is sought.

A pin-hole leak having an area equal to that of a 1/16-in. round hole can cause a steam loss of several hundred dollars per year, based on 100 psig steam. A steam trap which is not functioning as it should can cause a loss which is disastrous. A 1-in. steam hose also at 100 psig pressure is often necessary, but it must be shut off when not in use. Anyone who has observed the clouds of steam in various portions of an operating process facility on a cold day can see evidence of steam loss, aside from vented exhaust steam.

An economic problem that needs careful consideration is that of exhaust steam and how to handle it, or rather what to do with it. Both latent and sensible heat are recoverable from the exhaust steam; but heat recovery, as such, is not the sole point of interest. Recovered condensate can be used as very excellent boiler feed-water with a certain amount of contained preheat as it enters the boiler if the condensate is oil free. If oils are present in the condensate, either foaming or priming or both will occur in the boiler. This factor must be carefully considered.

As the steam generating equipment is installed, the drum internals will effectively prevent carry-over of boiler water with the steam according to specified conditions; but checks should be made from time to time to make sure that the internals are functioning as they should by tests of steam quality at the boiler outlet nozzle. Heat loss here is limited to sensible heat for the quantity of carry-over, but other undesirable factors are present when there is excessive carry-over in the generation of steam.

There can be no relaxation of a program devoted to fuel economy in all its aspects. The condition of heaters and furnaces changes constantly. New steam leaks or sources of steam loss are constantly found. Fuels and firing conditions change. Process conditions change. Instrument malfunction is an ever-present possibility. And last but far from least, the men who have to do with a program directed toward fuel economy in heater operation can, in the press of plant operation in all its devious details, neglect certain aspects of the program which may be essential.

Unit operators will perform their work in a manner best suited to the solution of problems. Once the problem has been met and the source of an upset has been found and corrected, there is reason to suggest return to a program devoted to fuel economy after the pressure of emergency conditions is relieved.

A significant number of companies engaged in refining and chemical process work have separate departments with engineers who have no duties other than attention to problems related to the burning of fuels in the most economical manner. There are various names for these groups such as power-engineers, fuel engineers, efficiency engineers or heat conservation engineers. The groups may range in number from one to as many as ten, but over a period of many years such groups have proven to be the most profitable of all engineering groups.

4

Heat Transfer

Heat is a discrete form of energy. It is the energy source that accomplishes the end effect of all processing. Heat is also the energy that has provided the lifestyle of the late twentieth century. Without the use of fossil fuel-derived heat-energy, life would probably be less enjoyable. Yet, even engineers think of heat-energy as something that is limitless despite what has been spoken of repeatedly as "the energy crisis."

It is of interest to be aware of why "heat" and "energy" denote similar functions, and what is the energy form of heat. Heat represents kinetic energy. A heat level is proportional to the square of average molecular motion on an absolute temperature basis. Molecules (however tiny) have mass and are in constant motion, so the classic kinetic energy formula $MV^2/2$ represents the energy level based on absolute temperature. Heat transfer, in any form, can be said to be an energy transfer that is accomplished because of molecular functions. Unfortunately, few engineers can offer upon request a correct definition of heat despite its universal use in many processes. A valid definition of heat is: energy that is transferred between masses because of differences in their temperatures.

It is probable that no element associated with manufacturing of useful materials has attracted more attention on the part of researchers than that of useful heat transfer. This is understandable in that fuel must be burned to produce the heat which is later delivered to some raw material being prepared for alteration into more useful products through softening, hardening, distillation, chemical alteration or evaporation. Literally, it might be said that industry operates through the use of heat produced through the burning of fuels.

Prior to the introduction of atomic-powered generating facilities, heat was produced from the burning of wood or fossil fuels. Fuel costs in 1979 were about \$4.20/million Btu's. With trillions of Btu's released per hour in process work, it is not at all difficult to understand the need for fuel conservation.

In other parts of this book the production and conservation of heat has been discussed. We will now consider the use of heat produced through the burning of fuels. Particular reference will be made to the petroleum, petrochemical and chemical industries where heat is delivered through the tube walls to material flowing within the tubes.

If the tubes through which the fluid is flowing are suitably arranged, heat will be transferred to the fluid based on the furnace temperature versus the fluid temperature, the speed with which the fluid is moving within the tubes, and the relative ability of the fluid to absorb heat from the inner wall of the tube at the flowing condition.

Heat Transfer Mechanisms

There are several mechanisms for heat transfer from the furnace to the tube for subsequent delivery of heat to the fluid material within the tube. The mechanism of greatest significance, in view of the quantity of heat transferred is that of radiation. For heat transfer by radiation, the well known Stefan-Boltzmann law governs *(Chemical Engineers' Handbook)*.

The mechanism of next greatest significance is that of convection. Heat is transferred through the flow of fluid over the tube surface to or from which heat is being transferred according to the tube-fluid temperature relationship. Consider the flowing fluid as hot gases with the gas temperature greater than the tube temperature. The literature is replete with calculations of convected heat transfer.

Conduction of heat played a very small part in the overall transfer of heat in process service until the use of fin tubes or tubes with extended surface came into common use in the interest of heat conservation. At the present time, such tubes have shown great ability to increase convected heat transfer to significantly improve economy of operation through reduction in fuel demand. Thus, conduction of heat becomes a factor in utilization of heat from fuel as fired. All heat transfer mechanisms are due for consideration as the operation of fired heaters is studied.

Transfer of heat is accomplished through three mechanisms: radiation, convection and conduction. It is easy to understand transfer by conduction and convection. However, in radiation, which is known and accepted with the production of heat and the burning of fuels, there is uncertainty as to the reasons why the radiation exists. It is beyond question that the heat energy dissipates through functions associated with infrared energy waves; but the source of infrared heat energy dissipation is not entirely clear.

Molecular Radiation

It is also unclear why some molecules are capable of heat dissipation or absorption through infrared activity, but other molecules at identical temperature levels are not capable of heat absorption or dissipation by radiation to any appreciable degree. It is true that these molecules are in the gaseous phase and are diatomic in their structure, but other molecules which are also in the gaseous phase but have binary structure can and do produce infrared rays and absorb infrared energy.

Radiant energy has the same nature as visible light. It is caused by electromagnetic waves within a specific frequency range or wavelength ranges which are lower in frequency and longer in wavelength than visible light. Photographs can be made with special films in complete darkness with infrared rays rather than with visible light rays. Because the frequency is quite high, infrared wavelengths are measured in microns rather than in feet, inches, yards or meters.

A micron is one-millionth of a meter. Electromagnetic waves travel at approximately 186,000 mi./sec. Waves in the infrared spectrum range in length from approximately 0.7 microns at the greatest frequency to approximately 14 microns at the lowest significant frequency. Solids radiate heat energy throughout the infrared spectrum. There is a very rapid increase in quantity beginning at 0.70 microns and up to 1.75-3.00 microns according to the temperature level, then, a less abrupt decrease in energy level to approximately 8.00 microns. In the wavelength range to 14 microns there is a very small decrease until energy radiation stops. This is shown graphically through curves on page 65, *Process Heat Transfer*, by Kern (McGraw-Hill Book Co.). The infrared wavelength range is from 0.70 to approximately 400 microns.

Data referred to are for radiant energy from solids. There is radiation of heat energy throughout the entire spectrum at levels influenced by temperature, with peak radiation at specific frequencies and lesser radiation at other frequencies. This state of heat dissipation, as influenced by temperature and frequency, justifies the Stefan-Boltzmann calculations in reference to the fourth-powers of absolute temperatures in the case of radiation from solids.

A very significant difference in radiant characteristics of gases and solids exists because radiation from gases does not occur throughout the infrared spectrum, as is true with solids, but does occur in relatively small portions of the spectrum and at various wavelengths. Thus, at equivalent temperatures and with no reference to relative emissivities, there will be a significant difference in the quantity of infrared energy dissipated. Trinks takes this into account as he points out that in radiation from gases the fourth-power laws do not hold (*Industrial Furnaces*, Vol. 1, John Wiley & Sons).

Emissivity Factors

The term *emissivity* is used to denote the relative abilities of matter to emit infrared energy at identical temperature levels. Kirchoff's law states that the ability to radiate and the ability to absorb radiation are identical for each substance. Thus, great radiant ability for a specific material also denotes an equally great ability to absorb heat received as radiant energy.

Emissivity, as such, is based on the ability of a theoretical "black body" to absorb or to radiate heat energy as unity or emissivity = 1.00. To say that the emissivity of a substance is 0.70 is to say that the condition of heat absorption or dissipation of the substance is 70% that of the theoretical perfect black body. It is a bit shocking to know that in tests of 40 different refractory materials in the temperature range from just above 1,100°F to slightly more than 1,800°F, emissivities ranged from a low of approximately 0.65 to a high of nearly 0.90. (See Table 4-1.)

Molecular Motion

Present-day thinking is that radiation of infrared energy as heat is due to some function associated with the molecular structure of the radiant mass. There is universal acceptance that the temperature level is proportional to the state of molecular motion within a mass. As the temperature level rises, there is an increase in molecular motion or activity. As the temperature level falls, there is a decrease in molecular motion with complete cessation of molecular motion at absolute zero. As the temperature level rises, there is an increase in heat energy radiation potential from the mass and as the temperature falls there is a decrease in radiation potential.

In all cases, except for water as it freezes, there is a decrease in volume as the temperature falls and, again except for water, there is an increase in volume as the temperature rises. It may be said, then, that the volume of a mass is proportional to the temperature level within the mass if the pressure remains constant. The single exception is that of water as it freezes or as ice melts. Since the volume of a mass is proportional to the state of molecular motion within the mass, if the pressure remains the same, and since the infrared heat energy radiated is also proportional to the temperature level of the mass, the conclusion may be drawn that the quantity of heat radiated is in proportion to molecular motion.

Radiation Function

If we assume this postulation is correct, we must theorize as to which particular function causes the mass to insist on dissipation of heat energy in proportion to an increment of heat or temperature with the heat energy in the form of electromagnetic waves which behave as light, which traverse a state of complete vacuum and which are capable of travel for infinite distances if not absorbed. This identical function is character-

Table 4-1
Typical Surface Emissivities

Surface	Temperature Range (°F)	Emissivity
Aluminum plate (unpolished)	78 - 1000	.055 - .150
Aluminum surfaced roofing	100	.214
Oxidized steel	70 - 950	.633 - .800
Rough cast iron	100 - 500	.930 - .955
Typical oxide coated steel tube	900	.750 - .795
301 stainless steel	450 - 1700	.512 - .701
316 stainless steel	460 - 1900	.265 - .662
310 stainless steel	460 - 1000	.880 - .967
347 stainless steel	450 - 1600	.500 - .655
304 stainless steel	900 - 980	.600 - .740
Monel	450 - 1600	.450 - .640
Alumina - Fine Grain Surface	1800 - 2900	.180 - .300
Alumina - Coarse Grain Surface	1800 - 2900	.410 - .500
Alumina-Silica-Low Iron	1800 - 2900	.400 - .600
Alumina-Silica-Medium Iron	1800 - 2900	.600 - .770
Alumina-Silica-High Iron	1800 - 2900	.680 - .790
Typical Fireclay	1800	.750

Note: Emissivities are shown as ranges to indicate disagreement of data from various sources. It is recommended that the supplier furnish specific and guaranteed data for tubes and refractories within specified temperature ranges to assist in choice of material and supply source. The surface characteristics in the same material influence emissivity; therefore, emissivity for a particular refractory or tube will depend on surface characteristics as operated.

istic of radio waves, with heat quantity absorbed by another surface or mass being inversely proportional to the square of distance the waves travel.

If we pursue this postulation and note that radio waves are generated by fairly or precisely linear oscillators it may be presumed that infrared waves are also generated by some function of linear oscillation characteristic of molecules as the temperature level is altered. It is puzzling to note that all molecules do not possess the ability to become linear oscillators as is the case with the molecules of diatomic gases such as O_2 and N_2. It must be presumed that if the molecular structure is suitable, the molecule can become a linear oscillator. If the molecular structure is not suitable, the molecule cannot become so and thus does not dissipate its heat content in the form of infrared rays. Such molecules require contact with other molecules at lower temperature levels to dissipate or deliver their heat content.

Combustion Gases

This condition of possession of or lack of ability to radiate heat becomes interesting as we consider a mixture of CO_2 and H_2O with N_2 and O_2 typical of combustion gases. The CO_2 and the H_2O as binary gases can and do radiate heat and absorb heat by radiation, but the N_2 and the O_2 as diatomic gases have no or very little radiant capabilities. It must be presumed that there is transfer of heat energy from the diatomics to the binaries as the binaries separately lose their heat energy through radiation, while the diatomics lose no heat energy except through contact with molecules at a lower temperature level. Within the same mass of mixed gases, there are potentially different temperature or activity levels in the separate molecules present in the mixture.

Physicists, as they study these phenomena, tend to consider matter in the atomic sense rather than in the molecular sense in an effort to provide logical postulations for radiant phenomena. Atomic functions are less complex than molecular functions due to consideration of a single mass rather than a mass composed of plural atoms. Bohr presents the atom as a nucleus about which electrons move in elliptical orbits and at various distances from the nucleus. The outermost orbital electrons possess energies composed of kinetic and potential elements. Addition of heat accelerates the motion and increases the energy level so that in collision with other electrons or atoms there is dissipation of heat energy in proportion to the energy spent in the collision. In this case, there is decreased atomic activity because there is less energy present.

In this approach, it is proposed that radiation of energy as heat is largely due to functions of movement of electrons in orbit about their various nuclei or displacement of electrons from normal orbital paths which suggests ionization. Ionization exists within a flame because of orbital displacement of electrons in bond alteration, but this state of detectable ionization ceases at the flame boundary because the flame is conductive for electricity but at high resistance while the gases following the flame burst are infinitely resistive and cannot be said to be conductive. Energy released in ionization is normally expressed as visible light seen in the visible blue flame burning or, for that matter, the visible light of the aurora borealis.

Molecular Vibration or Oscillation

Another theory proposes that heat radiation is due to functions of physics other than those of electrons in orbit and is due to a state of vibration or oscillation in and of the nuclei. Increased temperature produces an increment in amplitude of vibration or oscillation. Decreased temperature produces decrement of vibration. The effect of radiation is due to the relative energy with which the oscillation or vibration is occurring within the masses of the molecule. It is suggested that the nucleus establishes the mass of the atom and heat content or availability can be considered as a function of mass except that relative energy as heat is reflected in electron movement. Thus, two separate functions of physics can either be solely responsible for or can contribute separately to emission of energy as heat within the infrared spectrum range. At this time, there is no firm resolution of the effects which cause mass at elevated temperature to dissipate heat energy.

As an example, it is significant to note that at this time there is no firm and acceptable explanation of gravity or the attraction of one mass to another. It is common knowledge that gravity exists just as there is common knowledge that a state of radiation exists.

Up to this point, discussion and comment has pertained to binary gases typical of combustion reaction because such gases are of greatest concern. The term *binary* can be accepted as denoting lack of molecular symmetry because CO, which is a diatomic gas and unsymmetrical in mass structure, has appreciable emissivity as distinguished from characteristics of the symmetrical molecules O_2 and N_2. Therefore, the degree of emissivity of a gas is a function of the degree of lack of molecular mass symmetry or the mass ratio. In this case, a greater mass ratio denotes greater emissive ability at any temperature. Mass ratios are based on atomic weights. In nitrogen, which is a diatomic and thus not emissive, the ratio is 14/14 = 1. In CO, which is appreciably emissive, the ratio is 16/12 = 1.33. In CO_2, the ratio is (16+16)/12 = 1.916 for much greater emissivity. In H_2O, the ratio is 16/2 = 8 for greatest emissive ability. In process heater service, successful design is distinctly correlated with careful study of emission/absorption factors.

Radiant heat is thus derived from bodies or substances which are capable of emitting energy as heat within the infrared spectral range. All bodies or substances are not equally able to emit energy at any specific temperature level. Thus, substances or bodies have characteristic emissivity according to their ability to emit heat. Bodies or substances which have good emissivity characteristics have equally good ability to absorb heat by radiation. Good process heater design will provide high emissivity for both the internal structure of the furnace, such as refractory material and the furnace tubes, to obtain the best conditions for heat transfer since radiant heat transfer is the predominant mechanism involved.

Radiant Capability

Radiant heat quantity from solids follows the Stefan-Boltzmann fourth-power law because solids emit heat throughout the infrared range and at all wave lengths within the range. The same is not true of the binary gases present as the fuel burns. Binary gases such as CO_2, H_2O and at times SO_2-SO_3 emit energy only in relatively narrow bands or band-portions of the infrared spectrum range—not throughout the range—and the fourth-power functions do not hold for such radiation according to Trinks (*Industrial Furnaces*, Vol. 1, 4th edition).

Diatomic gases such as O_2 and N_2 which are present in combustion gases have no appreciable radiating ability and neither do they absorb heat by radiation; thus any consideration of radiant ability for the gases must pertain to the binary gases which are present. Manglesdorf and Hottel have developed the black body reference curves for gaseous radiation, based on the partial pressures of the gases as well as on the average length of radiant beam at various temperature levels.

Firm information for transfer of heat based on data of the black-body curves is difficult for two reasons. First, the mass of gases within the furnace is not static but is in varying conditions of movement, based on unpredictable forces within the furnace. The temperature contours within the mass of gases are anything but predictable to within several hundred degrees F or more. Secondly, in a homogeneous mixture of gases there are quite different states of emissivity between the binary and the diatomic gases of the mixture. As the heat content of the binary gases is depleted by radiation, the heat content of the diatomic gases remains. When there is very brisk molecular motion, what time interval is required to attain thermal equilibrium in the gas mixture? Does a temperature indication, taken within the mass of gases, reflect the temperature level of the binaries, the diatomics, or a mean of the respective temperature levels in a condition where a small temperature error can make a most significant error occur as heat delivery is calculated?

Heat Transfer Formulas

In developing formulas for radiant heat transfer functions, there have been giants such as Hottel, Lobo, Evans and McAdams. Their magnificent work made it possible to design the modern process heater to replace the shell stills and earlier tubular heaters on a much more reliable basis.

However, as the various designers applied the formula data supplied to them according to their particular preferences, it was discovered that all of the heaters failed to perform in keeping with the data. Some of the heaters failed to meet their performance guarantees and some performed far in excess of prediction. Differences in firing techniques accounted for a portion of both conditions in deviation with predictions; but this difference did not account for all deviation. The formula approach was used in all designs with variations to suit the particular heater problem at hand.

If the heater performance exceeded design condition, there was satisfaction on the part of the purchaser. From the designer's standpoint it was evident that some factors were missing in the formula approach. The designer was supplying more service than had been purchased and sometimes as much as 100% more than had been purchased. Because at times the heaters failed to meet performance guarantees, there was a need for a better design approach.

Even with a deviation in performance of heaters designed using the formula approach, these heaters were so greatly superior to those based on "catch-as-catch-can" procedure that there was, to the best of my knowledge, no organized research program to determine the cause of the deviation.

A heater is studied in separate sections. The greatest portion considered is the radiant section and the minor portion considered is the convection section to define the greatest source of heat transfer in the respective sections. This nomenclature is very convenient but is hardly accurate. In typical heaters where binary gases at significant temperature levels are present in combustion gases along with diatomic gases in the various sections of the heater, there is no line of demarcation between heat transfer by radiation and heat transfer by convection. Both heat transfer mechanisms are present and functioning as the gases flow through the furnace to the stack. It is quite true that the predominant heat transfer mechanism in the radiant section is radiation, principally because the conditions of temperature and gas flow in the radiant section favor this mechanism. The opposite is true for surfaces in the convection section, with the exception of the initial rows of tubes. In these rows, there is a condition of heat transfer based on both high temperature and quite great acceleration of gases causing radiant transfer to remain high plus a great quantity of heat transfer by convection at high temperature.

These cumulative conditions provide a heat-transfer condition to these initial convection tubes which is so great that they are referred to as shock tubes in which the quantity of heat transferred is much greater than in any other tubes within the furnace. Gas temperature determines the quantity of heat to be transferred by either convection or radiation; but in radiation, heat transfer varies substantially as the fourth power of the temperature difference. Convection heat transfer is substantially linear with the temperature difference. Thus, temperature is far more significant in the radiant section. The quantity of convective heat transferred is governed by the number of pounds of gas forced into contact with the tubes and the velocity with which it is moving as it strikes in addition to the temperature level of the gases.

The governing factor in the radiant section is predominantly temperature, and in the convection section mass velocity is most significant. In the average heater, about 80% of the total heat transferred comes from the radiant section and approximately 20% comes from the convection section. With this ratio of heat transfer in the heater sections, it is obvious that the most fruitful area to search for deviation factors must lie within the radiant section.

Radiant Heat Sources

In the radiant section, heat is derived by radiation from the flame burst at the burner, from radiant planes and areas within the furnace, and from the binary content of the furnace gases. Here we encounter some factors which need further investigation. According to the literature, there is certain radiation of heat from the flame burst when gas is the fuel. As much as three to four times this radiation quantity can come from the flame burst if the fuel is oil. These data are taken on the basis of the flame burst as a point source of heat. The distance from the point source to the various furnace areas is widely variable, which prompts the relation of another law which governs radiant transfer. This is the law which states that radiant transfer varies inversely as the square of the distance between the radiant and the absorptive bodies. It is thus impossible for flame radiation to be uniformly delivered to all portions of the furnace inner areas, even with a large number of burners—which is seldom, if ever, the case. Furthermore, there is reason to question the quantity of heat which the literature teaches is radiated by the flame burst, particularly with gas as the fuel.

Flame Radiation

The quantity of heat radiated by the flame is in question for a number of reasons, not the least of which is the extreme difficulty with which the data can be taken experimentally and on the necessarily small-scale operation typical of research.

A second reason is that flame-burst radiation is derived from the binary gases present in the flame. While the temperature of the flame is admittedly greater than that of the combustion gases, at some small distance beyond the flame envelope the gases do not stop radiating because of a relatively small drop in temperature. It is true that the binary gases a small distance beyond the flame are not as richly radiant as the same gases at slightly higher temperature levels in the flame-burst. Attention is called to Trink's postulation to the effect that there is deviation from the fourth-power laws in gaseous radiation. Any effort to offer truly firm data on flame-gas radiation, based on burners operating in typical process heaters, would be so burdened with problems that a solution would be impossible. Operating experience teaches conclusively that published flame-radiation data are considerably greater than that which is actually present. If this were not true, it would be impossible to design a suitable vertical cylindrical process heater where both gas and oil flames move very close to tubes without any serious upset in heat transfer unless the flames actually touch the tubes. There are many vertical cylindrical heaters in which flames have been literally within inches of the tubes for years of satisfactory operation without tube loss or, for that matter, tube or process damage.

There is much discussion of radiation and radiant effect in the published literature. Without question, the laws governing the radiant ability of a body or surface at a specific temperature are quite proven. Therefore, it is not the author's intention to cast any shadow of doubt on these laws.

However, there is an unanswered question of great importance. If we accept as factual and beyond question that the body or surface can and does emit a stated quantity of heat, as set forth by the laws, the body or surface cannot continue to emit the identical quantity of heat unless it is supplied with heat at the precise rate at which it is dissipating it. If heat is dissipated from the body or surface, the temperature must fall and the heat dissipation decrease as the temperature falls unless the temperature level is maintained. This is to say

that in a typical process furnace, radiant surfaces reach and maintain equilibrium temperature levels which are based on the heat radiated or emitted versus the continuing supply of heat to reach the state of equilibrium.

It can now be said that the unanswered question pertains to the mechanisms or phenomena through or by which heat delivery to radiant surfaces occurs to permit continued emission of heat energy. According to published data, the answer to this problem cannot be found in the total of flame and binary gas radiation. Since the radiant functions as such cannot be said to be the total source of heat supply, it must be presumed that the prime source lies in use of the heat content of the diatomic gases within the radiant areas. If the heat source is the diatomic gases (N_2 and O_2), then heat delivery is by contact of the diatomics with the surface which is radiating and such a condition requires continuous movement of gases for continuous heat delivery.

There are reasons to presume that the added heat source does lie in functions associated with the diatomic gases which require contact to deliver heat and therefore continuous and active movement of the gases. In recent years it has become possible to attain virtually flameless combustion. In this condition, there is little flame body to provide a source of radiation normally attributable to the flame. Also, as the combustion gases are created only about 33% of the heat produced in burning is contained in the radiant-capable binary gases. A third reason lies within the experience of the steel industry. It has been found that ingots normally heated in reverberatory furnaces, where there is small access of combustion gas in quantity to them, the ingots are heated much more rapidly at the same furnace temperature level when the combustion gases are directed to and over the ingots with appreciable vigor.

Burner Functions

It would appear, then, that the function of the burner is ample production of heat-laden gases for entry to the furnace where, due to inertial energy plus other forces which are discussed elsewhere, the furnace gas content is maintained in a continual state of movement through and to the various furnace areas where heat delivery is demanded. The gases and their state of movement provide the vehicle for heat delivery.

We may say then that the state of heat transfer in any particular furnace is governed by the state of gas movement within the furnace. However, the capability of the gases for delivery of heat will be found to be quite limited or governed by the temperature of the gases as they come into contact with surfaces where there is heat demand. Thus, there is a requirement for nearly instantaneous dispersion of heat from the burner or burners in order that the gas temperature will be as nearly uniform as possible in all areas of the furnace to assure reasonably good heat distribution.

Combustion Gas Heat Content

Another factor merits serious consideration, but this factor does not seem to appear in the literature. As has been pointed out, only about 33% of the heat produced in burning appears in the binary gases produced as the fuel burns, and approximately 63% of the heat is contained in the diatomic gases produced as the fuel burns when the excess air is 10%. The chemistry of burning methane at 10% excess air is as follows:

$$CH_4 + 2.20 \, O_2 + 8.36 \, N_2 =$$

$$CO_2 + 2\text{-}H_2O + 0.20 \, O_2 + 8.36 \, N_2$$

Gaseous products are:

1 mol of CO_2
2 mols H_2O
8.36 mols N_2
0.20 mols of O_2

Consider a lb.-mol of methane as 380 scf. At 910 Btu/cu.ft., the lower heating value of a lb.-mol of methane is 345,800 Btu. If it is presumed that 10% of the heat is radiated directly by the flame burst, the heat content of the gases is 311,220

Btu. The respective heat contents of the component gases are, then, as follows:

$CO_2 = 37,700$		$= 104,900$ Btu $= 33.7\%$
$H_2O = 67,200$		
$O_2 = 4,800$		$= 206,320$ Btu $= 63.3\%$
$N_2 = 201,520$		

The total heat content of the binary gases (CO_2 and H_2O) is 104,900 Btu. Heat content of the diatomic gases is 206,320 Btu immediately following the flame burst. These gases are in a homogeneous mixture in which a portion of the gases is radiant capable and a portion is radiation inert. This presents a situation which is difficult to explain as further heat is usefully delivered. (See Table 4-2.)

The explanation is difficult because the heat energy of a portion of the gases is being dissipated by radiation to produce a steady decrease in heat content within these gases. Another portion of the gases, which happens to contain the greatest portion of heat, cannot and does not lose any of its heat content by radiation but does, through molecular collision, deliver heat to the radiation-depleted gases. Thus, there is effort toward heat-content equilibrium between the binary gases and the diatomic gases as created through molecular collision.

Combustion Gas Radiation

However, the emissivity of gases is quite low. Even though there is a tendency for temperature equilibrium, as heat is dissipated by radiation, the quantity of heat radiated is a relatively small portion of the total heat content of the gases. Furthermore, of the residual heat content of the gases, approximately 63% is contained in the nonradiant diatomic gases which demand contact with a heat-absorptive surface for useful extraction of heat content. The surface over which the gases move for heat extraction can be either directly absorptive surfaces such as tubes or it can be refractory, which can absorb and reradiate the heat energy.

Table 4-2
Radiant Capability of Combustion Gases at 25%
and 50% Excess Air

25% excess air: $CH_4 + 2.5\,O_2 + 9.5\,N_2 = CO_2 + 2\,H_2O + 0.5\,O_2 + 9.5\,N_2$

Binaries (radiant capable)	CO_2	35,620 Btu
	H_2O	58,554 Btu
		94,174 Btu = 30.25% of total heat

Diatomics (radiant inert)	O_2	10,856 Btu
	N_2	206,280 Btu
		217,136 Btu = 69.75% of total heat

50% excess air: $CH_4 + 3\,O_2 + 11.4\,N_2 = CO_2 + 2\,H_2O + O_2 + 11.4\,N_2$

Binaries (radiant capable)	CO_2	30,176 Btu
	H_2O	49,509 Btu
		79,685 Btu = 25.60% of total heat

Diatomics (radiant inert)	O_2	18,672 Btu
	N_2	212,861 Btu
		231,533 Btu = 74.40 % of total heat

Note: These data will show that radiant capability decreases to a greater degree than the simple cooling effect of higher excess air factors might be expected to produce. It also adds greater urgency to the need for operation at the lowest excess air condition in the furnaces of heaters as fired. However, pursuit of minimal excess air must not be allowed to interfere with process, and excess air factors less than 10% may be questionable.

Gases can and do produce radiant energy; but the quantity of heat thus available, while significant, cannot by any means account for the heat absorbed by the radiant tubes. The radiant potential is restricted by the relative heat contents of the gases as they move through the furnace. As the gases complete their radiant function their major heat content is still to be extracted, regardless of the degree to which radiation, as such, has extracted heat from them. Continued heat extraction must be through some process involving direct contact of the gases with heat extractive surfaces, which places the mechanism within the realm of convection but not necessarily by direct convection to the tubes. Refractory surfaces over and against which the gases flow are continuously supplied with heat for reradiation to directly absorptive surfaces.

Temperature Equilibrium

If a refractory surface is to continue radiating heat, it must be supplied with heat continuously and in equilibrium with the rate of heat dissipation. The flow or movement of furnace gases is the vehicle which delivers heat to the radiant surfaces as any operating process furnace is carefully examined. This is not to say that a portion of the heat to the refractory radiant surfaces is not by radiation from other areas but the portion thus delivered is a relatively small part of the total heat received.

One of the most respected authorities on heat transfer, with special reference to the steel industry, is Trinks, Emeritus Professor of Mechanical Engineering, late of Carnegie Institute, whose time-proven information is to be found in his book *Industrial Furnaces* (John Wiley & Sons). Trinks points out, with emphasis, that in the transfer of heat to steel billets and the like, especially in the low-to-medium temperature ranges typical of process heaters as they operate, that brisk movement of furnace gases is demanded for adequately rapid transfer of heat to the steel. He further states that there must be brisk movement of gases over and in contact with the steel as well as the refractory walls, roof and floor of the furnace allowing gas movement to enhance radiation as well as convection as means of accelerating heat transfer.

Here Trinks is in advance agreement with the position that the movement of furnace gases is extremely important for heat transfer functions. In addition, the beneficial effect of accelerated transfer of heat is not that of direct convection alone to the surface receiving heat but is instead a combination of the effects of enhanced radiation as well as convection which are directly attributable to the movement of gases.

As has been discussed earlier, there is inevitably a state of equilibrium in temperature level between the binaries and the diatomics. Just where and how the state of equilibrium is being reached is also a subject for speculation. But speculation does not solve matters pertaining to radiation on a firm basis.

Without question, the presence of solid matter as carbon in the flame derived from dissociation of fuel adds most significantly to the total heat radiated from the flame. This can be proven quite readily if not quantitatively in an experiment with a Bunsen burner. Place the palm of your hand fairly close to a blue flame at a point where radiant heat is felt clearly but not painfully. Note that as the primary-air adjustment of the burner is closed and the flame turns yellow with carbon at incandescence in the flame envelope, it is necessary to remove your hand rather quickly to avoid painful burning. This experiment repeated with a coupon of metal to which a thermocouple has been attached will show up to four times as much radiation.

The oil flame which is yellow, yellow-white or white with the incandescent carbon present in the typical oil flame is, accordingly, a better source of radiant heat than a clear gas flame. Again, consider the typical vertical cylindrical heater. Oil is used very successfully and without damage by simply increasing the space between the oil flame and the tubes; but the space is seldom as much as doubled to again cast doubt on the overall effect of direct flame radiation.

Refractory Emission

It is common to consider as radiant planes only those refractory areas which glow with heat at a color in keeping with heat level. This is quite erroneous because all of the refractory surfaces are at heat levels which will permit them to radiate to a greater or lesser degree to the heat-absorptive surfaces of the furnace. Thus, all refractory is radiant at the inner surfaces of the heater regardless of where it may be.

Generally speaking, refractory surfaces possess high emissivity and thus rapidly deliver their heat by radiation. Or, if it is preferred, they dissipate their heat readily through radiation. If heat is dissipated rapidly and if the heat transfer level remains high there must be some means for delivering heat in quantity to the refractory for it to continue radiating at a satisfactory level. This is to say that there must be some source of continued delivery of heat in quantity and at a temperature level suitable for the amount of heat dissipated in radiant energy by the refractory.

Experimentation shows clearly that the heat delivery mechanism is not some function of radiant energy due either to radiation from the flame burst or to radiant energy from the gas content of the furnace structure. Such a suggestion leaves only some function of mass movement of gases as the source of heat. Since mass movement of gases is now considered and since convected heat transfer is due to mass movement of gases at significant temperature levels, it is easy to presume that the heat source is convection. But this is not true.

Gases within the furnace are never static and neither is their movement at any fixed rate. The movement of gases is largely at random and at varying velocities according to thermal contours within the furnace and according to other energy contours such as inertia at discharge from the burner or acceleration as the gases approach the furnace exit.

Thus, as furnace gases move within the furnace they come into contact with the tubes and, of course, transfer a quantity of heat to the tubes by convection. But the total area of the tubes is much less than the total area of the inner surfaces of the furnace. Here, again, the gases sweep over the refractory surfaces. Since the gases are hotter than the refractory surfaces, heat is delivered to the refractory by both radiation from the binaries and by convection from the diatomics. The heat thus delivered is then reradiated by the refractory surfaces to the tubes or other heat-absorptive surfaces.

Refractory Heat Color

Much of the refractory surface is behind the tubes. As the average process heater is studied, it is seldom that any heat-color is observed in the refractory areas behind the tubes. This state of affairs tends to be misleading as over-all heat transfer conditions are considered because the presumption may be made that in order for refractory to be significantly radiant it must show *heat color* or be visibly radiant. This presumption may be caused by too great a consideration of heat transfer based on the Stefan-Boltzmann equation, at the cost of neglecting the second law which governs radiant transfer. This is the law which states that radiant heat transfer varies inversely as the square of the distance between the radiant and the absorptive bodies.

In view of the fact that tube-to-wall spacings are measured in inches rather than in feet, it is not necessary for the wall behind the tubes to be so hot to transfer an optimum amount of heat. However, it is vitally necessary for the wall behind the tubes to be continually supplied with heat to maintain the required heat transfer to the total tube area.

Since the statement is made that the means for heat delivery to the refractory areas is a function of gas movement within the furnace, it is in order to examine the means for causing gases to sweep the refractory areas behind the tubes.

Energy for such gas movement is due to a simple thermosiphon effect that exists in the areas before and behind the tubes. The effect is set up and maintained because as the gases approach and flow over the tube surfaces they lose heat by both radiation from the binaries and convection as the gases move into contact with the tube surface. The loss of heat causes the gases to become cooler and therefore more dense. Since the remainder of the gas content of the furnace is losing heat much less rapidly and is considerably hotter, as well as less dense, the cooler gases begin to descend at increasing velocity until they reach the furnace floor and on both the front and the back sides of the tubes. On reaching the floor, the gases are reheated to either make another circuit or to exit from the furnace en route to the stack.

Gases in such flow pass over the entire tube areas as well as the wall behind the tubes scrubbing the tube surfaces for heat transfer by convection. Far more importantly, they also scrub the refractory wall behind the tubes to continually deliver heat to the wall surface. Because the space between the tube and the wall is relatively small, the state of radiation from the wall becomes quite significant as the wall temperature rises. Because of the small distance between the radiant surface of the wall and the absorptive surface of the tube, it is not necessary or preferred that the wall temperature be such as to show temperature color which can be seen in the typical process heater.

The descending gases move at surprising velocities en route to the floor, at times more than 50 ft./sec., to produce additional effects which are beneficial to heat transfer. Their movement adds to convected heat transfer. The zone of low pressure set up by the descending velocity causes hot gases from the open part of the furnace to be drawn into the tube area to further assist in heat transfer. Note that tube orientation, whether vertical or horizontal, makes no difference in this effect of recirculation. The effect of recirculation becomes optimum when the tubes are on typical two-diameter centers and is decreased as the center-to-center distance is less than two diameters.

Tube-to-Wall Spacing

Operational experience provides an excellent basis for research in heat transfer as was shown clearly in the case of a heater in which there were both roof and wall tubes. The heater had operated for years in a most satisfactory manner. As operation progressed, it was noted that the heater was rapidly losing heat transfer ability despite the fact that there had been no change in operation which might account for the decrease. There was no change in pressure drop through the coil which would indicate coke lay-down, if coking should be the cause of the loss of heat transfer capability. Yet, the loss came about in less than six months and noticeably on a day-to-day basis as the heater operated.

The heater was quite old. It had been in service for many years and was due for repairs which included replacing side walls which were failing inwardly. The walls, supported independently of the steel which supported the tubes, were gradually moving toward the tubes. The space between the walls and the back sides of the tubes was reduced to such a degree that most of the side walls were actually resting against the tubes.

The heater was shut down and the side walls were repaired to make the space between the tubes and the wall one full tube diameter, which in this case was 4½ in. When the heater was again fired and put into service, it had regained its heat transfer capability. Note that there had been no addition of tubes, there had been no change in burners or firing. Thus it was surprisingly evident that the increased space between the tubes and the wall accounted for increased heat absorbing ability. The heater performed as it had in the period before the failure of the walls.

This case history which obviously offered a clue to heat transfer capability was personally observed by the writer and brought about pilot-scale studies of the effect of tube-to-wall spacing on heat transfer capability. A test heater was constructed using ¼-in. OD tubes in a furnace 18x18x27 in. There was a provision to accurately adjust the tube-to-wall spacing and to adjust the relationship of the burner to the tubes. Accurately metered, saturated air was passed through the 3/16-in. ID tubes as the source of heat absorption. A thermocouple was used in the air stream at exit from the tubes to measure temperature of the exiting air. Thus a means was provided for calculation of heat absorbed on the basis of sensible heat for accuracy when the firing rate and excess air, as well as furnace temperature, were closely controlled to identical conditions for all tests.

The results of this test series were published (Reed-WPRA TECH-53-15) as a paper which was read at the 1953 meeting of the Western Petroleum Refiners Association, now the National Petroleum Refiners Association. At a later date, similar research was reported in the literature by engineers of the C F Braun Company with the exception that in the Braun research the tube diameter was 4 in., yet there is very close agreement with the Reed paper in evaluation of tube-to-wall spacing.

The papers report that for a tube spaced one-half diameter off the wall, the heat transfer to the tube is increased 13% over the condition where the tube is tangent to the wall. If the tube is spaced one diameter off the wall, the heat transfer to the tube is increased approximately 29% over the condition where the tube is tangent to the wall. All furnace conditions as to firing, excess air and furnace temperature were unchanged in the tube-spacing test.

It was further found that if the tube-to-wall spacing was increased past one diameter to as much as three to four diameters, there was no further increase in heat transfer. At still greater spacing, there was a decrease in heat transfer. Therefore—and fortunately—the optimum spacing of tubes off the walls of the furnace is one diameter for maximum heat transfer.

There was some question that the increase in heat transfer was due to improved access of radiant heat from other planes and areas within the furnace and not due to gas movement as has been suggested. To resolve the source of increased heat transfer, a further experiment which is not reported in the literature was conducted.

In this experiment, the tubes were spaced one diameter off the wall to produce the 29% increase in transfer. Strips of mica 0.003-in. thick were placed in the space between the tubes and the wall at the centerlines of the tubes so as to fill the space between the tubes and the wall with material which is substantially transparent to infra-red. The purpose was to avoid blockage of radiant transfer but to completely block the flow path for gases in the space between the tubes and the wall behind them. With the mica strips thus placed, the heat transfer to the tubes was exactly the same as it would have been if the tubes had been moved back to a tangent condition with the wall rather than a full diameter off the wall. This experiment offers proof that movement of gases in the tube-to-wall space is the source of increased heat transfer as the tubes are moved away from the wall. In this experiment the increase was 29%, which is very significant.

With this research offering proof of the vital role in heat transfer attributable to the movement of furnace gases, there was further investigation of gas flow phenomena as factors in heat transfer. In this study, it was necessary to take data from operating furnaces as the phenomena were observed. Laboratory scale procedures would be largely inconclusive in reference to specific areas of the furnace volume when the entire furnace is being studied.

Furnace Gas Flow

Such study required establishment of a means for definitive observation of furnace gas flow patterns. At first, bronze powder was introduced into furnace areas. This procedure left much to be desired because the typical blue-green glow of the copper tended to persist much longer than was ideal for area observation of hot furnace gases. A nearly satisfactory substitute is sodium bicarbonate powder, which produces a brilliant yellow flame. When introduced through the burner, sodium-yellow can be seen in the burner flame with visible extension of the flame area showing area of very hot gases but with abrupt cessation of the brilliant yellow at approximately the 1,800-2,000°F contour about the flame as the very hot flame gases are cooled.

After considerable experimentation for a means of observing gas flow patterns in which many chemicals were tested, powdered hard coke, such as is "rattled" from tubes, was found to be superior. The powdered coke as scooped up on impulse consisted of all grades of fines ranging in size from that which would pass through a 200-mesh screen to that which would pass through 16-mesh screen.

The burning of the very small fines produces a flame much like that of the sodium bicarbonate; but the larger particles carry with the gases from the burner and can be clearly and easily observed as they flow throughout the space within the furnace. Initial observation of the coke fines as they wander through the furnace is usually a source of considerable surprise. The flow patterns shown by the glowing small particles of carbon at times appear to move in aimless manners and directions.

Stack Number and Location

Using coke fines for the observation of gas flow patterns and following many years of such observation in literally hundreds of furnaces of all makes, types, forms and shapes, a number of most significant conclusions can be drawn with time-proven reliability. The first is the somewhat startling observation that the state of heat transfer in any furnace—regardless of its form, type, configuration or design basis—is directly controlled by the flow of the furnace gases. This is true of the typical process heater as well as in furnaces designed for highly pyrolytic service such as steam reforming or ethylene production. Energy sources influencing the flow of furnace gases are the inertia of the gas flow directly away from the burners and the thermosiphon effect in the tube areas. After many years of observation, there has not been a single case where stack location or number of stacks attached to a single furnace had any appreciable effect on the flow within the furnace proper if the space above the convection tubes and in the breeching above them was even reasonably adequate. In the breeching and immediately above the convection tubes, the area should be large enough to deliver uniform draft effect to all areas immediately down stream of the convection tubes. Such draft will secure reasonably uniform gas flow/heat transfer to all areas of the convection tubes. The typical heater is adequately designed for this function. It is not typical for stack location or numbers of stacks on a single heater to make an observable difference. However, if the space above the convection tubes is unduly restricted there can be an upset in heat transfer contours in the convection section and furnace flow can be seriously upset. But even with this design, considerable correction can be obtained if suitable revision of convection baffling is made. Such a procedure is seldom justified. A careful study of the heater design should be made to determine justification for this because there are few things quite so distressing as a fairly expensive course of action which produces little, if any, benefit.

The sole, truly controllable factor in the gas movement/energy picture is that of the inertia derived from the burners. For heaters to provide transfer of heat to material for process in the best manner the burners must provide inertial patterns and energies to the gases effluent from the burners and directly at the burners where the inertias, energies and patterns are properly suited to the specific heater which is being fired. The greater the departure from these preferred conditions, the less satisfactory the heater becomes from either tube failure through over heating or failure to deliver heat at the required time or quantity.

After more than 40 years of heater observation, there has been no instance where a heater was, by any standards, considered perfect. There have been scores of instances where near perfection was such that very little was left to be desired. In each case of near perfection, study of the gas flow patterns showed quite excellent uniformity throughout the furnace and minimal distortion of gas flow to any part.

The heater designer creates a furnace structure which, provided the gas-flow patterns are as he wishes them to be, will perform its function as intended. But, in view of the influence of burner design on the heater and the relatively small consideration given to overall burner function, it is truly remarkable that there is not greater difficulty.

Burner Design Benefits

However, the requirement for meeting guaranty conditions despite something less than preferred firing conditions often leads the designer to over-design. If after a period of operation at or near guaranty conditions, inspection of the heater firing shows undesirable conditions in the furnace, better service from the heater may be obtained by substituting burners better suited to the service required. Such increase in service from the heater may range from as little as 5% to as much as 50%, but either is interesting if the heater operation is at all profitable.

Experience shows clearly that if there is trouble in the heater, even though superficial inspection of firing provides no clue as to the source of the difficulty, study of the gas-flow patterns from each individual burner will reveal the source of the undesirable furnace conditions. Many times it will be found that the difficulty has its source in a burner located in a reasonably remote part of the furnace and there is no flame within many feet of the trouble area. Flow of the glowing coke particles will show the travel of overly hot gases to the critical area. The gas flow may follow a quite devious path. It may be horizontal or partially downward and it may curl back on itself.

Gas Recirculation Factors

Recirculation energy factors, other than those peculiar to the burner design, have a great bearing on gaseous flow. Recirculation energy factors are completely unpredictable in their order of magnitude and effect. Firm predictions of the precise state of heat transfer in any particular part of the heaters is most difficult because of recirculation energy factors.

Heat transfer to any coil of tubes will conform to an average; but the greatest single cause of heater difficulty is serious departure from the average. Heat transfer will be high in comparatively restricted portions of the tube surface allowing average conditions to exist because of low heat transfer in other tube areas. The results of such a condition are burned tubes, coking inside the tubes, serious interference with the process because of accelerated skin cracking and other equally unpleasant conditions.

A question which will frequently occur to the average process man might well be, "Just how much heat input can a tube be expected to take?" A reply to this question must be considered highly empirical because it may be said that a particular tube in any service is capable of average heat transfer without particular damage. Small areas may be absorbing from 5 to 50% more heat than the average because other areas are absorbing less than the average. While there is no observable tube damage in the high heat areas, is the ability of the tube to be limited to the average figure or can a much higher figure, based on the actual state of heat transfer, be considered safe and operable?

Heat Release vs Furnace Volume

Improvement in the art of burning fuels in heaters has been so very great in the years 1956-1980 and furnace conditions of gaseous flow and heat distribution are so improved that some very significant increases in average heat transfer are becoming common to petroleum and petrochemical operations. As an example, consider that heat release in the order of 10,000 Btu/cu.ft. of furnace volume was considered daring in the not-too-distant past. Present-day process heaters run upwards of 50,000 Btu/cu.ft. and at the moment there is excellent reason to state that more than 150,000 Btu/cu.ft. are quite possible for some elements of process operation.

The term "Btu/cu.ft. of combustion volume" is most misleading because we speak of the entire furnace volume when the phrase is used, whereas it is quite commonly known that the actual flame volume as the fuel burns is a rather small portion of the furnace volume. However the fact that the flame ceases to exist at a particular point in flame travel does not mean that the gas temperature immediately following the flame instantly drops to that of the mean temperature of the furnace. The gases immediately following the flame are at slightly lower temperatures than that of the flame but are almost too hot for contact with tubes or heat transfer surfaces. Gas heat content must be dissipated by radiation or admixture with cooler furnace gases before they can safely come in contact with tubes or heat transfer surfaces. This is the basic function involved in the distribution of heat from and at the source of heat. If the flame or the hot gases following the flame should reach the tubes or heat transfer surfaces, there would be damage due to excessive delivery of heat to the surfaces.

Burner Functions

The function of the burner equipment is to deliver heat to the gas content of the furnace as uniformly as possible to produce a temperature contour throughout the mass of the furnace gases which is as nearly even as possible. Reaching this ideal condition is impossible without an infinitely large number of small burners, which is economically unfeasible. Since less than ideal conditions must exist in firing, it is probable that something less than ideal furnace conditions will exist. The burner equipment used must possess superior ability to disperse heat to the gaseous furnace atmosphere if the heater is to be satisfactory. It is the relative ability to disperse heat by a particular burner that may make it badly suited to firing a specific heater. If the burner is applied to another furnace having a different configuration, it may be quite satisfactory.

Simple release of an adequate amount of heat to the furnace atmosphere, for the amount of heat to be absorbed, may be a very far cry from a satisfactory heater. No element in the basic design of the heater is more important than the choice of proper burner equipment, for the service to be performed, with the available fuel. There are no hard and fast rules to govern choice of burners. Consultation with the burner manufacturer as to the type of burner equipment best suited for the service is considered wise provided a very responsible burner manufacturer is chosen. It is further recommended that the choice of a burner manufacturer be made on the basis that he is capable of offering his version of all typical basic burner designs, so that his opinion is unbiased as he recommends a particular burner.

There is no single burner for any fuel which can be considered satisfactory for all firing conditions required for heat transfer to materials for processing. We have suggested that the burner is the prime source of energy for establishing satisfactory conditions of gas movement. In addition to supplying inertial energy for gas movement, the burner must also be capable of satisfactory heat diffusion to the furnace gases without damage to tubes or heat transfer areas. All functions are so important that it is difficult to determine which is of the greatest significance.

Burner flames must be shaped and directed to allow the required heat diffusion to the furnace gases without delivering excessive heat to any transfer area. At times, the flame shape is that of a rigid cylinder of quite small diameter and great length. At other times, the flame is in the form of a less rigid cylinder of greater diameter and lesser length. Other flames must be still less rigid and of still greater diameter to the point where there is no flame rigidity and where the flame moves at right angles to the burner axis and against the furnace wall with absolute zero length or forward motion. Any of these conditions of flame shape or travel may be required—or perhaps some intermediate shape or travel. Suggested flame shapes can be obtained in suitably designed burner equipment for either gas or oil fuels, with the exception that flame travel parallel to the furnace wall requires fuels in the distillate range rather than in the residual range when liquid fuel such as oil is being burned. At times the flame may be required to be in the shape of a fan, narrow at the bottom and wide at the top, viewed in elevation but quite thin in cross section. Fan shapes allow firing of quite long but relatively narrow spaces without heat damage to transfer surface.

Flame Impingement

It is interesting that in some conditions in which there is damage to tubes or heat transfer surfaces there is no flame impingement on the surfaces. It is quite common, but erroneous, to say that such damage is caused by flame impingement when the conditions causing heat damage might much better be described as impingement of hot gases. Visible impingement of the flame on tubes can be seen and should be corrected immediately to avoid severe damage. Impingement of overly hot gases can be almost as severe, yet without the use of coke fines, as discussed previously, there is no visible evidence of the source of overheating. There is a case on record in which one of the burners diagonally across the furnace from an area in which there had been severe tube damage was the source of the difficulty. The process heater was almost totally inoperable until a study of the flow of furnace gases with coke fines indicated a burner revision in an area at least 50 ft. from the point of tube damage.

It is comparatively common to find the source of heat damage at a point quite remote from the area of damage. This condition may be found in many operating heaters. Such conditions limit heater operation unnecessarily and can be the source of a less profitable operation. A proper examination of furnace gas flow could reveal the source of the difficulty and with few exceptions the difficulty is subject to improvement through burner correction.

Great consideration is given to flame length, despite the fact that flame length and heat dispersion are not necessarily in a fixed relationship, but heat dispersion is really the governing factor in heater performance. To say that the burner is capable of producing a short flame for the required heat release is not necessarily to say also that the ability of the flame to deliver heat to the furnace gases will be suited to the firing requirements of the heater. At times, it is necessary to provide a long flame with considerable forward inertia to drive the hot gases to the furnace areas where maximum heat transfer is required. For example, in the typical floor-fired steam reformer it is necessary to drive the hot gases from the furnace floor to the top of the furnace to distribute heat to the tube areas where maximum heat density is demanded for suitable operation. The contrary is true in side-wall fired steam reformers.

In side-wall firing, burners are located in areas where maximum heat transfer is demanded. Absolutely zero forward flame is required when the burners are located quite close to the tubes in narrow furnaces in which the tubes may be either vertically or horizontally oriented at the center of the furnace. Such heaters require a relatively large number of small burners to secure the heat delivery required for reforming. As a prime example of preference for heat dispersion, as distinguished from flame length, there is a heater design for the identical service which forms the side walls as terraces against which the flame moves. In this design, the flame is considerably longer yet the service performed is identical. The flame heats the wall which in turn radiates to the tubes despite the greater flame length.

In a typical process heater, the demand for very precise control of heat density per lineal foot of tube is not so great as in a steam-reformer furnace. It is possible to use a smaller number of larger burners to obtain satisfactory firing conditions and heat dispersion, but the burners must be suited to the service. Many times, burners capable of reasonably short-flame production have not had satisfactory heat dispersive characteristics and were replaced to very greatly improve heater operation because of tube damage and the amount of material charged to the heater. Within the short flame concept, there are not only degrees of flame shortness but, again, the presence of a short flame does not assure proper heat dispersion to the furnace. It is erroneous to presume that a furnace is well fired when flames are short, as visually inspected, in the absence of hot-gas projection as would be shown through the use of pulverized coke.

Continued use of pulverized coke in examining hundreds of furnaces, in all petroleum and petrochemical process services, has shown clearly that without a pulverized coke check, examination of the furnace cannot conclusively establish heat transfer quality in a particular furnace. Visual inspection can clearly show there are no hot spots or danger areas, but visual inspection cannot show the areas in which there is less than preferred transfer of heat. Experienced observers find that by quick, visual inspection of furnaces they can obtain a fairly rough estimate of heat transfer through observing the heat color of the hangers which support the tubes. Hanger ends glow with color according to the heat level they are "seeing." Brighter colors denote maximum heat transfer and duller colors denote minimal transfer. The brightest hanger should not be more than bright cherry red or there is danger of tube damage. Heat color may grade downwardly to deep blood-red which can be observed as color with difficulty. However, the tube hangers are present only at widely spaced intervals along the side walls and at the arch or roof of the furnace and cannot show heat density for the entire tube length. Thus, visual observations of tube hangers leave a great deal to be desired in determining heat density in the various furnace areas.

Wall or Floor Firing

Preference for excellent distribution of heat and cost for construction collide head-on at times and very notably in the decision as whether to floor-fire, end-wall or side-wall fire the heater. Wall firing will, in most instances, cost less because there are usually fewer burners and the cost of elevating the heater to provide head room is not required; thus the heater, ready to fire, costs less. However, in wall firing, the reduced first cost of the heater is gained at the cost of reduced potential through-put. At the same limiting conditions, a heater can be fired up to 25% harder from the floor than from the walls. This is true for a number of reasons such as better use of combustion volume, better heat distribution, better heat control and more uniform firing of all tube areas. In any firing method there will be greater service from the heater when a relatively large number of small burners is used rather than a small number of large burners. In any event, the ability of the burners to disperse heat to the furnace atmosphere will be proportional to the number of burners firing.

If there is a relatively small number of large burners there is a greater mass of gas issuing from each burner and a greater concentration of heat before the burner. This disproportionately large mass of gases and quantity of heat must then be dispersed evenly to the furnace atmosphere if the heater is to perform in the best manner. It is far more difficult to disperse these gases and this quantity of heat to the furnace evenly than it would if the mass of gases were half as great and the quantity of heat half as much, as would be the case with twice as many burners. The typical floor-fired heater has from three to four times as many burners as the average wall-fired heater. The fact that there can be as much as a 25% increase with floor-firing more than justifies the added expense of the greater numbers of burners.

It is well to consider that the heater is erected especially to produce a useful and profitable product. Any procedure that will permit the heater to produce a greater quantity of product at a small extra expense in terms of percentage of total cost can be considered wise. However, the problem here is the eternal conflict between capital investment and tax factors versus process considerations in view of net return at the end of the year or over a period of years.

The heater design and configuration are fixed factors as supplied; but the service from the heater thus supplied is governed completely by proper observation of all factors connected with heat transfer. If this were not true, it would not be possible to increase heat transfer to the designed heater as much as 50% without damage to any of the heat transfer surfaces, through replacing or revising burners, as has been done hundreds of times.

Operators of heaters should always be aware that poor heater performance is not necessarily due to improper design or design error but may be due to factors other than design, which may be causing substandard heater performance. However, substandard heater performance can usually be corrected if both the heater manufacturer and the burner manufacturer are consulted promptly.

5

Stacks, Draft and Flow of Furnace Gases

A prime source of energy for induction of combustion air becomes available when gases are heated and are confined within a structure which isolates them from air at atmospheric temperature. This energy is commonly referred to as *draft*. Since the draft or energy occurs due to natural physical functions, it is called *natural draft*.

Buoyancy

As gases are heated at constant pressure they expand. A cubic foot of gas at elevated temperature is less dense than a cubic foot of gas at atmospheric temperature, or the heated gas becomes buoyant. The degree of buoyancy is thus governed by the degree of temperature elevation with all buoyancy calculations based on absolute temperature (degrees Rankine). Since buoyancy is proportional to expansion at elevated temperature, the volume of the gases is also proportional to the degree of temperature elevation.

Calculation of volume at elevated temperature for gases is as follows:

$$V_2 = V_1 (T_2 + 460 / T_1 + 460)$$

where:

V_1 = Volume at 60°F at 760 mm Hg. pressure,

V_2 = Volume at elevated temperature (°F) and 760 mm Hg. pressure,

T_1 = 60°F,

T_2 = Elevated temperature, °F

Because of expansion of the gases, the weight per cubic foot at elevated temperature, is inversely proportional to the 60°F temperature and is as follows:

$$M_2 = M_1 (T_1 + 460 / T_2 + 460)$$

where:

M_1 = 0.076 lbs./ cu. ft. at 60°F and 760 mm Hg. pressure,

M_2 = Weight per cu. ft. at elevated temperature and at 760 mm Hg. pressure,

T_1 = 60° F,

T_2 = Elevated temperature

Calculation shows that while the volume of gases increases with an increase in temperature, the weight per cubic foot becomes less. If the gas is confined in a column of suitable height, the buoyancy of the gas as contained in the column is capable of creating draft or less than atmospheric pressure required to cause atmospheric air to be drawn into the heated space supplying oxygen for fuel burning. As the fuel burns, the heated space supplies a self-regenerative source of energy, inducing more air for the continued burning of fuel.

Natural Draft and Stacks

An overwhelming number of furnaces designed for process work use natural draft for induction of air. Stacks or chimneys are supplied at calculated heights to supply the required draft and also to serve the important function of discharging combustion gases containing residual heat at a point significantly above grade. High discharge of combustion gases avoids hazards caused by the hot gases as well as reducing air pollution hazards due to oxides of sulfur which may be present in the stack gases. Other potential pollutants may also be present.

The air pollution factor is becoming increasingly important in stack design as emphasis on air pollution reduction at grade, to comply with local regulations as well as impending federal laws, becomes critical. If there is any significant quantity of sulfur in the fuel such as H_2S, mercaptans, organic sulfides or elemental sulfur, both principal sulfur oxides will be present in the stack gases as either SO_2 or SO_3. Closely held research shows that as much as 10% by weight of the sulfur present can appear in the stack gases as SO_3 due to some obscure catalytic conversion of SO_2 to SO_3; but the remainder of the sulfur appears as SO_2.

Other pollutants such as Cl_2 or F may also be present according to the nature of the fuel which is burned and according to the disposal requirements of the operation. There are changing but quite specific requirements for both chlorine and fluorine. If local or national requirements for tolerable concentrations at grade are to be met, a wise designer will learn the requirements before erecting the heater and before establishing the required stack height.

Stack Height

A significant means for reducing pollutant concentration at grade and down wind of the stack, is found in increasing the stack height. Pollution may well be the deciding factor in establishing stack height rather than the normal factor which is to supply the required amount of furnace draft. There has been a great deal of research in determining diffusion or volumetric reduction of pollutants as stack gases return to grade in the down-wind direction from the stack. However, there is considerable disagreement in the formulations proposed. One authority is quite punitively conservative. In small-scale experimentation as in wind tunnels, faulty data will likely be obtained because conditions vary considerably with actual full-scale operations.

A formulation which has been found reasonably satisfactory for calculating stack height based on pollutant concentration in parts-per-million as the stack gases return to grade in the down-wind direction is

$$\text{Stack Height} = 2.15 \ (Q) \ (100{,}000) \ 0.50/ \ 10 \ (H)^2$$

where:

Q = Std. cu. ft./sec. of pollutant gases

H = 1.50 times physical height of stack (at 1600° F)

At 750 to 1,000°F, H = (1.20) Physical Height

At 1,100 to 1,460°F, H = (1.35) Physical Height

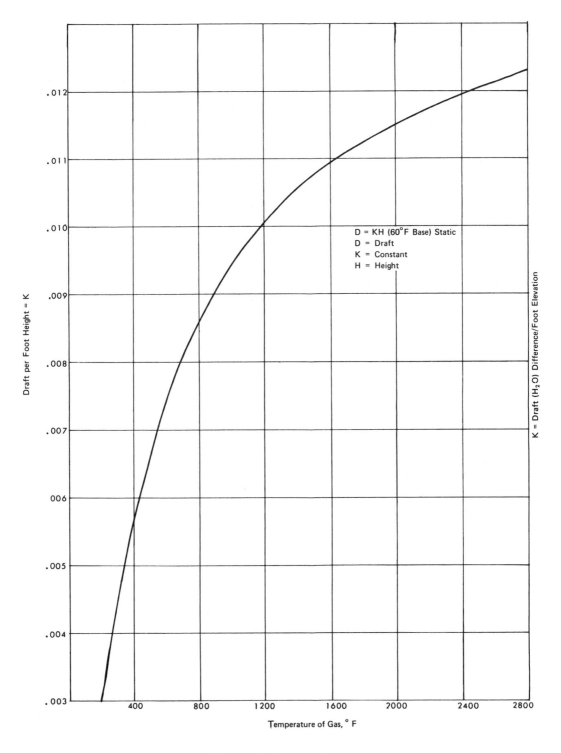

Figure 5-1. Static draft data.

This formulation, based on typical calculations of Sutton and Lowery, is simplified for easier use. The equation takes into account the much greater thermal rise typical of gases at temperature levels which are in excess of normal temperatures for smoke stacks, which is the basis upon which typical standard formulations are based.

Stacks based on this formulation will be punitively high. There is great need for better procedures based on typical conditions in process heater stacks where temperatures commonly are as great as or greater than 1,000°F. A number of research groups are now seeking better data to calculate reasonable stack heights which will produce a required state of diffusion of pollutants. One major point of contention is that in the standard calculation procedures the pollutant gas is considered in its pure state, whereas as discharged the pollutant gases, such as SO_2/SO_3 are greatly diluted by the CO_2, H_2O, N_2 and O_2 as they emerge from the stack.

As typical of the need for better caluclation procedure consider one stack in which the calculated height for diffusion of a relatively small quantity of SO_2 was over 600 ft. to meet air pollution requirements in a desert area. In another instance stacks were erected to heights dictated by a requirement not to exceed 0.10 ppm of SO_2 at grade are now in operation at greater than design conditions and constant sampling surveys out to 20 mi. from the plant site have failed to show any detectable SO_2 at grade.

At the present time there is reason to believe that the ultimate requirement for SO_2 concentration at grade will be in the order of 0.10 ppm as the effect of SO_2 on vegetation becomes better understood. While such a requirement may be considered as punitive in view of present practice, it should be noted that in some European areas the minimum stack height permitted is 100 m. to avoid pollution at grade.

Stack height, for available draft only, is that height which will produce draft or less than atmospheric pressure at the entry to the stack such that at no point within the furnace structure can a condition of atmospheric pressure or greater than atmospheric pressure exist. The sole function of the stack draft is to overcome the pressure drop of combustion gases in their flow from the furnace proper to the point of entry to the stack plus 0.03-in. WC. The 0.03-in. WC is added because this is the minimum draft which should exist at any point within the furnace structure.

In any event, where draft exists there is a decrease in draft with upward movement and an increase in draft with downward movement. This is true of the stack as well as the furnace and is due to the buoyancy of the heated gas above the point where the draft is being measured. At 1,200°F gas temperature, the draft or pressure changes 0.01-in. WC per foot of height. Thus, if we measure draft at a particular point and then move up 10 ft. and measure draft again, within the same structure, there will be 0.10-in. less draft at the point which is 10 ft. above the point of first measurement. The draft effect is proportional to the temperature level. With an increase in temperature, the draft effect increases, however, this is *static* draft or draft which exists in the presence of very small linear movement of the gas so that linear pressure drop is not a factor in draft measurement. (See Figure 5-1.)

Furnace Draft

Because of its buoyant energy, hot gas is quite capable of producing pressures greater than atmospheric, if there is interference with its flow. Thus, in the typical furnace convection section, breeching and stack configuration, the pressure contours as the gases pass become quite complex and do require understanding. Each portion of the assembly is to be considered as entirely separate as pressure contours within the assembly are studied.

In the furnace radiant section, if the furnace height is 10 ft. and the temperature is 1,200°F, the change in pressure (draft) in the furnace is 0.01-in. WC per foot of height. (See Figure 5-2.) If the draft at the roof or arch is 0.03-in. WC, the draft at the floor will be 0.13-in. (0.10 + 0.03) when the draft from the stack is adequate to overcome the pressure drop across the convection section and the breeching plus 0.03 in. If the stack draft should be decreased by 0.06 in, there would no longer be adequate energy by stack draft to overcome the pressure drop across the convection section breeching, but the requirement for energy remains unchanged.

In this case, the buoyant gases within the furnace raise the pressure at the entry to the convection section to supply the required pressure drop. If the stack draft has failed by 0.06 in, the pressure at the top of the furnace must rise 0.06 in. to change from -0.03 in. to +0.03 in. The draft at the floor is then changed to 0.07-in. WC (0.13-0.06) which may not be enough draft to permit burning the fuel without burner adjustment; even with burner adjustment the draft may still be inadequate.

However, the lack of adequate draft for fuel burning may be the least serious result of the draft failure. As the pressure within the furnace becomes greater than atmospheric, cooling air is no longer drawn in through the various cracks and apertures in the furnace. Instead, there is outward movement of hot gases to cause loss of fuel as well as serious overheating of the steel elements in the furnace structure. Overheating can result in failure of various parts in the furnace structure or there can be serious warpage or corrosion. A prime rule for heater operation is that there should never be greater than atmospheric pressure at any point within the heater structure or very serious damage as well as loss of fuel may result.

There are numerous symptoms of greater than atmospheric pressure within the heater structure. When the arch or the furnace roof is inspected visually, if the cracks between the refractory segments of the roof or arch are hotter than the faces of the segments, the draft is not adequate. The cracks will be darker than the faces of the segments if draft exists at the level of the arch or roof. If cracks should exist in other parts of the furnace, the same thing is true.

When appreciable quantities of sulfur are present in the fuel, the combustion gases will produce a faint blue-gray smoke which is SO_3 at the dew point as it cools to near atmospheric temperature. This smoke should be visible against a clear blue sky and quite close to the top of the stack alone if there is no furnace leakage due to pressure greater than atmospheric within the furnace. However, if

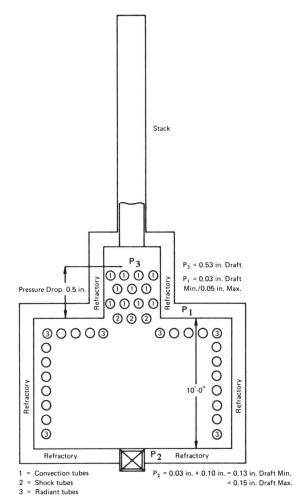

Figure 5-2. Draft/pressure contours typical of a fired heater where furnace temperature (mean) is 1,200° F. Drafts are indicated in inches WC.

the furnace is under pressure, the same smoke will be seen floating away from the roof of the heater. This condition, if observed, requires immediate correction if damage is to be prevented. The correction to be made is increasing furnace draft and appropriate closure of air registers to hold an identical excess air factor. A requirement for this adjustment is damper control of draft above the convection section in combination with a stack designed for creation of the required draft above the stack damper, permitting an increase in draft below the damper as it is opened.

Stack Dampers

If, as is frequently the case, the stack has been under-designed so that with the damper in the wide open position it is impossible to obtain sufficient draft, there is a choice between continued operation at the risk of furnace damage or decreased rate of firing accompanied by a proportional reduction in product production. Neither choice is pleasant.

Dampers are subjected to considerable heat attack. As the months of operation pass, it is occasionally discovered that moving the damper to a new position will result in an unexpected draft change. The movement may be either toward the closed or open position. As a last resort, this maneuver should not be neglected if there is a draft failure.

Tube Fouling

Furnace draft failure can quite frequently be caused by fouling of the convection passages for the gas. Such fouling is to be expected where significant quantities of oil are burned as fuel. However, the fouling can also occur in gas firing because so-called clean air will contain a few milligrams of dust per thousand cubic feet of air. By the time billions of cubic feet of air pass through the furnace, in normal operation, dust tends to accumulate, seriously interferring with both heat transfer and draft. When oil is the fuel, there will always be some mineral ash, which combines with dust to speed the accumulation. This tendency for speedy accumulation of mineral matter is particularly serious with extended surface tubes in the convection section such as fins or studs. Consideration of this factor must be made in gas firing and experience shows that in oil firing, extended surfaces are not advisable. If extended surfaces are demanded, stud tubes should be used, at considerably greater expense.

Experience with soot blowers for such draft or heat transfer impairment in convection sections has been uniformly good, even where gas alone is the fuel. An increase in convective transfer temperature of as much as 20-30°F has been found as the soot or accumulated mineral matter is blown. In one particular installation where oil was the fuel and the soot blowers were operated at 8-hr. intervals, each blow produced a 15°F rise in convection outlet temperture to very quickly pay for installation of the soot blowers and the cost of their operation.

Stack Design

In the design of stacks and breechings, the design basis should be conservative to provide ample draft for a potential increase in charge rate or for the normal state of fouling which is to be expected. The cost increase for designing the stack on a conservative basis rather than on a tightly designed basis is quite small.

A conservative basis for calculating stack area for the flow of stack gases presumes that the velocity with which stack gases flow is approximately 25 ft./sec. (linear velocity). A formula for such calculation is as follows:

$$A = Q \left[(T_2 + 460)/(T_1 + 460)\right]/(3600 \times 25)$$

where

A = Stack cross-sectional area in square feet required for a velocity of 25 ft/sec.

Q = Volume of stack gases in scfh (60°F and 760 mm Hg.),

T_1 = 60°F

T_2 = Temperature of stack gases as they flow, °F.

The result of this calculation will determine the number of square feet of stack area required for a stack gas velocity of 25 ft./sec. The required stack diameter is easy to determine once the required area is known; however, the same calculation can be used for ducts and breeching which may be rectangular in cross section and should be designed around the same cross-sectional velocity.

Table 5-1
Pressure Drop vs Velocity

Press. Drop, in. WC	V-60	V-250	V-500	V-750	V-1,000	V-1,250	V-1,500
0.10	21.1	24.2	28.7	32.1	35.2	38.2	40.9
0.20	29.8	34.1	40.5	45.3	49.8	54.0	57.8
0.30	36.6	41.9	49.7	55.6	61.1	66.2	71.0
0.40	42.2	48.3	57.4	64.2	70.5	76.5	81.9
0.50	47.2	54.0	64.2	71.7	78.6	85.5	91.6
0.60	50.2	57.6	68.2	76.3	84.0	91.0	97.4
0.70	55.5	63.6	75.5	84.3	92.8	100.5	107.8
0.80	59.6	68.3	81.1	90.6	99.6	107.8	115.7
0.90	62.3	71.3	84.8	94.7	104.0	112.7	120.9
1.00	66.7	76.3	09.8	101.5	111.4	120.8	129.5
2.00	94.5	108.1	128.5	143.5	158.0	171.0	183.5
3.00	115.5	132.4	157.0	175.0	193.0	209.0	224.3
4.00	133.5	152.5	181.5	203.0	223.0	242.0	259.2
5.00	149.0	170.0	203.0	226.5	249.0	270.0	289.3
7.00	176.5	202.0	240.0	269.0	295.1	319.0	342.7
10.00	211.0	241.5	287.0	321.0	352.0	382.0	410.0

Direct, simple calculation of area required for flow of a specific volume of air or typical combustion gases at a specific temperature can be made by using the equations:

$$V_1 = V_2 \; \sqrt{[(520)/(T + 460)]}$$

$$V_2 = V_1 \; \sqrt{[(T + 460)/520]}$$

$$A = [Q \, (T_2/T_1)/(3{,}600 \; V_2)] \; 1/C$$

where:

V_1 = Velocity at 60°F
(See Table 5-1)
V_2 = Velocity at other than 60°F
(See Table 5-1)
Q = Volume of gases (scfh)
T_1 = 460 + 60
T_2 = 460 + T
C = Orifice coefficient
A = Area (in square feet)
T = Temperature (°F)

(Note: The value of C is taken as 0.85 for sharp-edged approach with L/D greater than 0.5 and up to 0.95 for rounded approaches.

In making velocity correction for other gases, use the equation:

$$\sqrt{\frac{MW\text{-}1 \times R\text{-}2}{MW\text{-}2 \times 1.41}}$$

where:

MW-1 = 29
MW-2 = Molecular weight of other gases
R-2 = Cp/Cv for other gas (ratio of specific heats)

This data is based on 14.70 psi absolute pressure. For other absolute pressure (P) at pressure drop (Vp), use the following equation:

$$Vp = V \; \sqrt{[(14.70/P)]} .$$

Gas Velocity Factors

In stacks, ducts, and breechings the velocity can reach some higher velocity without serious loss of draft; but at greater velocities the loss in draft rapidly becomes serious and can interfere with the required operation. Stack gas velocity is proportional to the firing rate.

In stacks, there is a certain static draft condition due to the temperature of the gases confined within the stack. But since there is movement of gases at quite appreciable velocity in the stack, the draft available from the stack will be the static draft minus the linear pressure drop caused by the movement of the gases. The pressure drop in the stack is influenced by the roughness of the interior and a roughness factor must enter into the stack pressure drop calculation.

Static draft for the stack will be the height of the stack in feet above the entry of the breeching to the stack multiplied by the static draft effect per foot of height at the temperature of the gases within the stack. There is always loss of temperature as the gases pass up the stack, therefore the entering gas temperature is not the proper temperature basis for the static draft calculation. In most instances, it is safe and conservative to accept the entering gas temperature minus 100°F as the temperature level for calculating the average steel stack which is almost universally used in preference to ceramic stacks.

Table 5-2 which is based on air temperature at 60°F, provides static draft effect per foot of height at various corrected stack temperatures. Note that the draft effects per foot of height are based on the temperature difference between the corrected stack gas temperature and 60°F atmospheric temperature. Therefore, if the atmospheric temperature is higher there will be less draft effect per foot of height in proportion to the absolute temperature differential; at lower atmospheric temperatures there will be greater draft because the temperature differential will be increased.

Static draft calculation is, then, based on the draft effect per foot of height (K) times the height in feet above the breeching entry to the stack (H). Expressed in equation form, draft (D) is $D = KH$. But note that static draft is not available draft because there is movement of gases in the stack at very appreciable velocities. Therefore, linear pressure drop and inertial resistance must be deducted from static draft to arrive at the draft which will be available from the stack.

A convenient and reasonably accurate formula for calculating draft losses (DL) due to movement of the gases is as follows:

$$DL = fW^2 \ CH \ / \ A^3 = \text{inches Water Column}$$

where:

f (steel stacks) = 0.0015
f (smooth refractory) = 0.002
f (brick lining) = 0.0025-0.003
W = Lb./sec. of stack gases
C = Circumference (inside) in feet
H = Effective height in feet
A = Area of inside of stack in square feet

Inertial loss of draft, which may be exit loss or acceleration loss, is defined as the pressure drop required for establishing the actual stack gas velocity. However, this loss is based at stack gas temperature rather than at standard conditions. The loss of draft, in inches of Water Column, for acceleration at various temperatures is listed in Table 5-1 for entry to the stack which is safest as a base for calculation. The linear loss, or the loss due to flow, adds to the acceleration loss to subtract from the static draft of which the stack is capable at operating temperature. This calculation produces the effective draft availability for the stack at the effective height. In other words, the total of the losses must be subtracted from the calculated static draft effect.

Table 5-2
Static Draft Effect per Foot of Height
(Air Temperature 60°F.)

300°F = 0.0044 in.	800°F = 0.0086 in.
400°F = 0.0056 in.	900°F = 0.0090+ in.
500°F = 0.0066 in.	1,000°F = 0.0094 in.
600°F = 0.0074 in.	1,100°F = 0.0097+ in.
700°F = 0.0080 in.	1,200°F = 0.010 in.

The discussion for available draft and static draft to this point is suitable for elevation of the stack base above sea level not to exceed approximately 500 ft. If the stack is located at a greater altitude, correction for the reduced absolute pressure is required. (See Table 5-3.)

Table 5-3
Absolute Pressure Corrections

P at sea level	=	14.70 psi
P at 1,000 ft.	=	14.21 psi
P at 2,000 ft.	=	13.72 psi
P at 3,000 ft.	=	13.23 psi
P at 4,000 ft.	=	12.77 psi
P at 5,000 ft.	=	12.31 psi
P at 6,000 ft.	=	11.89 psi
P at 7,000 ft.	=	11.47 psi

As these data show, there is need for a much greater increase in stack height than in stack area. It is recommended that all calculation be on the basis of standard conditions at sea level initially and then corrected for altitude as necessary. In altitude correction, it is suggested that the next highest altitude value taken if the altitude at the job site is at or near the midpoint between altitude figures. Thus, if the job site altitude is 4,500 ft., calculation of stack diameter and height should be on the basis of 5,000 ft. or at an interpolation between indicated altitude figures and that of the job site elevation might well be used. The former suggestion is most conservative.

Friction

Where there is an abrupt change in flow direction, such as at an abrupt right angle turn, there is loss of draft energy in addition to the losses due to friction.

$$\text{Friction} = fW^2\, CH\,/\,A^3$$

where:

f = 0.002
W = Lb./sec. of gases
C = Internal circumference of stack
H = Height of hot column (A')
A = Internal stack area, sq. ft.

Acceleration = pressure drop due to flow at t_1 and at calculated velocity per Table 5-1 multiplied by 1.176

Friction loss may be calculated for ducts and breechings exactly as in the stack, with the provision that if the breeching or duct is square the friction loss is to be multiplied by a factor of 1.12 and by 1.15 if the duct is rectangular. (See Figure 5-3.)

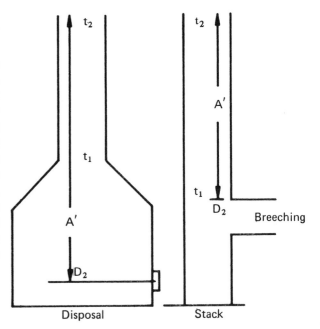

Figure 5-3. Friction Loss. Kt_2—*see static draft curve at* t_2; t_1 = *gas temperature at entry to stack;* t_2 = t_1 − *100°F;* D_2 = d_1 *(friction + acceleration);* D_1 = *static draft;* D_2 = *effective draft;* A' = *height (feet);* D_1 = $Kt_2 \cdot A'$.

The energy loss due to each right angle turn in the breeching can be correctly assumed to be 0.05-in. WC when the duct velocity is 30 ft./sec., 0.09-in. WC at 40 ft./sec. and 0.14-in. WC at 50 ft./sec. It is a serious error to disregard these turning losses as will be seen.

If the turning losses are seriously interfering with draft, it is possible to reduce the losses with well-designed turning vanes to relieve the abruptness of the turn. However, the relief that will be obtained is not great. If a few hundredths of an inch increase in draft is all that may be needed, turning vanes in the right angle turns may provide the needed draft increase.

The purpose of the stack is to overcome the pressure drop of gas flow between the furnace proper where the fuel is being burned, through the convection section, through the breeching and finally to the stack for discharge to atmosphere. There is a further requirement in that the stack must supply at least 0.03-in. WC in addition to the pressure drops just discussed. This is true because the stack must supply draft to maintain at least 0.03-in. WC draft in the highest portion of the furnace proper. At no time should the pressure within the furnace proper be allowed to equal or exceed atmospheric pressure. There must be no out flow of hot gases from the furnace in areas other than through the normal convection outlet or connection to the stack. Such an out flow will occur if the furnace pressure should rise unduly. (See Figure 3-2a.)

Application of Draft Data

What is the available draft at the burner level in the case of a thermal oxidizer in which the top of the stack is 150 ft.-0 in. above the burner centerline; with t_2 at 1,250°F; with design stack gas velocity at 50 ft./sec. in a 4 ft.-9 in. inside diameter stack with gas flow rate at 24.16 psi/sec. Altitude is 3,000 ft.

$A^1 = 150$ ft -0 in.
$Kt_2 = 0.0102$ (draft curve at $1.250°F$)
$D_1 = (150)(0.0102) = 1.53$ in. WC
$f = 0.002; W^2 = (24.16)(24.16) = 583.70; C = (3.14)(4.75) = 14.93; H = 150$ ft.
$A = 17.72$ square-feet $A^3 = 5,564$ square feet

$$\text{Friction} = \frac{(0.002)(583.70)(14.93)(150)}{5,564} = 0.469 \text{ in. WC}$$

$$\text{Acceleration} = (50)(1.176)\sqrt{\frac{14.70}{13.23}} = $$

$$61.91 \text{ ft./sec. at } 1.250$$

and at 3.000 ft.

The chart pressure drop (Table 5-1) for 0.30 in. shows velocity at 66.2 ft/sec. Therefore at 61.91 ft./sec. the pressure drop is:

$$\sqrt{0.30}\,(61.91/66.20)$$

$$= 0.272 \text{ in. WC acceleration pressure drop}$$

D_2 (effective draft) $= D_1$ (static draft) $- (0.469 + 0.272) = 1.53 - 0.741 = 0.789$ in.

Therefore, the calculated draft at the burner level is 0.789 in. WC and, under design conditions of operation, the calculated draft is quite close to correct. However, meterological conditions, atmospheric temperature, and deviation from design excess air can seriously interfere with burner operation. For this reason, *burner* design might well be based on lower draft at the burner based on the following:

$$0.95 \cdot (\sqrt{\text{Calculated Draft}})^2$$

Draft Regulation

Furnace draft and stack draft then become tools which can be very valuable if they are properly used and if the stack and damper design allow proper use. If there is excessive stack draft and the furnace draft is allowed to get too high, there will be excessive air leakage into the furnace, resulting in fuel loss. If because of either misadjustment of the stack damper or lack of stack draft capability the furnace becomes pressurized, there will be an outflow of hot gases resulting in heat loss as well as heat damage to the heater.

There must always be adequate furnace draft to cause air to enter through the burners in the required quantity for burning the fuel. However, the basis for draft demand at the burners lies very much with the basic design of the burners. As an example, gas burners designed for self-inspiration of air are essentially free of furnace draft limitations because there is no reliance on draft for air inspiration. When the burner is designed to rely on furnace draft for all or a portion of the air required to burn the fuel, draft becomes very critical to satisfactory operation. It becomes very critical because the draft must not only cause an adequate quantity of air to flow across the burner to consume the fuel but it must control excess air and also be great enough to hold less than atmospheric pressure in all parts of the furnace. The burners must have secondary air registers adjusted in such manner that the required total amount of air is allowed to pass across the burner air register when the furnace draft is adjusted by the stack damper to hold a minimum of 0.03-in. WC draft at the highest part of the furnace. The maximum draft in the highest part of the furnace should not exceed 0.05-in. WC.

Damper and Burner Adjustment

Establishing the draft condition just discussed requires an adjustment of burner air registers as well as the stack damper in steps. If the stack damper is opened too wide, the furnace draft will be too high and the burner air dampers must be closed too tightly to hold economical excess air. The high furnace draft will greatly increase air leakage causing fuel loss.

If the stack damper is not open enough, the burner air registers are too open, the draft in the furnace is too low to hold draft at the highest part of the furnace in the 0.03-0.05 in. range and there is danger of furnace damage.

As the adjustment between the burner air register setting and stack damper setting progresses, all adjustments should be on the slow and careful side with no major changes. It is common to make as many as eight to ten changes in settings before reaching the preferred draft condition at the burner level and at the top or highest part of the furnace.

Once there is proper balance between the stack damper setting and the burner air register setting to hold economical excess air and proper furnace draft, there is little need for further adjustment until there is a change in the firing rate or in the fuel. If such a change should occur, the firing condition and the excess air should again be checked to determine any possible necessity for new air register and stack damper adjustments to suit the new firing condition.

Combustion Air Sources

Such adjustment should be made if the burners are designed to receive as much as 30-40% of their total air supply from furnace draft as would be the case with raw gas or nonpremixed gas burners, with oil burners or with premix burners where all air is not inspirated by gas energy. The term "total air supply" is intended to mean theoretical air plus such excess air as may be required. The term "premix" as applied to burners has many meanings because a burner is called premix if all or any part of the theoretical air is entrained by and mixed with the fuel prior to entry of the fuel to the combustion zone. There is mixture of air with the fuel enroute to the combustion zone.

Thus, the burners which are in service may merit the term premix, but the portion of air entrained may be from 20% to more than 100% of theoretical to provide a small quantity of excess air. Burners which entrain or draw in all air for burning the fuel are termed "100% premix" burners. With certain exceptions, such burners operate completely without reference to the state of furnace draft. Burners which inspirate their total air are somewhat limited in their tolerance for fuel changes. Other such burners are equipped with small secondary air registers to permit the furnace draft to pull in about 10% of the theoretical air. Because air deficiency caused by a change in fuel can be compensated for through admission of secondary air, these burners are much more tolerant of changes in fuel characteristics. Burners which are not equipped with secondary air registers are of the so-called sealed-port type because the burner is actually sealed into the wall or floor of the furnace.

Greater flexibility for tolerance to change in fuel characteristics is to be had as the design amount of theoretical air inspirated decreases. Burners which inspirate from 50 to 70% of the theoretical air can accept and burn fuels in which the fuel's calorific value changes as much as 200% or more. Burners designed for about 35% inspiration of theoretical air can accept fuel changes of 250% or more. Such changes usually do not require adjustment of burners as the fuel calorific value shifts without warning in the average process plant if the excess air with the lowest calorific value gas is satisfactory. This presumes no significant change in furnace draft as the fuel changes because furnace draft is the source of the greater portion of the total air supply to the burner.

The area within the furnace where there must be a positive means for measuring draft is at or quite near the arch or roof of the furnace, this is the highest part of the furnace and the point at which minimum draft exists as the furnace operates. A draft gage is used, preferably with the capability for measuring draft to the nearest 1/100 of an inch WC. Many such gages are commercially available and are in service. Their operation is that of a manometer which measures the difference between the pressure within the furnace and atmospheric pressure. Their indications measure the draft or less than atmospheric pressure which exists within the furnace.

Such gages are useful for close draft measurement only if there is no wind whatsoever at the time the draft is measured; wind energy upsets atmospheric pressure in areas around the furnace. If the draft gage is located at the up-wind side of the furnace, the impact of the wind against the side of the furnace causes an elevation in atmospheric pressure in the impact area. If the atmospheric pressure opening of the draft gage is in the impact area, the draft indication will be higher than the actual draft which exists within the furnace and the deviation, according to wind velocity can be 0.20-in. WC or perhaps more. If the draft gage is located at the down-wind side of the furnace, acceleration of the wind following a pressure rise at impact and flowing past the furnace causes the pressure at the down-wind area to be less than true atmospheric pressure; thus, the gage will show less draft than that which exists. In a brisk wind which shifts direction as it blows, the draft gage indication can vary as much as 3/10 in. quite rapidly, making the draft gage completely useless in any condition other than fairly still air.

Means for complete stabilization of draft gage indication can be had quite simply through application of an isolated piezometric atmospheric pressure point connected to the atmospheric pressure side of the draft gage through suitable tubing as shown in Figure 5-4. A single piezometric point can be applied to as many draft gages as may be required. The piezometric, atmospheric pressure probe is to be located in an area away from any structure and in an area where the wind can blow over it freely from any direction. It is recommended that the 1 in. pipe of the probe be made of Series 300 stainless steel (types, 302, 303, 304, 309, 316 or 310). Very careful machining is important, especially port drilling and internal and external polishing. Care should be taken in welding the upper end closed to avoid spattering of weld metal.

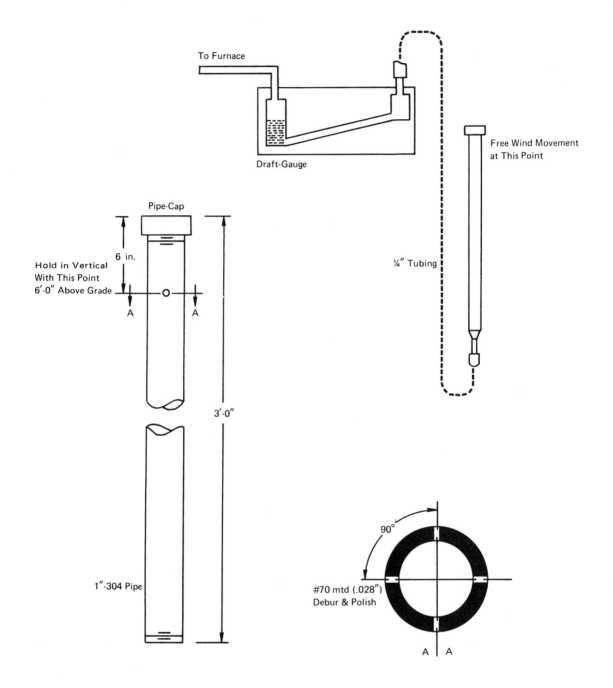

Figure 5-4. Piezometric atmospheric pressure stabilization for windy conditions.

Wind Effects

Where a furnace is to be operated in a windy area, the choice of burners should presume inspiration of a great majority of air for burning fuel. The change in atmospheric pressure which makes the draft gage useless also changes the quantity of air which can pass through the burner to produce some very unsatisfactory firing conditions such as much too much air or lack of sufficient air according to whether the atmospheric pressure rises or falls as the wind blows. The amount of air that can pass through the burner by draft action varys according to the square root of the pressure drop across the burner. In a windless condition, if the pressure drop across the burner is 0.25-in. WC but as the wind blows and because of pressure rise the pressure drop becomes 0.45-in. WC, the amount of air across the burner would be increased by approximately 34%. If wind action should cause the pressure drop to be decreased to 0.10 in., there would be only approximately 63% as much air, which in all probability would cause incomplete burning of the fuel and relatively severe puffing in the furnace as air flow is restored. If the burners are capable of inspirating as much as 70-80% of their air supply by gas energy, these unpleasant conditions will not exist. If the inspirated air is not so great or if the burners rely entirely on furnace draft for their air supply in the burning of either gas or oil, or if fuel characteristics change rapidly, a furnace can be completely inoperable in a high wind. The condition of inoperability can occur with either floor or wall firing if there is reliance on furnace draft for combustion air. Inoperability will not occur in a wind if the burners do not rely on furnace draft for more than 30% of the total air, as is the case with inspirating burners where the state of inspiration is great enough.

Where there is significant use of draft for air delivery and where high winds are common there are no means of maintaining operation other than some means of shielding the burners from wind action or to using forced draft. In the latter, air delivery is through closed wind boxes. Air is supplied by fans or blowers where the blower energy is so much greater than wind energy that there is no upset in air delivery to the furnace as the wind blows.

Where there is side-wall firing, a solution to wind problems is the erection of a wind fence to a height at least three burner diameters above the level of the burners and spaced outwardly approximately the same distance. Sheet iron in corrugated sections as well as corrugated asbestos roofing have been used for such fences, which should completely enclose the furnace.

In the vertically fired heater, it is necessary to stop the sweep of wind beneath the furnace. Wind fences as suggested for wall firing have been very successful for this service provided there is a means for rapid exit from the area beneath the furnace. It is dangerous to personnel to completely enclose this area. For personnel escape purposes, it is common to leave spaces wide enough for a man to pass between the vertically erected corrugated sheets.

Wind Turbulence and Down Drafts

There has been much debate concerning the effect of wind turbulence on the draft supplied by the stack. Some very complex as well as expensive devices have been added to the top of stacks because of the presumed wind effect on stack draft. All available evidence shows that if the top of the stack is above surrounding structures or is at least 2,000 ft. from a higher structure or hill, the effect of wind is to increase effective draft. However, if there are higher structures nearby or if the stack is located at or near the base of a higher hill, there can be a condition of down draft or draft reversal at the top of the stack. This condition will reduce the draft from the stack as the wind blows from the higher structure toward the stack. Wind is actually trying to blow down into the stack. The corrective procedure is to install a conical down draft diverter which is metallurgically suited to the temperature of the stack gases. The diameter of the conical section is at least twice the diameter of the stack; the skirt of the conical section should be 0.75 stack diameters above the stack opening. The conical section diverts the downwardly directed wind currents and can actually increase stack draft in this condition.

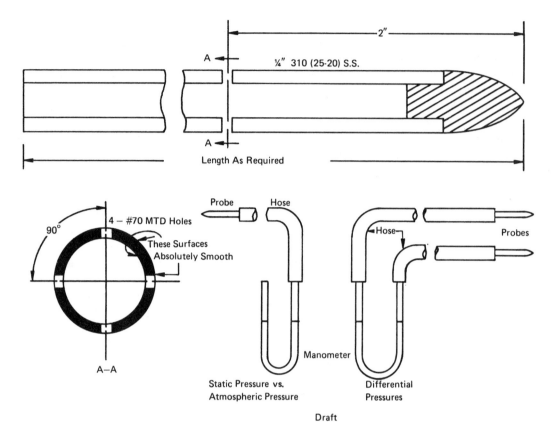

Figure 5-5. Piezometric static pressure probe.

Any increase in draft due to wind action is not harmful in the sense of maintaining operation but a decrease in stack draft cannot be tolerated. The result of reduced draft is usually lack of enough air to burn the fuel with puffing in the furnace and smoke at the stack if oil is the fuel. If the draft increases, there will be an increase in excess air but it is usually not significant. Windy areas demand immunity from wind effect on the burners through the use of gas energy for inspiration of air, through the use of forced draft and wind boxes or through erection of suitable wind fences.

In normal draft measurement, by means of a draft gage, the draft pressure measurement is taken from fixed points and in areas where the movement of gases at the point of measurement is too small to cause inertial upset in the pressure indica-tion. Thus, the indicated drafts can be accepted as reasonably accurate. However, if the draft meas-urement point is in an area where there is gas movement in excess of 10 ft./sec., the draft indica-tions as shown by the gage cannot be accepted and may be in error significantly according to the rela-tionship of the opening, for sensing the state of pressure, to the movement of gases.

When pressure is checked with a draft gage or with a manometer when measuring pressure drop in ducts or flue gas passages, where the speed of gas movement is over 10 ft./sec. in hot gases or more than 5 ft./sec. in cold gases, the probe in-serted into the gas passageway must be of piezo-metric design as shown in Figure 5-5. If an ordi-nary open-end tube is used, it is almost impossible to obtain a true static pressure at the point of insertion. If the end of an open tube is turned toward the direction from which the gases are moving, impact of gases into the open end of the tube will markedly increase the indicated pressure. If the tube is pointed in the opposite direction or at 90° to the flow, the indicated pressure will be less than the true pressure at the point of insertion.

In the piezometric tube with its end closed and with pressure sampling through the four ports which are 90° apart, each port samples different pressures which may be either higher or lower than the true static pressure. Since the ports open into a common space inside the tube, the pressure inside the tube is quite close to the true static pressure in the area into which the tube is inserted. However, the greatest accuracy may be obtained when the tube insertion is as near to 90° to the direction of gas movement as possible.

Draft Gage Tube Corrosion

Tubes leading from the draft sampling point down or around to the draft gage are particularly subject to corrosion or stoppage and should be checked at least twice a year to be sure the tube is open and that there are no leaks. When the tubes lead to less than atmospheric pressure points, it is good practice to leave the tubes open to the atmosphere so air flows through them constantly rather than closing them off with a valve. The air flow prevents corrosion and if the air is reasonably free from dust, the tubes tend to remain open.

It is common to use draft gage tubes as sample tubes for checks of excess air in the flue gas, but it is probable that this means for excess air checks will produce inaccurate results. The draft gage tube is seldom well sealed into the furnace wall, which allows extra air to appear in the sample. Since corrosive combustion gases are drawn through the tube there is a condition which can cause the tube to be stopped up or to be perforated by corrosion.

Air Movement Design Factors for Burners

In another section, it is pointed out that the speed and excellence of burning is governed by the state of turbulence as the fuel burns. In the burning of fuels there are two sources of turbulence. Both can be quite significant in securing excellent burner performance. One source is the velocity with which the fuel is discharged for burning, with greater velocity producing better turbulence and accordingly better burning conditions. The second source of turbulence is the velocity with which air meets fuel as it burns and the angle at which the air strikes the fuel.

If it is possible to cause the air to strike the fuel at 90°, there is maximum benefit from air velocity. Such a condition of air entry is very difficult to obtain in typical burner designs. If countercurrent air and fuel flow were possible, there would be still greater benefit. The average angular relationship of air strike to fuel flow is in the order of 60°, but these are basic design considerations which may well be observed in the choice of burners.

Velocity of air flow, in most cases, is established by the state of draft or air pressure drop across the burner. Velocity of air flow varies as the square root of the air pressure drop. If the air velocity and turbulence are to be doubled, the pressure drop must be increased so that it is four times as great.

In by far the greatest number of furnaces, the source of air pressure drop across the burner is the state of natural draft which is typical of the furnace when the draft at the arch is maintained at 0.03-in. WC. A typical furnace draft in this condition will be in the order of 0.15-in. WC. In rectangular and vertical cylindrical heaters, the draft may be much greater.

Burner Sizing vs. Draft

Using all of the draft energy for turbulence and better burning conditions should be considered of great importance. But if the burners chosen are too large or are improperly designed, poor use of the draft is the result because the air pressure drop is taken across the burner register or in other parts of the burner rather than immediately at the point where fuel and air come together. To avoid heat damage the burner air register is located as remotely as possible from the area where fuel and air come together.

Forced Draft for Air Supply

It is possible to significantly increase the quantity of fuel burned in a specific furnace by adapting forced draft to the burners, replacing natural draft operation. Forced draft will increase the air pressure drop across the burners enough to obtain faster burning for increased heat release. But this must not be done at the expense of pressurizing the furnace. The stack breeching, convection section pressure drop relationship must be such that the stack can still hold a minimum draft of 0.03-in. WC at the arch or roof of the furnace. Increased heat release requires that more gas pass through the convection section and breeching. It is probable that the gas temperature will be higher; therefore, the pressure drop is increased because of a greater quantity of flue gases and because of increased temperature at the same time.

If you need to know the new pressure drop condition with altered firing conditions, the first procedure is to measure the pressure drop between a point just under the convection section and the stack, at the level to which the breeching is attached, and in the breeching. All pressure measurement tubes should be of the piezometric type attached to a manometer through suitable tubing. The difference in pressures, as indicated by the manometer, is the pressure drop required for an original amount of flue gas being passed from the furnace to the stack at the temperature existing in the original flue gases.

In calculating the pressure drop by increased firing with a new quantity of flue gases at a new temperature level, estimated at approximately 100°F greater than the original temperature level, the following equation will be of assistance:

$$(PN)^{\frac{1}{2}} = (PO)^{\frac{1}{2}} (QN/QO) (TN/TO)^{\frac{1}{2}}$$

where:

QO = Original quantity of flue gases
QN = New quantity of flue gases
PO = Original pressure drop as measured in inches WC
PN = New pressure drop with increased firing in inches WC
TO = Original flue gas temperature, degrees absolute (Rankine)
TN = New flue gas temperature, degrees absolute (Rankine)

If the firing rate is to be increased 25% then QN will be 25% greater than QO if the excess air remains unchanged at the new rate of heater firing. TO should be measured directly below the convection tubes and preferably with a velocity thermocouple.

As an example, if PO should be 0.60-in. WC at 1,160°R (700°F) and the preferred increase in firing rate is 25% with the suggested increase of 100°F for TN, then PN is approximately 1.02 in. WC. When opening the stack damper, the draft at the breeching cannot be increased to at least 1.00-in. WC, it is very probable that the increased firing rate cannot be reached because of stack limitations, if disastrous pressurization of the furnace is to be avoided. If it is possible to add to the stack height or use induced draft fans for draft energy, the increased firing rate will be possible. There will be a certain increase in the stack's static draft potential because of increased stack temperature, but this will be largely cancelled by the increased linear drop in the stack resulting from increased amounts of flue gas (25%). A tightly designed stack, based on original process design requirements, is probably one of the very best examples of saving capital cost at the expense of later loss of ability for increased profitability. The very small saving in capital cost by restricting stack design severely limits future increases in the firing rate which limits increased process stream thruput to the heater.

Furnace Puffing

Where there is failure of draft because of over firing a heater or because of wind action, a condition of puffing or breathing at the burners, there is a very dangerous condition in the furnace. The danger applies to both the furnace structure and to operating personnel. Puffing or breathing starts when the burners are short of air for a period, causing the furnace atmosphere to be laden with combustibles. If any air at all gets by the burners to enter the furnace unconsumed, there is a minor puff or explosion. The gas expansion following the increased burning reverses air flow at the burners, causing flame and hot gases to be driven with some violence out through the burner openings. The condition can occur rhythmically.

Safety During Furnace Upsets

If this state is not promptly stopped, the furnace can be damaged as the puffing violence increases. If operating personnel are standing in the burner area, it is quite possible for them to receive serious burns as the flame and hot gases flash outside the burners.

If the furnace is puffing or is about to puff, it is a very great error to open the burner air registers or the stack damper because such action will greatly increase the violence of the puffing. The proper procedure is to immediately reduce the fuel to the burners to approximately 25% of the volume which caused the puffing. Immediately check all burners to see that the puffing has not extinguished some of them. If all burners continue to operate properly, slowly increase the fuel flow to the burners, restoring operation at a more conservative firing level. If it is found that some burners have been extinguished immediately stop all fuel flow to the burners and flood the furnace with steam if possible. Stay away from all peep holes while the furnace is upset and move to a corner of the furnace if it is rectangular. Controls, valves and all apparatus should be located at a furnace *corner* near the burners in rectangular furnaces and at a point well clear of the area under a vertical cylindrical furnace. The corners of a rectangular furnace are last to fail since the flat walls between the corners go first and a truly violent explosion would be required to cause the corners to fail. The vertical cylindrical furnace structure resists internal pressure very well but the flow of flame and hot gases from the burners in the floor make the area under the furnace quite dangerous.

Before a single burner is placed in operation, there will be some small draft in the furnace due to wind action at the top of the stack or other effects. This initial draft, without any hot gas in the stack, is adequate for light-off of the burners. As the burners are ignited, the rate of firing should be only a small portion of the heat release capability of the burners until the hot gases from operating burners have had an opportunity to reach and pass through the stack. The rate of firing can then be increased to place the heater in operating condition.

Start-up Firing

If the firing rate is increased too rapidly, the furnace will almost certainly puff unless there has been a suitable lapse of time to allow the stack gas temperature to rise and establish a condition of draft for normal operation. In cold firing of a furnace, a period of five minutes or more should intervene between light-off and the beginning of increased firing. A shorter period will be satisfactory if the furnace has been firing at a reduced rate or is still comparatively warm as light-off of burners begins. In no case should firing be significantly increased until the draft gage shows a reasonable state of draft; and in no case should the firing rate be abruptly increased, particularly when a furnace is approaching its design firing condition or following light-off of the burners.

6

Burners, Fuels and Firing

There is a great aura of mystery surrounding the burning of fuels for delivery of useful heat to process units. Because the transformation of wood or vegetation into heat and light, with a little ash residue, appeared to be something attributable to powers beyond his understanding, primitive man was in great awe of the fire which produced so many beneficial effects. Some of this awe remains among those who are daily responsible for effectively burning millions of dollars worth of fuel. However, the awe is partially a product of amazement at successful fuel burning despite the very great state of contradiction in the theories of authorities as to what happens, how it happens, when it happens and why it happens.

There has been long and loud argument for more than a hundred years as to just how fuels burn. Many theories by respected authorities have entered the literature. Each authority vigorously defends his particular position, has observed phenomena and has offered his explanation of what he has seen. He has performed experiments to lead him to his conclusions. This type of research is all too frequently conducted in the interest of proof rather than in the interest of discovering what is happening. The student of combustion will discover that scanning the literature for factual data is difficult. A typical problem can be found in a respected chemistry handbook where in one place the autoignition temperature of methane is stated as 999°F while in another place in the same handbook the ignition temperature of methane is stated as ranging from 1201 to 1,382°F (Tables 6-1, 6-2, and 6-3). In late editions of another chemistry handbook the calorific values for fuels have been abandoned because of the great variation in data available for particular fuels. It is not my intention to discredit all data because each researcher faithfully reports what he finds. My intention is to say that the approaches have influenced the findings, and since there are variations in approach there are variations in the results. Since there is complete ignorance on the part of the reader as to the approach for the findings and since the reader is uncertain as to the relation of his problems to the data as reported, there can be very serious error.

Table 6-1
Ignition Temperatures of Gases °F

Gas	Authority #1	Authority #2	Authority #3	Deviation (%)
CH4	1170	999	1382	38.33
C2H6	882	950	1166	22.73
C2H4	914	1009	1018	11.37
C3H8	898	871	997	14.46
C3H6	856	822	940	14.35
C4H 10	826	806	912	13.15
C4H8	829	809	918	13.47
H2	1065	1076	1094	2.72
CO	1128	1204	1216	7.80
H2S	558	635	701	25.62
NH3	1203	1290	1436	19.36

Note: The purpose of this tabulation is to show the great deviation in ignition temperatures for typical fuel gases as reported into the literature by very respected research authorities who have faithfully reported their findings. Names and references are purposely omitted.

Table 6-2
Speeds of Flame Propagation - Feet Per Second

Fuel	Authority #1	Authority #2	Authority #3	Authority #4
CH4	1.25	2.20	2.35	0.83
C2H6	1.50	2.80	2.65	0.92
C3H8	2.30	2.75	2.50	0.94
H2	8.20	21.70	15.90	9.30
C2H2	4.75	9.30	9.70	9.40
CO	1.4	4.20	4.10	1.69

Note: The differing factors for Tables 6-1, 6-2, and 6-3 have been taken from published literature but not separately identified. Literature sources are: American Gas Association; *Lange's Handbook of Chemistry*—McGraw-Hill; *Chemical Rubber Company Handbook; NGSMA Data Book;* Lewis & von Elbe—Academic Press; Haslam & Russell—McGraw-Hill; *Manual for Process Engineering*—McGraw-Hill; *Gas Engineers' Handbook*—McGraw-Hill.

Table 6-3
Ultimate Flame Temperature °F

Gas	Authority #1	Authority #2	Authority #3	Deviation (%)
CH4	3640	3750	3416	9.77
C2H6	3710	3820	3443	10.94
C2H4	3910	4250	3587	18.48
C3H8	3770	3840	3497	9.80
C3H6	3830	4090	3515	16.35
C4H 10	3780	3870	3443	12.40
C4H8	3810	4030	3506	14.94
H2	3960	4010	4112	3.83
C0	3960	4475	4212	6.36

Note: This tabulation shows the very considerable deviation in ultimate flame temperatures for typical fuel gases as reported into the literature by very respected research authorities who have faithfully reported their findings. Names and literature references are purposely omitted.

Combustion is based on scientific principles, no one is certain exactly what these scientific principles may be. For a person to become knowledgable about the burning of fuel, he must personally observe conditions and results to reach reasonable conclusions as to the hows, whats, whys and whens of combustion. But he does so always at the extreme hazard of misinterpretation which may lead him to errors greater than those in the literature.

Only after a particular phenomenon is observed repeatedly and considered in the light of all the chemical and physical effects can even reasonable conclusions be drawn as to the areas of reaction which may correctly be assumed to be responsible for the observed phenomenon.

Because of a lack of firm knowledge concerning the many combustion phenomena, improvement in burners has been limited to the results of "cut-and-try" experiments—at best, a very slow process. Slow development of improved burners has had a slowing effect on furnace (heater) design with particular reference to reduction in size. However, recent years have seen

significant advances in burner performance and in reduction in fired-heater proportions. Further burner design research is virtually certain to produce additional improvement. Process fired-heaters were designed initially to provide not more than 8,000 Btu's/cubic foot of furnace combustion volume. Today's furnaces are being designed around 50,000 Btu's/cubic foot of internal volume in some cases. While process heaters do not fully reflect a size ratio of 8,000/50,000, they are markedly more compact.

A good example of incorrect assumptions by refinery operators is as follows. In the early days of petroleum refining, gas was considered as an undesirable fuel. It was "known" that to burn tower overhead gases with even reasonably acceptable flame condition, it was necessary to run a large steam line to each gas burner and jet the steam into the gas flame. The steam lines were ½ in. or larger. It was common to find 100 psig steam pressure applied to the lines with little restriction as the steam was discharged.

It is small wonder that the boiler plants of early refineries were considerably large—to supply steam for fuel burning alone. It is true that the turbulence generated by discharging high-pressure steam plus the chemistry of combining hydrocarbons with water vapor made satisfactory gas flames when the gas was supplied at 1-2 psig.

There was immediate improvement in gas burning when the very rich tower overhead gases were stripped of their heavier hydrocarbons in vapor recovery plants by absorption or compression. A truly significant improvement was noted when gas pressure to the burners was elevated to 5 psig to produce satisfactory firing in a hot furnace. The great drawback to using the higher gas pressure was that it was very difficult to keep the burners lit when the furnace was cold. This brought about rules prohibiting fuel supply pressures greater than about 5 psig because unstable burners produced some notable explosions. In turn, this brought about the design of refractory adjuncts to furnaces such as dutch ovens, ducks nests and breaker walls, into which and against which burners fired to rapidly develop hot surfaces promoting flame retention or at best to avoid explosions. The ultimate in this design trend was the lattice wall, which was a partly open refractory wall situated a short distance from the burners.

Refractory Furnace Adjuncts

During this period there were theories as to the whys and wherefores of the refractory structures, with considerable debate about the reasons for the desirable effects of the structures. Some insisted that preservation of temperature level did the trick, while others, with equal assurance, insisted that some catalytic effect of the refractory was responsible. These entries in the literature were contributed by authorities who commanded considerable respect at the time.

This period of refractory glory began to die a slow death when burner inventors made the discovery that if the burner design was suitable, the burner did not become unstable at any applied gas pressure. Furthermore, there was a tremendous improvement in burner performance when the burner

gas pressure was 25 psig rather than 5 psig. Despite the obvious benefits of greatly improved fuel burning with higher pressure burners, almost 20 years passed before the last refinery to retain the 5 psig limitation on fuel gas pressure finally shifted to higher pressure.

This period of transition was literally the heyday of the burner expert who spoke mysteriously about the wonders his particular brand of burner could perform. One of them went so far as to proclaim a great state of superiority for his burner because his burner "burned up the water" formed as the fuel burned. Engineers are generally the least gullible of all people, but engineers bought the burner that burned-up the water; however, they bought the burners because they performed despite the odd explanation for their performance.

Old Refinery Operating Practices

Those who recall these days will be aware that the operation of refineries was comparable to the early days of flying. Refinery operation was very much of seat-of-the-pants operation based on experience in the absence of engineering assistance. If a distillation unit was performing improperly the procedure for correction was opening or closing valves "two spokes" or some such procedure. The required skill in correction was a statement of the number of spokes the valve adjustment was to be changed. Strangely enough, the correction usually worked!

The ancestor of the bubble tower, which was then called a dephlegmator or packed tower, was coming into common use. Plant operators viewed the coming of engineers into the refineries with mixed feelings as well as a little outright hostility. It was not unusual to find the 10-point potentiometer as the sole temperature indicator for refineries in the 5,000-10,000 bpd category refinery.

With this background, it is hardly strange that the air of mystery pertaining to burners, burner operation and results obtainable with particular burner configurations should be accepted as normal and incorporated into the philosophy of refinery operators. It was made a part of operational philosophy because, despite ridiculous claims made for them, the burners did bring about great improvement in product yields as well as increased capacity and improved fuel economy.

It is a little strange that some of the mystery associated with burners and the firing of heaters remained for such a long time after engineering took over the refining of oils and the production of petrochemicals and reduced these operations within very finite limits. In defense of engineering generally, engineers tend to rely on the theories of accepted literature or research. Since it is quite probable that there will be deviation between the predicted results of the literature and the results obtained in practice with little if any explanation for the deviation, the element of mystery enters even at this late date.

Heat Transfer Fallacies

As an excellent example of the lack of predictability consider theories about the quantity of heat to be absorbed per square foot of tube surface. Such data are basically experience factors in which a coil of tubes in a particular service and of particular metallurgy has been satisfactorily used and it has been shown that the *mean* heat transfer rate is X Btu/sq. ft. of tube. Data are taken on the basis of observed heat transfer conditions which existed in the furnace. In the observed condition there is no symmetry of heat transfer per linear foot of tube, yet the mean figure is designated as safe for the tube in question. In another heater fired in a different manner and at other conditions of excess air, the identical tube surface may show an ability to transfer considerably more or less heat according to furnace conditions. Tube failure or tube damage is the limiting factor in all instances.

A research program was conducted to show what the transfer rate *per tube* might be when the tube was a part of a heater coil, when heat transfer was measured as sensible heat in each tube, when the mean transfer rate for the coil was carefully observed through measurement of coil inlet versus

outlet temperature, and neither latent heat nor heat of reaction were factors. This research was at the time considered proprietary and as such has never been reported in the literature. It was discovered that some tubes in the coil were receiving less than 20% of the mean transfer rate while other tubes in the coil were receiving as much as 250% of the mean transfer rate. The mean transfer rate at that time was considered as the absolute maximum for the tube metallurgy in the coil.

There are critical areas in tube coils which distinctly limit operation to a maximum firing condition. Certain areas of tube coils are prone to receive a greater quantity of heat as the heater is fired. This lack of symmetry of heat transfer is one of the continuing mystery factors which will not disappear. If the firing is altered through a change in burners for better heat distribution in the furnace, it is at times possible to very markedly increase the total amount of heat transferred to the coil. The same conditions of tube attrition limit the maximum firing rate.

If a change in firing through burner adjustment or through a change in burners produces an increase in process capability or improvement in heat transfer within a fired heater without an increase in heat damage, there is reason to be grateful. If the improvement comes about through a burner change, without a very good and logical explanation of the reasons for improvement, a certain element of mystery will be associated with the change.

It is common within the industry to consider all elements of furnace design with exquisite care until design considerations reach the stage of burner choice. Either through a state of exhaustion resulting from work with prior considerations or tax reasons, the choice of burner equipment is then relegated to the status of hardware. This tendency leads to one of the most profitable sources for replacement burner sales. It is quite true that replacement burners are purchased with 50¢ maintenance dollars so this cost factor has some relief for the purchaser, but the purchaser buys the replacement burners only when they are economically or operationally necessary. The lost profit due to unsatisfactory firing may well be many times greater than the cost of the new burners—and there is no tax relief for this loss!

Economy obtained through the purchase of less expensive burners to reduce capital costs has proved to be "penny wise and dollar foolish." It is a brave designer who has the temerity to contradict the wishes of management dedicated to tax factors in planning new process facilities.

Let us for a moment consider the widely held theory that if a furnace needs X-million Btu's fired, it is only necessary to put that amount of Btu's into the furnace in any convenient way and the furnace will operate satisfactorily. Or, if you please, the ultimate is the design of the furnace structure. Once furnace design is set, the burners to supply the needed quantity of heat can be considered as just so much hardware. Not so! If this were true the benefits gained through a change in burners could not exist, as has been repeatedly shown.

Process design of the heater is very important and errors in process design are difficult to resolve, thus there is excellent reason to carefully check each single factor. Remember, as the checking proceeds, that the proper function of the heater depends on burners for heat delivery at rates and in quantities such that the process is not hindered and that heat delivery to areas and at particular points depends entirely on the ability of the burners to supply heat properly.

In the strictest sense, a fired heater performs its service according to the cooperation between process design and the manner in which the heater is being fired. To separate these functions is as impossible as separating the functions or importance of the organs of the human body because all are vital. Burners in the fired heater perform the vital function of metabolism in the body. Metabolism is not the entire cause of healthy and happy living but it is difficult to imagine healthy and happy living in the absence of proper metabolism.

In the final analysis, the excellence with which burners fire a heater is directly proportional to the ability of a particular burner configuration to supply heat to the furnace. It must do so in a manner suited to the heat requirements of various parts of the heater even when there is never symmetry of heat delivery or heat demand for the process. The heater is poorly or improperly fired when there is maximum of heat delivery to an area of minimum heat demand. The reverse is also true but the former is much more serious since this is one of the sources of tube damage while the latter simply limits the process capability of the heater.

Basic Gas Burner Design

When considering burners it is well to remember that there are 12 basic designs. Any burner conforming to basic design parameters will have heat-dispersive characteristics typical of the basic design configuration, regardless of the manufacturer. However, some effect in dispersion is attributable to design variations of the basic type. When the firing of a heater leaves something to be desired, a very careful study will in all probability determine what the required firing or heat dispersive effect may be and selection of replacement burners should be made according to the required conditions. This practice can be profitable. A combination unit in a refinery limited to 70,000 bpd by severe tube attrition is today running close to 100,000 bpd at the identical limiting conditions after a change in burners to a design better suited to the heat requirements of this particular heater.

Burner changes directed toward improved firing can always be justified if the improved firing results from the burner change. However, burner changes directed toward improved fuel economy are questionable. An exception is if existing burner performance prevents proper excess air reduction. Another exception is if the heat-dispersive characteristics of existing burners are severely overloading certain tube areas, allowing other areas to receive a relatively small fraction of the heat. The latter provides a very poor condition for heat transfer. Generally speaking, firing efficiency is directly governed by the quantity of excess air present in the furnace proper as well as in the stack. Furnace excess air is controlled by the burners if the furnace is tight. The stack excess air will indicate the state of air leakage between the furnace and the point in the stack where the sample for analysis is taken. Note that the heat loss is governed by the state of excess air at either point. The stack sample should be used to indicate the necessity for stopping air leakage between the furnace and the stack, since the stack excess air is not necessarily governed by burner adjustment or performance characteristics. Many burner changes are made in the interest of low excess air when the high excess air as measured is caused by air leakage. Air leakage is not controllable by the burners. When there is air leakage, a burner change will produce no or very small improvement.

It is a poorly kept secret that there is never symmetry in transfer of heat in process heaters. It is not necessarily true that complete symmetry of heat transfer is desirable in all cases. As process material flows through the tubes, there are areas in which relatively high heat transfer rates are preferred while in other areas the heat demand is not so great.

An excellent example is to be found in highly pyrolytic processes. In certain tube areas the heat demand is great for heats of reaction. In other areas of the same tube the heat demand is sharply reduced. For these services, highly specialized heaters with somewhat complex burner arrangements are provided. It is well known to those who operate such process facilities that success or failure of the process depends greatly on controlling heat density in particular tube areas with almost exquisite precision.

It is true that such heaters may be considered exceptions. The great preference is for distribution of heat as evenly as possible in most instances. In applications where a much less expensive and elaborate burner configuration is used, there is greater demand on the burners for widespread distribution of heat. It is virtually impossible to secure ideal furnace conditions. But with care, conditions can well approach the ideal and provide completely satisfactory heat contours.

The approach to ideal conditions is largely governed by the number of burners or heat sources provided for the heater. The larger the number of burners, within economic limits, the more nearly the ideal is approached.

Floor Firing vs Wall Firing

There is much debate about the relative merits of wall firing versus floor firing, both as to costs and firing excellence. There is a recurrent question of the safety for operating personnel who are required to go below the heater while it is firing. Despite the validity of the question, experience over many years with hundreds of floor-fired heaters shows an excellent safety record in all conditions of operation and upset.

Repeated experience shows that the identical heater in tube surface can be fired at least 25% harder from the floor than from either the end or side walls. Identical limiting conditions exist in either type furnace, for maximum firing. Existing wall-fired heaters have been altered to provide floor firing, with suitable burners, to produce more than the noted 25% increase in firing rate. However, burners for floor firing can cost up to 100% more than burners for wall firing. Justification for the added cost must be based on improvement in process capability.

It is probable that the improvement in firing potential results from more comprehensive use of the combustion volume within the heater. In addition, there is an improvement in basic characteristics for heat distribution resulting from better use of available combustion volume. Floor firing requires a much larger number of burners than is typical of wall firing and the heat release per-burner is accordingly reduced.

Use of a specific number of Btu/hr./cu. ft. of combustion volume was at one time considered the prime limiting factor in the design of process heaters. Figures as low as 5,000-8,000 Btu/cu. ft. were typical, accounting for the huge size of heaters designed and erected during this period. The limitation was imposed because the flames produced in burning fuel at that time were relatively large. To avoid direct flame impingement on tube surfaces, the heater proportions were suited to the flame proportions produced by the burners.

As burner manufacturers devised means for more rapid burning of fuel and as the volume of flame per million Btu's decreased sharply, the old limitation for heat release per cubic foot began to disappear. Improved burner performance became accepted.

It is not uncommon at this time to find heat densities approaching 50,000 Btu/cu. ft. in process service with completely satisfactory operation. It becomes obvious that current burners produce much less flame per million Btu's than was typical when the heat release per cubic foot limitation was established at such low figures. The people who design and supply heaters have been quick to take advantage of improved fuel burning. Today's heaters are relatively small compared to those built 20 years ago. They are admittedly more satisfactory if the designer-builder is not too cost conscious in proposing a price 1-5% greater than his competitor.

Heaters purchased 10 years ago or more were purchased for a specific service at specific charge rates. Following the acceptance run the purchaser would immediately find the bottleneck in the heater's process capability. When the bottleneck was reached it was not at all unusual to find the heater delivering 20-50% more than had been purchased. This state of affairs no longer exists. It is rare to find the heater performing much more than 10% in excess of design and purchase rate.

Some of the unresolved factors involved in close design for process service have been resolved in the past few years. At this time, any heater purchased will perform the service for which it was obtained. It will also do little more. A wise purchaser specifies performance and process conditions which will allow him to use all the charge he will have and produce all the product he requires.

From a first cost standpoint for a process facility, today's practice is better. Because of competition, the heater manufacturer literally scrapes the bottom of the barrel in seeking means for cutting cost as he prepares his proposal. He must do so if he is to survive!

From a total profitability standpoint, today's practice is decidedly inferior. Suppose the projected pay-out over a period of years is based on the sale of product based on X-thousand barrels per day. If the operating company finds that the heater will allow operation at 1.50 X barrels per day, with the same profitability, either the pay-out time is decreased or there is increased profit.

Profitability vs Capital Cost

First cost for the facility determines what capitalization will be required. At times, the "woods" of reduced capital expense completely hides the "trees" of incremental profitability. There is currently a very great deal of emphasis on matters pertaining to tax costs on the part of management, where expenditure decision must originate.

As the purchaser's process group studies specification details it is inevitable that they will become aware of superior materials and components which can well increase profitability. But if the superior elements add cost to increase capital cost, it is difficult if not impossible to convince management that the added capital cost can be justified. There is much to be said for both sides. The process group should not be permitted to "gold plate" the facility and the management group should not insist on reduced cost until economy becomes cheapness.

One of the truly significant elements in setting up a new or revised process facility is the matter of the fuel supply for the heaters. (See Figures 6-1 and 6-2 and Table 2.2.) The current state of burner design will allow the satisfactory use of just about any burnable fuel. Fuels include gases down to 50-75 Btu/cu. ft. and pitches. Burner design, however, can be flexible from the standpoint of fuel characteristics only to a limited degree. Therefore, if there is potential change in fuel, a wise process group makes it clear just what the fuel change may be as burner equipment is specified. Excessive difficulty, when a fuel change is required, will be avoided.

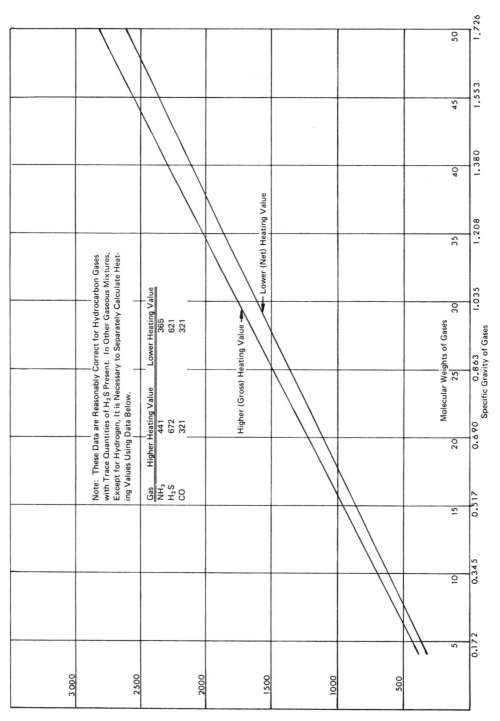

Figure 6-1. Heating values.

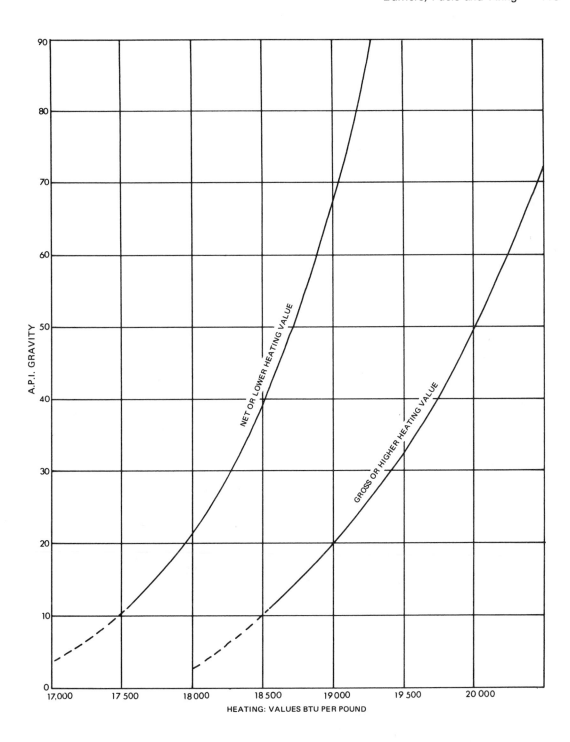

Figure 6-2. Relation of heating values and API gravity.

Fuels Availability

In the process plant, fuels must be fired as they become available. Gas is more nearly an ideal fuel than oil and is therefore preferred. If gas is not available, oil must be fired in its place. It is well to understand that a heater designed around the characteristics of gas firing can be extremely difficult to convert to oil firing. In some cases it is almost impossible to convert a gas-fired heater to oil firing. In the process planning stage, if there is possibility of oil firing, you should purchase heaters and burners which will be suitable for the altered firing. It is not the author's intention to create the impression that oil firing is a source of great difficulty. Many operators actually prefer to fire oil. But if oil firing can become a factor, it is wise to be prepared. Because of different burning characteristics, oil demands a furnace suited to its greater flame volume and radiation.

Process operators in certain gas-rich areas, such as the U.S. Gulf Coast, are prone to consider only gas firing. At the time, there is ample cheap natural gas for supplementary firing if the process should fail to produce enough gas for fuel. It is beginning to appear that such a philosophy may be in error. It may be necessary or expedient to fire fuel oil rather than natural gas.

Change in fuel availability is not the cause. There is continued discovery of additional reserves of natural gas but the cost of the natural gas is reaching the point where it will be less expensive to fire oil than gas. In 1939, a 25,000-bpd refinery purchased natural gas fuel for $500.00 per month because oil producers were forced to stop flaring their gas production. Conservation took over.

Fuel Cost Factors

Fuel cost, as well as fuel availability, is a serious problem in process operations. The combination of a natural gas shortage and a constantly escalating fuel oil price are making reasonable forecasts for operations guesswork. There is an ongoing replacement of gas firing with oil firing where possible, and waste gas fuels previously considered as "useless" are now being employed in various ways. These process waste gases often have only 60-80 Btu's/cubic foot. However, after careful study, process waste gas use has proven worthwhile despite special provisions for its burning—sometimes at significant cost.

When a gas-fuel system for a plant is being considered, review the following: Consider not only existing gas sources but look five to ten years ahead for a fuel supply. Consider the influence of production demands by existing facilities as well as demands by future units which may be placed in service.

As the firing of new or revised units is planned it is of great importance to have firm data as to what fuels are to be burned. The mol-percent analysis of the gas fuel should be as firm as is possible. Selection of burner type is almost entirely governed by the nature of the fuel if the heaters are to be reasonably and properly fired. If oil is to be fired, the equipment for heating and pumping it must be suited to changing oil characteristics as it is burned. A major change in the fuel system is anything but cheap. A change of burners to accommodate fuel changes is expensive.

A problem for gas fuels of considerable magnitude is that caused by the addition of free hydrogen. Present trends in process work are causing significantly greater mol-percentages of free hydrogen in gas fuels. The volume of gas as produced is perhaps large. But, the heating value is reduced to such a degree that burner changes may be required either because of pressure limitations or because of a tendency for the burners to flash back as the free hydrogen increases. Thus, if the fuel is changed from a low hydrogen content to higher hydrogen, difficulty may be expected.

Oil Fuels

If fuel oil is being fired, a change in fuel oil properties need not be of such great concern. The properties are assumed to be markedly similar in viscosity and in specific hydrocarbon content. There is need for concern, however, if there is a sharp increase in aromatics, if the fuel is a decanted oil from cat cracking, if the oil contains coke particles or polymer solids, or if there is a great change in the viscosity index.

If the aromatics concentration increases markedly, greater quantities of steam will be required for atomization. More steam is necessary to produce the firing excellence typical of low-aromatics fuel. If the steam is available and if the small added cost for the increase in steam consumption is not a factor, there should be small difficulty.

Oils typical of decanted fuels, which are residual oils from cat cracking operations inevitably carry some catalyst fines. These oils are very abrasive as they are burned. It is not at all uncommon to find oil atomizers eroded beyond use within two weeks or less.

If the solids carried by the oil are large enough in particle size, there can be great difficulty with plugged burner parts or valves which greatly interfere with firing. Suitable strainers with mesh apertures small enough to trap the solids can relieve this difficulty. The strainers must be cleaned regularly. There will be a pressure drop across the strainers. Strainers should be installed at each point where fuel oil is withdrawn from the supply header.

The viscosity index of oils is the tendency for the oil viscosity to be altered by temperature or its resistance to viscosity change as the temperature is changed. When changing fuel oils, the viscosity as a function of temperature can be a source of considerable difficulty. A temperature level which was completely satisfactory for one oil may not be at all satisfactory for another oil. When there is a change in fuel oils, the viscosity of the new oil should be carefully checked to determine the oil temperature required for a satisfactory state of viscosity as burned.

Fuel burning is subject to misinformation in any case, especially where oil fuel is concerned. Steam is typically used as the atomizing medium in oil burning and, since steam conservation is important in process operation, it is not uncommon for significant sums to be spent for new atomizers when an existing set of atomizers is thought to require an excessive quantity of steam for atomization. Unless existing atomizers *do* require excessive steam for best adjustment to proper firing conditions, the significant sums are wasted. Several factors influence atomizing steam

demand. Many operators prefer dazzling white oil flames. This preference wastes steam. After the burner is in stable operation, the flame color/appearance depends on steam usage. With less steam, the test-proven flame color should be yellowish with an orange tinge. Excessive steam produces the dazzling white oil flames.

Fuel oil characteristics such as viscosity *as burned* and relative aromatics content greatly influence atomizing steam demand for suitable flame appearance. If the fuel oil viscosity is excessively high as it is burned, the steam demand is very great. A prime source of excessive viscosity as the old is burned is heat loss from fuel oil lines after the heating and pumping set. No line insulation is more important! The viscosity of the fuel oil can, and does, vary widely with fuel oil supply. A temperature which sufficiently lowers viscosity in one oil may be far too low for another oil. Delivered temperature/viscosity as the oil is burned is heat loss from If the viscosity, as checked, exceeds 250 SSU, atomizing steam requirement is probably excessive. Oils containing aromatics require more steam than oils which are olefinic or paraffinic. In some cases, because of less-than-good air register design, flame proportions become far too great with minimal steam usage and tube impingement results. Here, increase in atomizing steam will shorten flames and may be necessary. Atomizing steam demand, in terms of pounds of steam per pound of oil, is always minimal at full atomizer capacity, but the weight ratio of steam-to-oil increases rapidly as atomizer capacity is reduced.

Completely satisfactory firing with oil as the fuel is common in the industry. Burners must be checked regularly to make sure they are operating properly and are in proper adjustment. Thus, there is greater demand for attention with oil than with gas firing.

The preference for gas fuels is largely due to the greater need for burner attention and their operation when oil is the fuel. Also, because of differences in burning characteristics, the range of operability is less with oil than with gas.

In all process facilities it is necessary at times to change the fuel(s) fired as fuel availability or economic conditions change. If the required fuel change is from oil firing to gas firing, few (if any) problems must be solved because a furnace is, with rare exception, more easily fired with gas than with oil; less attention to firing factors are required. However, change from gas to oil firing can present problems. One potential problem is the adaptability of the furnace to oil firing whether or not new burners are required. A furnace that has been designed around the clean and very rapid burning characteristics of gas fuel is, inevitably, difficult to convert to oil firing. Indeed, at times the change can be virtually impossible. Highly specialized burners for complete duplication of gas firing with distillate oil fuels can solve this problem at some initial cost for burners plus added cost for the distillate fuel as an operating expense. However, some relief from operating expense is possible with highly specialized burners because their forced draft is readily adaptable to preheat. Where there is any question as to the fuel adaptability for a furnace, great care should be used.

The process industries, particularly in the Gulf Coast area, have largely relied on gas firing, and there is a marked reluctance to a change to oil firing. The reluctance is partially justified because a preferred fuel for ease of firing is one with a higher H/C weight ratio of from 0.33 to 0.25 such as methane or ethane. A typical H/C weight ratio of 0.12 is characteristic of # 6 oil. However, the aversion to oil firing is not justified because oil burning equipment now available is capable of doing a fine job of firing compared to earlier oil burning equipment. More attention to oil firing is required, although automatic firing controls for oil firing now closely approach the excellence of gas-firing controls.

The ancient truism that oil firing requires more excess air is simply no longer true. It has been found that gas-firing excess air down to less than 10% can also be maintained for oil firing with comparatively few exceptions. This condition exists because theoretical air demand/ MM Btu's with methane firing is 27.9 mols, and with # 6 oil the air demand is 27.76 mols. If the air supply is adequate for methane, it is also adequate for # 6 oil to within less than 1%, and the difference favors oil firing. If identical excess air is not possible with both fuels, a complaint should immediately be made to the particular burner manufacturer for correction.

Because of natural gas shortages and increased demand for liquid-fuel firing where distillate fuels are acceptable, systems are available for the substitution of vaporized oil/steam (or other partial-pressure control gases) for natural gas without burner change when the vaporized oil/gas mixture is suitably superheated to avoid oil dew point. Piping and controls for such fuels must be carefully insulated after the superheat phase to avoid oil dew point from heat loss. Such fuels have been successfully adapted to original gas-fired primary reformers for hydrogen production and to pyrolysis heaters where heat density per cubic foot of furnace volume is very high. These are the most demanding services for process firing. Patents exist for this fuel alternative, including USA 4,025,282, and other patents are in application.

The traditional reluctance to abandon gas firing and resort to oil firing despite progress in oil burner design is essentially unjustified. Such conversion has proven to be productive of excellent operation. After the conversion, operators frequently prefer the oil-firing mode.

It is not uncommon to find gas burners operating quite satisfactorily in the range of from 15 to 100% of design heat release in automatic control. In the burning of oil in automatic control a range of operation of from 33 to 100% heat release is more typical. Where automatic control is required, the controls for gas firing are much more routine. However, controls for oil firing are now considered satisfactory if properly designed and operated. But there is a limitation to the heat release per burner as well as to the type of fuel burned. The burner manufacturer should be required to establish these limitations before any automatic control equipment is purchased so that the control equipment can meet the limitations as they are established, to permit proper firing.

For automatic control to function properly there must be completely stable fuel supply conditions up to control regulation regardless of the fuel being burned. When oil is the fuel not only must the oil supply pressure be constant but also the viscosity as well as the steam supply pressure for atomization. For the oil viscosity to remain constant, the oil temperature must remain constant at all conditions of flow. Line insulation between the control devices and the burners must be carefully applied and maintained. The steam lines must be properly insulated and trapped to avoid delivery of condensate slugs to the burners.

The calorific values of most fuel components can be readily referenced from current literature; however, they are not available for a growing number of compounds which are typical of CPI process residuals. This unavailability is particularly true for chemical or petrochemical operations. Correct and reliable heat balances for calorific values of these compounds are badly needed in process operations. Erratic operating data can be traced to a lack of research in fuel component calorific values.

When this condition exists, there is urgent need for a reliable procedure (within less than 1%) for computation of fuel calorific data. A formula procedure does exist to take into account the LHV of fuel molecule components either plus or minus the molecular heats of formation for compounds being studied. The molecular component heat value total is not the sole determinant for the calorific value of a specific compound. Molecular heats of formation can be found in chemical handbooks at f values in kilo-calories per gram-mol. There are 453.59 gram-mols per pound-mol, and a kilo-calorie is equal to 3.968 Btu's. Heats of formation can be either exothermal (carry a minus sign) or endothermal (carry no sign or the plus sign).

Heat-worthy molecular components are carbon (C), hydrogen (H), and sulphur (S). Each pound of carbon represents 14,093 Btu's, each pound of hydrogen represents 51,602 Btu's, and each pound of sulphur represents 3,983 Btu's. A pound-mol is the number of pounds of a molecular substance equal to its molecular weight; it is also (arbitrarily) 379 scf as a gas. Thus, a pound-mol of methane (CH_4) is 16.043 pounds

or 379 scf. Methane contains 12.011 pounds of carbon and 4.032 pounds of hydrogen. The heat of formation (f) for methane is -17.89.

The calorific value of a mol of methane is as follows:

$$[(12.011 \times 14,093) + (64.132 \times 3,983)] + (453.59 \times 3.968 \times 27.55) = 424,708 \text{ Btu's}$$

One pound of methane represents 345,151/ 16.043 = 21,513 Btu's and a cubic foot of methane represents 345,131/379 = 910.6 Btu's. Referring to published data verifies these figures.

A pound-mol of carbon disulfide (CS_2) contains 12.011 pounds of carbon and 64.132 pounds of sulphur. Its heat of formation is $+27.55$. The calorific value of a pound-mol of carbon disulfide is as follows:

$$[(12.011 \times 14,093) + (4,032 \times 51,602)] + (453.59 \times 3.968 \times -17.89) = 345,131 \text{ Btu's}$$

A pound of carbon disulfide represents 424,708/76.143 = 5,578 Btu's, and a cubic foot of carbon disulfide represents 424,708/379 = 1,121 Btu's.

A chemical handbook is not always readily available for determination of heats of formation. Table 6-4 provides the necessary data for a number of CPI residual fuel substances.

When the heater design is complete, the heater structure is very fixed. The process people have exercised their skills to the best of their ability as to tubes, tube surface, tube orientation, stack, breeching and all else within limits imposed upon them by cost factors. There has been good engineering in every respect and again within cost limitation for the materials and structure. This is assumed by the purchaser and rightfully so. But one of the facts of life in relation to process heaters is that many factors and forces which are not subject to firm prediction may cause the operation of the heater to leave a little or much to be desired. When this occurs, the problem is attacked through burner modification to set up altered conditions

Table 6-4
Fuel Component Calorific Value Computation

Fuel	Molecular Weight	Heat of Formation (f)
Acetaldehyde-gas	44.054 - C2,H4,O	− 39.76
Acetic Acid-gas	60.054 - C2,H4,O2	−104.72
Acetic Anhydride-gas	102.092 - C4,H6,O3	−148.82
Acrolein-gas	56.065 - C3,H4,O	− 20.50
Acetone-gas	58.081 - C3,H6,O	− 51.79
Amine-Dimethyl-gas	45.086 - C2,H7,N	− 6.6
Amine-Methyl-gas	31.059 - C,H5,N	− 6.7
Ammonia	17.032 - N,H3	− 11.04
Amyl Alcohol-n, liquid	88.151 - C5,H12,O	− 86.06
Amyl Alcohol-tert, liquid	88.151 - C5,H12,O	− 96.46
Benzene-gas	78.114 - C6,H6	+ 19.82
Benzaldehyde-gas	106.125 - C7,H6,O	− 9.57
Cyanide-gas	27.027 - H,C,N	− 31.20
Carbon Disulfide-gas	76.143 - C,S2	+ 27.55
Carbon Monoxide	28.011 - C,O	− 26.42
Cyclohexane-gas	84.162 - C6,H12	− 29.43
Cyclopentane-gas	70.135 - C5,H10	− 18.46
Formaldehyde	30.027 - C,H2,O	− 27.70
Formic Acid	46.027 - C,H2,O2	− 86.67
Mercaptan-Ethyl	62.136 - C2,H6,S	− 16.00
Mercaptan-Methyl	48.109 - C,H4,S	− 2.97
Phenol-gas	94.114 - C6,H6,O	− 21.71
Phenol-liquid	94.114 - C6,H6,O	− 37.80
Styrene-gas	104.152 - C8,H8	+ 35.11
Styrene-liquid	104.152 - C8,H8	+ 24.72
Toluene	92.141 - C7,H8	+ 11.95
Xylene-O, gas	106.168 - C8,H10	+ 4.54
Xylene-M, gas	106.168 - C8,H10	+ 4.12
Xylene-P, gas	106.168 - C8,H10	+ 4.29

Component Heat Values	Component Atomic Weight
C = 14,093 Btu's/lb	C = 12.011
H = 51,602 Btu's/lb	H = 1.008
S = 3,983 Btu's/lb	S = 32.066
	N = 14.008
	O = 16.000
	CL = 35.457

The LHV of a mol of any fuel is the sum of its component LHV (C, H, and S), either plus or minus its heat of formation factor *(f)* according to the sign preceding *f* as shown previously. *f* is kilo-calories per gram-mol, and there are 453.59 gram-mols per lb-mol. The *f* heat is 453.59 X *f* X 3.968 in Btu's. A lb-mol is the number of pounds equal to molecular weight and is, arbitrarily, 379 scf.

Methane has a molecular weight equal to 16.043, with 12.011 lbs of C, and 4.032 lbs of H. The heat from C is 12.011 X 14,093 = 169,271 Btu's. The heat from H is 4.032 X 51602 = 208,059 Btu's. The total heat is 377,330 Btu's. The *f* for methane is −17.89 (negative). The *f* heat is 453.59 X −17.89 X 3.968 = −32,199 Btu's, and 377,330 −32,199 = 345,131 Btu's per mol of methane net. Heating value per lb: 345,131/16.043 = 21,513 Btu's, and per cubic foot is 345,131/379 = 910.6 Btu's.

within what is really a well-designed heater. Such attack is invariably successful if the heater design is good. It is a rare circumstance today when the fundamental design of a heater leaves something to be desired. With this in mind, it is possible to have the impression that a less desirable burner has been supplied to fire the heater. This presumption is not necessarily correct. The fault will lie, in all probability, in some unexpected force within the furnace which is seriously distorting heat distribution patterns. Before any burner change is made, the gas flow patterns inside the heater should be carefully checked from *each* burner with ground-up adsorption charcoal powder. As the glowing charcoal particles travel through the furnace, they will clearly show where heat flow is deviating from expected paths. With this information, a capable burner manufacturer can quickly and accurately set up corrective procedures either by modification of existing burners or substitution of another design to correct the heat flow deviation. This suggests that the burner manufacturer should be capable of delivering all basic burner designs when the original design is chosen. However, the burner manufacturer who is capable of supplying any basic design should be consulted as to his choice when the heater is originally supplied. Burner choice is not necessarily a precision matter. Burner change for correction of heater problems is not peculiar to a single heater manufacturer or a single burner manufacturer and is, in fact, not really rare.

Fuel Supply Pressures

If there are limitations on fuel supply pressure, make sure these limitations are quite clear to the engineer who will be required to present his proposal. Fuel pressure limitations severely limit burner selection as well as burner performance. It is a significant error to limit fuel-gas pressures to perhaps 15 psig at the burner because of control preferences. Not only does such a limitation restrict the operating range of the burners, it may also result in inferior burner operation. An optimum operating gas pressure for burners is in the 25-35 psig range, as a general rule.

Engineering representatives of burner manufacturers should be allowed to present their argu-

ments in support of the recommendations they have made. There should be a careful analysis of each presentation which is based on experience. In this manner, the plus and minus factors in each case can be carefully considered. A selection can be made on the basis of merit alone. A priceless ingredient in any presentation by any engineer is the reputation held by his firm for the readiness with which service is supplied if trouble should develop as the heater operates. Service to them and burners go hand-in-hand no matter how carefully the burners may have been chosen due to factors which are almost completely imponderable as the selection is made. Some of these factors are: changes in fuel specifications, changes in the process at the last minute, or other changes governing the performance of a furnace-burner configuration. The performance of the heater is keyed to burner performance. If the burners cannot perform correctly after a change there must be service to make them deliver heat in a suitable manner. If the burners have been supplied by a competent manufacturer, his service staff will have the skill and experience to promptly correct the undesirable operation. Minimum difficulty and process impairment results from burner servicing.

Service is still another factor in the equation for burner selection; and it is a significant factor. A responsible burner manufacturer will propose those burners which seem most likely to provide satisfactory operation for any particular heater configuration. He will do so in the best of good faith. However, burner operation, even with a repeatedly proven burner design, is fraught with hazards which are largely unpredictable. Thus, there may be difficulty with any burner for any fuel. When difficulty arises, the burner manufacturer should be notified as soon as possible and in full detail as to what is happening. Again, the service factor is critical. If there is improper burner operation, there is an expensive impairment of the process. The choice of a burner manufacturer should be made on the basis of a long-time history of prompt service by people of proven competence. Competence is defined as the ability to observe burner performance and provide a prompt solution for the difficulty at minimum cost. This test should apply whether the cost involved was caused by the burner manufacturer or by some deviation from specified conditions when the burners were purchased.

In reporting difficulty to the burner manufacturer, provide full detail as to draft, fuel characteristics, fuel pressure at the burner (not at some point remote from the burner) as well as a clear statement of the nature of the difficulty. In all cases, the burner manufacturer should be required to provide a scaled drawing which is exact in detail for the burner installed in the particular heater. The reason for a specific drawing is that for any specific burner based on any specific basic burner design, it is probable that an alteration of burner structure will have been made to permit its installation. Unless the drawing is true for a particular burner's modification, it is difficult if not impossible to make a correction, in a reasonable time.

Basic Burner Functions

It is, perhaps, a great over-simplification to state the end-result expected of a burner. The result expected is the production of a specific quantity of hot gases directed in preferred manner into the space inside the furnace. The hot gases move within the furnace structure. There is a transfer of gaseous heat to the various areas and surfaces of the furnace, as calculated, through both radiation and convection.

We have thus placed the cart before the horse. We have dealt with the end result to this point rather than with the physical and chemical functions which allow the end result to occur. In the interest of clarity, it is in order to pose the question, "What, specifically, is a burner?"

A burner is a device made of metals and refractory which accepts specific amounts of air and fuel and mixes them as homogeneously as possible and then causes the fuel to burn through stable exothermic chemical processes. Functions of physics must be satisfactorily present and operative prior to chemical functions which produce the flame-hot gases. Mixture must precede burning. The state of mixture determines what state of burning may exist.

Mixture occurs in gases as the result of differential flowing energies of the gases involved or according to the degree of differential energies which are the results of flowing velocities. One gas stream must always be flowing at a significantly greater velocity than the gas stream with which it is to mix. Flowing velocity in gases or fluids is proportional to the square root of the pressure which caused the velocity of flow to exist up to sonic velocity. The energy at any velocity is $MV^2/2$ where M is mass and V is velocity. Velocity head is $V^2/2g$ where g is gravity (32.17 ft./sec.).

Flow Velocity Energy and Pressure Drop

Bernoulli teaches that when a gas or fluid is flowing into another gas or fluid, the pressure is lower in the stream flowing at greatest velocity. An effect of a stream of gas or fluid at greater velocity is to cause the second gas or fluid to be drawn into and mixed with the first stream. The degree of in-draft as well as the degree of mixture is in proportion to differential velocity functions. Since a goal of the burner designer is the production of a homogeneous mixture of fuel and air prior to burning, he must make use of such differential velocities as are available to produce a satisfactory fuel-air mixture. Sources of differential velocities are:

1. Air pressure drop across the burner structure
2. Fuel pressure drop to the atmosphere in which burning is to occur.

Air pressure drop is typically measured as a fraction of 1-in. WC or in inches water column. Fuel pressure drop is typically measured in lbs./sq. in. gage (psig). Therefore, flow velocity is least in air flow and greatest in fuel flow. These relationships limit the burner designer in creating a burner structure which will permit reasonably satisfactory burning of fuels.

Fuel supply pressures vary widely. Draft or air pressure drops across the burner structure vary almost as widely. The burner designer must accept conditions dictated by the nature of the service. He must provide a state of fuel mixture-burning acceptable for another factor which is the nature of the available fuel.

In the broadest sense, burners (particularly gas burners) are offered as either premix or nonpremix (raw gas) types. The term premix denotes an operating condition where a portion or all the air for burning is premixed with fuel before the fuel reaches a point at which burning can begin. Nonpremix burners cause the air-fuel mixture to occur coincidentally with burning. Oil burners are generically of the nonpremix type, unless the oil as a liquid can be converted to oil as a vapor immediately prior to burning. Oil as a liquid is in a quite different physical state from a gas. Substances in differing physical states cannot be homogeneously mixed. Thus, liquid oil must be converted to gaseous oil through either vaporization or atomization.

There are many burner manufacturers but the number of basic burner designs is somewhat limited. Each burner manufacturer offers his version of basic burner designs according to his preference. The firing characteristics of any specific burner as offered by any manufacturer will be in keeping with those of the basic design regardless of manufacture.

A description of basic gas burner designs to meet the many conditions for fuel burning is suggested as follows:

1. Refractory block, multiport gas burners.
2. Spider-type gas burners.
3. Peripheral gas, center-oil burners with and without spin louvers.
4. Center-gas and center-oil burners with and without spin louvers.
5. Single-aspirator, narrow-flame gas burners.
6. Single-aspirator, wide-flame burners.
7. Multiple-aspirator burners.
8. Fan-type burners for air induction.
9. High-radiance, premix burners.
10. Low gas pressure, spider-type burners.
11. Multiple refractory block, gas and oil burners.

12. High-intensity gas and oil burners for forced draft.

All of these burner types, when properly applied, will produce a state of fuel burning suited to particular limitations of air and fuel relative velocities, speed of burning and flame volume/length. Burner application is, then, a matter of choosing burners having characteristics suited to the service to be performed.

It has been stated earlier that the end result expected of a burner is stable burning. This can be restated as a requirement for stable burning throughout a normal control range in operation. There are few sources of danger in unsatisfactory operation which are more serious than unstable burners which may be extinguished or misbehave without warning. Unstable burning is a major hazard both in burner design and burner selection. What may be a perfectly satisfactory configuration for one operating condition, may be completely unsatisfactory for another. Therefore, burners should be chosen for their range of operability as well as fundamental burning characteristics.

Fundamentally, a burner may be said to consist of air and fuel admission or injection parts which cooperate to produce desirable conditions of fuel burning. Air admission parts may be an air register for secondary air, a controllable door for primary air entry or regulatable means for entry of tertiary air. Primary air is mixed with fuel before burning starts; secondary air is admitted directly to the burning zone and tertiary air is usually admitted after the burning zone. All can be controlled as required.

It is in the fuel admission/injection means that there is greatest variation. Each manufacturer establishes this function in keeping with the effect of burning which he hopes to attain. There are neither rules, metes nor bounds for fuel admission/injection. However, parts for fuel admission/injection are typically most subject to corrosion and heat attrition. These functions are matters for concern in all burner design. In some cases, cast-iron parts may be used very satisfactorily, according to the rate with which heat is dissipated.

In other cases, more exotic materials may be required to produce satisfactory continued operation.

Function of Atomization

Oil burning, generally, is more difficult than gas burning. As has been stated, oil as a liquid must be converted to oil as a gas (vapor) before it can mix with air and begin to burn. In typical operation, oil is delivered to the burner where it passes through an atomizer which converts the liquid to millions of tiny droplets which, hopefully, are not greater than 10-50 microns in size. Such conversion tremendously increases the ratio of surface-to-mass, permitting substantially instantaneous heat absorption by the droplets, altering their physical state from liquid to gas in microseconds. Gas thus produced mixes freely with air and burning begins. For burning to occur, there must be an ample supply of heat relative to the atomizer discharge. Atomization may be through the action of steam, air, or high-pressure gas. It may be attained by "pressure-atomization" or mechanical atomization in which the oil enters a swirl chamber through tangential ports or slots to be discharged as a conical spray resulting from an applied pressure of 100-400 psig. Another type of atomization, rarely used in the process industries, is the "rotary cup." Oil admitted to the interior of a rapidly spinning cup leaps clear of the cup lip as a relatively fine spray.

Mineral Content of Oils

Liquid fuels have a further undesirable characteristic in that they contain varying amounts of mineral matter which is typical of residual oils. Mineral matter may be present from brines initially in the crude oil as nondistillable products, or they may be as mineral components such as vanadium actually bonded into the hydrocarbons. Since the mineral is a portion of the hydrocarbons, it cannot be removed by desalting. This process is typically used by refiners to remove sodium, cal-

cium, magnesium and iron salts carried by emulsified brines present as B. S. & W. Such vanadium as is present burns to various oxides (principally V_2O_5—vanadium pentoxide) producing approximately 10.9% as much heat as an equivalent weight of carbon. Vanadium does have a certain heat value; but the problems presented by the presence of vanadium oxides can be serious, according to the amount of vanadium present in the oil as burned. Undesirable effects of vanadium oxides associated with furnace operation are as follows:

1. Severe metallurgical attack as temperature is elevated
2. Refractory attack through the formation of a eutectic (lower melting temperature) layer at the surface of the refractory which, at critical temperature can destroy the refractory
3. Since V_2O_5 is the prime catalyst for conversion of SO_2 to SO_3, it greatly increases the partial pressure of SO_3 in the furnace gases and accelerates sulfuric corrosion.

Metallurgical attack characteristics of V_2O_5 have been the subject of a doctoral program at a well-known university. The thesis produced indicates that attention to metallurgy can cut metal attrition to a degree, but the effect of selective metallurgy is disappointing and hardly amortizes added cost for more exotic alloys. As an example, it was found that there was little difference in metallurgical attack on type 304 steel, type 309 steel and type 310 steel if the tests were carried out at temperatures typical of process operation for tubes and heat-transfer surfaces and not to exceed 1,200°F. Tube hanger attack, where higher temperature levels are expected, is best resolved on the basis of temperature endurance of the alloy rather than through consideration of metallurgical functions as such.

Because of the capability for metallurgical attack when vanadium-bearing fuels are burned, there has been an effort to define maximum furnace temperature by technical service groups of various operating companies. But there is small agreement among them to within 100-200° F. It is obvious that there must be a lower furnace temperature than would be typical of gas fuel or vanadium-free oil fuel. But the point at which avoidance of attack begins to interfere with plant economics is difficult to define. Loss of return caused by temperature reduction must be balanced against all factors of gain due to avoidance of attack. Operating characteristics of the specific installation have been found to be the key to temperature reduction in a great majority of cases and by numerous operators of process facilities.

Vanadium concentrations in fuel oils vary quite widely. The factor of vanadium concentration in oil, as burned, should always be a matter for consideration. With 20 ppm or less, there is small reason for concern except for processes such as steam reforming where tube temperatures are exceptionally high. Typical concentrations can vary from less than 1 ppm to more than 20 ppm. Note that care for attack presumes a decrease in furnace temperature with decreased productivity the result. Choice of fuels can well be dictated by this factor.

Eutectic attack of refractories is largely in proportion to the concentration of vanadium in the fuel oil. With a specific oil, furnace temperature must be adjusted to avoid this attack. When eutectic attack is present, it will continue at a fixed furnace temperature to accomplish essentially complete destruction of the refractory. Avoidance of such damage must, inevitably, be a reduction in furnace temperature to a point where the eutectic action ceases to be serious. In defining the furnace temperature which will avoid such attack, there is little if any agreement as to the allowable amounts of vanadium. Lack of agreement is thought to be due to variations in specific furnace temperatures and furnace areas. Judgment as to temperature reduction is required for each heater or furnace.

There is a tendency for SO_3 to be present in the gases produced in the burning of sulfur-bearing fuels in the apparent absence of a catalyst which is required for conversion of SO_2 to SO_3. The SO_3 has been discussed as a material which can greatly accelerate corrosion because of elevated dew point. (See Figure 3-7.) Vanadium in the fuel appears as V_2O_5 in the furnace structure. As has been suggested, this is the prime catalyst for SO_3 production. Therefore, this catalyst produces greater quantities of SO_3 than would be typical in its absence. There is significant further elevation of dew point to increase corrosion potential when vanadium-bearing fuels are burned. It is, therefore, necessary to exercise greater caution to avoid corrosion when vanadium is present in the fuel. Only carefully conducted tests for SO_3 concentration in furnace gases can be relied upon.

Vanadium and Group I Metals

Vanadium oxides are not, however, the sole source of such eutectic attack. Sodium oxides are serious but perhaps not equally so; however, the presence of sodium as mineral in fuel oil is far more common than the presence of vanadium since sodium is typical of oil-well brines. There is some relief from the presence of sodium through typical desalting processes.

A carefully conducted research program devoted to vanadium eutectic attack has produced conclusive evidence that the vanadium ion alone is little more serious than the sodium ion alone. Also, the attack is greater when both sodium and vanadium ions are present. Thus, there is reason to consider far more comprehensive desalting as a means for avoiding vanadium attack. However, at this time, there is not conclusive evidence to support this consideration despite some favorable data. There is reason to believe that a greater degree of desalting is preferred.

Sodium is a Group I metal. Any of the metals of this group seem to exhibit the same characteristic of eutectic attack on refractories. There has been no specific reference to potassium, as an example of another Group I metal, having the identical accelerative attack characteristic when combined with vanadium. It may be presumed that any Group I metal will accelerate attack when combined with vanadium.

When firing process heaters, there is no substitute for a capable and conscientious operator despite the obvious value of controls and the functions they perform. This is to say that the operator who is genuinely interested in his work develops what is essentially a seat-of-the-pants feeling for corrective and operational techniques which, in many instances, is priceless. The average operator may not fully understand functions of chemistry and physics which cause his corrective procedures to work. He has simply learned that if he makes an adjustment under a fixed set of conditions the effect of the adjustment will be good.

As a typical example one operator, who just happened to be a graduate chemical engineer, discovered that the heater ran better and consumed less fuel per barrel of useful product when the stack damper was closed to a point which caused positive pressure to exist at the arch or roof of the furnace. His explanation of the improvement—strange as it seems—was that the pressure in the furnace did a better job of driving heat into the tubes. He did complain that the furnace arch was failing rapidly. The true explanation is that in closing the stack damper he was reducing excess air. This was demonstrated to him by closing the burner air dampers with enough draft to avoid pressure at the heater arch. This procedure stopped the arch damage and provided an even greater improvement in operation. The engineer who supervises operation can make no operational mistake greater than failure to listen carefully to what his operators tell him and then, in his own way, seek an explanation for what he has been told.

Because each furnace will have its own characteristics, the adjustment of furnaces is essentially an art, despite the fact that there is a scientific explanation for what happens when the adjustments are made. It is not at all unusual for identical heaters to have quite different adjustment characteristics because the gas flow characteristics are not identical. A certain method of burner fuel-air adjustment may have been proposed as ideal; but

because of specific individual furnace conditions, other adjustment techniques may be required so that the heater can perform satisfactorily.

Generally speaking, burner adjustments are made to either improve firing conditions or to reduce excess air and the two may be closely related. Such adjustments are made to the air register or the air-control parts or perhaps to the amount of fuel allowed to reach particular burners at a fixed control setting for the fuel. Each adjustment should be followed by careful furnace inspection to avoid flame impingement and hot spots which may appear as a result of the adjustment or other undesirable conditions such as pressure at the arch, which should never exist. A good draft gage which is in good repair and which has been "zeroed" is a must for reasonably good firing control in any circumstance. This is because air adjustment for burners is either through control of burner air-flow devices or through control of the stack damper.

Burner air-flow devices control the quantity of air which can enter the burner to the furnace according to the state of draft or air pressure drop at a particular burner, as adjusted. But, the state of draft or air pressure drop is controlled by the stack damper. Air-flow quantity is proportional to air-flow areas as the burner is adjusted. If the air-flow area is altered significantly, without a corresponding alteration of furnace draft or observation of draft to see that there has been no significant change, the adjustment in air-flow area does not produce a proportional effect in air quantity. Control becomes difficult and only careful balancing of furnace draft, by damper adjustment with burner adjustment, can establish a reliable state of control. (See Table 6-5).

The function of the stack damper portion of the heater is solely to overcome flow pressure drop between entry to the convection section and to the stack. Since pressure drop will vary nonlinearly with flow quantity, at the same temperature level, for double the volume the pressure drop is quadrupled. It becomes evident that fixed, stack damper adjustment for a range of control is not possible if control is to be suitable and if pressure at the arch or top of the furnace is to be avoided.

In any state of operation, stack-damper adjustment should be made to cause a draft condition above the convection tubes which is equal to the pressure drop across the convection section plus 0.03-in. WC with the draft at 0.03-in. WC existing at the arch or roof of the furnace. Tell-tale for this condition is measurement of draft at the arch. If with the stack damper in the wide-open condition it is not possible to avoid pressure at the furnace arch due to stack limitations for draft capability, the decision for continued operation at that condition should be made by management. Management should always be notified of the condition immediately: such draft limitation may be due to overload or design error. The latter is truly rare as the design condition for operation is set up when the heater is supplied. However, if the design stack velocity of gas movement is set too high, there is no stack provision for the overfiring which is typical if not inevitable. Specification for stack design velocity should never exceed 25 ft./sec. if the heater is to perform properly. In normal operation, the stack damper should always be partially closed to provide a safe and satisfactory basis for overload firing.

In this discussion, it is the author's intention to point out that heater design is the function of the heater manufacturer, who through experience will undoubtedly be capable. Heater operation is the function of firing personnel and successful service from the heater is largely a matter of the excellence or lack of excellence in firing. Heater firing is not at all a simple matter of fuel turn on and ignition. It is, instead, a combination of the turn on and ignition plus judicious adjustment of fuel, air, draft, flame length, appearance and spread as well as constant furnace inspection. The operation of heaters is not yet a push button operation, despite control excellence.

For this reason the firemen are, in essence, in firm control of plant operation as they work with the unit operators. For this reason, it is difficult to find a job which carries greater responsibility than that of the firemen. No plant is well operated until the firemen are proven capable either through their experience or through suitable training by capable people. But, the training should be by people who can communicate with the firemen or who "speak the fireman's language" rather than the more erudite language of higher education.

Table 6-5
Burner-Sizing (Free Area) and
Pressure-Drop (Air) Correction for Altitude

Altitude in Feet	"B" Factor	Altitude in Feet	"B" Factor
1000'	732	4000'	655
1500'	718	4500'	644
2000'	705	5000'	632
2500'	693	5500'	621
3000'	681	6000'	610
3500'	668	6500'	599
		7000'	586

S = Sea-Level Size
DP = Sea-Level Pressure-Drop
DP_1 = Altitude Pressure-Drop
S_1 = Sx $\sqrt{760/B}$
DP_1 = ($\sqrt{DP}$ X $\sqrt{760/B})^2$ for Sea-Level Burner at Altitude

Sea-Level Barometer = 760 MM HG
Altitude Barometer − MM Hg = B
S_1 = Size Corrected for Altitude

7

Flow of Fluids

Avogadro gave us the law that at identical temperatures and pressures, all gaseous materials have identical numbers of molecules present within a unit volume. Avogadro's law combines with the laws of Boyle, Charles and Gay-Lussac on the basis of the kinetic theory to provide the ideal gas law which is expressed as:

$$pv = nRT$$

where:

p = Pressure
v = Volume
R = Ideal gas constant
T = Temperature on the Kelvin or Rankine scale

This formula is a bit awkward because the value of the R factor depends on the units in which other factors are expressed. A much more convenient formula which avoids the use of the ideal gas constant for volumetric calculation with gases is:

$$v_2 = v_1 (p_1/p_2) (t_2/t_1)$$

where:

v_1 = Volume at standard conditions
v_2 = Volume at calculated conditions
p_1 = Pressure at standard conditions, absolute
p_2 = Pressure at calculated conditions, absolute
T_1 = Standard temperature, absolute
T_2 = Temperature at calculated conditions, absolute

Metric and English Standards

Standard conditions under the English and metric systems vary in defining the temperature which is considered standard. In the metric system, the standard temperature is zero degrees Centigrade (32°F). In the English system, the standard temperature is 60°F and this condition is quite frequently a source of significant error as volumes are calculated.

The standard unit of gas volume may be either a gram-mol (or a number of grams of the gas equal to the molecular weight of the gas) or the pound-mol which is a number of pounds of the gas equal to the molecular weight of the gas. According to the literature, the volume of a gram-mol of gas is equal to 22.40 liters and the volume of a pound-mol is 359 cu. ft. Note that these volumes are at 32°F.

When a pound-molal volume at 32°F is corrected to the English standard of 60°F, the volume becomes 379.4271 cu. ft. For calculation in the English system, it is common to use 380 cu. ft. as the volume of a pound-mol of gas with the very small error of 0.16%. In view of the fact that gases do not behave in perfect keeping with the ideal gas law, the error becomes insignificant unless micrometric calculation is demanded.

A unit of volume typical of the metric system is the normal cubic meter which is 35.310 cu. ft. at 32°F. When this volume is converted for calculation in the English system (60°F) the volume becomes 37.329 std. cu. ft., based on a temperature correction factor of 1.0569 for volume.

All gases deviate to greater or lesser degree from the ideal gas law. (See Table 7-1.) There is greater deviation of hydrocarbons and, in general, the deviations become greater as the molecular weights increase. In all cases, the deviation becomes greater as states of critical pressure and temperature are approached. For air and the gases produced in combustion as well as water vapor in relatively low partial pressures typical of humid air and combustion gases the ideal gas law is considered as a fair approximation. Within limits of engineering tolerance, it may be used. Where there is

deviation, the molal volume is less than the ideal gas law would predict. Calculated volumes will, therefore, be greater than actual volumes.

In mixtures of gases, the partial pressures of the component gases are equal to the mol-percentages or volume percentages of the respective gases. In a mixture, the total pressure is the sum of the partial pressures of the component gases. Thus, mol-percentage and partial pressure for the component gases are identical.

Mixture of Gases

Where there is a mixture of gases at any total pressure and where one of the component gases reaches the dew point and is altered to the liquid phase, the remaining partial pressures in gaseous components are increased by virtue of withdrawal of the volume of the dew point product from the volume of the confining space. In a mixture of gases composed of 1/3 butane, 1/3 pentane and 1/3 hexane, the partial pressures for each of the component gases would be 1/3 the total pressure. If the hexane should go to the dew point and no longer be present as a gas, the volume would be reduced by approximately 1/3, leaving the pentane and butane in the gaseous phase. The partial pressures of the remaining two gases would be, for each of the remaining gases, 1/2 of the total pressure. Partial pressures are absolute pressures or gage pressure plus atmospheric pressure.

Dew Point in Mixtures of Gases

Because dew-point conditions for gases must take into account the partial pressures of component gases at any specific condition of temperature and pressure, the alteration in partial pressures as the individual components go to dew point must be considered and entered into the calculation for dew point potential in mixtures of gases at specific conditions of temperature alteration at pressure conditions.

There should always be calculation of dew point potential for gases and mixtures of gases if the vapor pressures of the gases can cause dew

Table 7-1
Actual Pound-Molal Volumes and Volumes Per Pound of Gases
After Correction for Perfect Gas Law Deviation

Gas	Actual Cubic Feet per Pound-Mol	Deviation from 380 cf/mol	Cubic Feet per Pound
CH_4	378	.994	23.565
C_2H_6	374.5	.985	12.455
C_2H_4	376.2	.990	13.412
C_3H_8	368.8	.970	8.365
C_3H_6	378.9	.997	9.007
C_4H_{10}	367.4	.966	6.321
C_4H_8	379	.997	6.756
C_5H_{12}	378.9	.997	5.252
C_5H_{10}	378.7	.996	5.400
C_6H_{14}	378.9	.997	4.398
C_6H_{12}	----	----	----
C_2H_2	373.5	.982	14.334
NH_3	373.2	.982	21.914
CH_3OH	378.7	.996	11.820
C_2H_5OH	378.7	.996	8.221
H_2S	374.1	.984	10.979
SO_2	369.6	.972	5.770
H_2O	378.6	.996	21.017
Air	378.4	.995	13.083
N_2	376.5	.990	13.443
O_2	378.2	.995	11.819
CO	378.3	.995	13.506
CO_2	376.2	.990	8.548
H_2	378.4	.995	187.723

Note: Data are taken from American Gas Association table of combustion-constants and, while opinion as to the actual volume of a pound-mol can be said to vary, AGA's procedure is thought to be sufficiently accurate.

point to exist at known conditions of absolute pressure and temperature. Neglect of this factor can be the source of considerable difficulty with two-phase flow where two-phase flow should not exist in gas lines as well as severe interference with the operation of burners.

Calculation is not required if the gases are nitrogen, oxygen, hydrogen, methane, ethane and ethylene unless pressures are unusually high or temperatures are unusually low. But natural gases, process gases and gas streams which contain very low mol-percentages of water vapor, such as acid gases or sweetened hydrocarbon gases which have passed through an MEA system, must be considered as suspect. The presence of water vapor can present the hazard of freezing with badly plugged or burst lines resulting.

Dew-point calculation can be quite simple if the mol-percentages of the components of a gas stream are known with reasonable accuracy and if suitable data for vapor pressures are available. Excellent references for these data are *Engineering Data Book*, published by the Natural Gasoline Supply Men's Association, and the *Data Book on Hydrocarbons* by J. B. Maxwell (Van Nostrand).

Vapor pressures are absolute pressures (gage pressure plus atmospheric pressure) at temperatures. Mol-percentages of the components of the gases times the total pressure will determine the partial pressure (absolute) for the components. From the partial pressures, the dew-point temperatures can be established for all the components. As the separate components go to dew point, the partial pressures of the remaining gaseous components are altered and dew-point calculation must then be a step-by-step process.

The volume of gases in transit in a line and at fairly constant pressure can change because of a number of phenomena such as a drop in volume due to a dew-point condition within the line, a drop in volume due to decrease in gas temperature or increase in volume due to rise in temperature. If the entering volume is based on pound-molal calculation using either 379.4271 cu. ft./pound-mol or the suggested 380 cu. ft/pound-mol and if the calculation is to be very accurate, deviation from the perfect gas law should be taken into account. In a perfect gas, the volume of 1 pound-mol is 379.4271 cu. ft. at standard conditions of temperature and pressure. Because of gas law deviation, the molal volumes for some gases are difficult to determine.

Gas Temperature Change in Lines

Temperature changes within the line, as the gases flow, depend on a number of factors such as the exposure of the line to weather conditions, the state of flow within the line (i.e., turbulent or laminar flow), and the area of the line which is exposed to heat loss. A fair basis for estimating line heat loss is to presume that the loss can be based on a temperature differential basis with a minimum of 3 Btu/sq. ft./hr./°F difference and a maximum of 10 Btu/sq. ft./hr./°F difference, according to wind and rain action on the exposed pipe. The effect of cooling of warm or hot gases at initial entry to a line is quite great and relatively abrupt due to sensible heat loss to the metal or structure of the line which can be calculated.

Gas Flow Inertial Factors

A critical factor in thoroughly understanding the flow characteristics of gases is the potential energy of the gas flow as it is confined within a line at constant or relatively constant velocity or as it is expanded to larger volume. Inertial energy results from the mass movement of the gas and causes some misunderstanding. Common understanding of the term inertia presumes resistance to initiation of movement from a static condition or resistance to acceleration of movement. Inertia is accurately defined as the tendency of a physical body to remain in unchanged condition either in a state of uniform motion if moving or at rest if resting. Thus, due to inertial functions, energy is required to produce initial movement and acceleration of a physical mass. Once the mass has made the initial movement and acceleration, it has a quantity of energy equal to that which produced the initial movement and acceleration.

In flow of gases at entry to and through pipes, energy as pressure drop is required for initial acceleration of the gases into the line. As the gas flows within the line, there is energy loss due to friction. Pressure drop is the energy source, and it becomes greater than that for the initial acceleration to the line for flow of a stated volume of gas through a line of any significant length.

For gas lines of known internal diameter, where the entering and terminal pressures are known, it is possible to calculate the volume of flow through the line by use of the Weymouth formula which is

$$Q_s = 443.45 \, (T_s/P_s) \, (d^{2 \cdot 667})$$

$$\left((P_1{}^2 - P_2{}^2)/_{LST} \right)^{1/2}$$

where:

Q_s = Gas flow in scf/day
d = Internal diameter of pipe, in.
P_1 = Initial pressure, lb./sq. in., absolute
P_2 = Final pressure, lb./sq. in., absolute
L = Length of line in miles
S = Specific gravity of gas
T = Absolute temperature of flowing gas
T_s = Standard absolute temperature (60 + 460)
P_s = Standard pressure (14.7 psia)

There are three states of pressure within a pipeline which are of interest. The first is the static pressure in the line as the gas flows, or the gage pressure in the line. The second is the velocity pressure as the gas flows. The third is the total pressure, which is the static pressure plus the velocity pressure or velocity head. Therefore, the velocity pressure is the total pressure minus the static pressure. Velocity pressure is the potential pressure head due to the velocity at which the gas is moving; this also is impact pressure. However, velocity head does exist and is measurable where the flowing gas is not confined within a pipeline as in the case of a jet of gas in discharge from gage pressure to the atmosphere.

Velocity pressure or velocity head is measured with a pressure sampling port or tube which is oriented at 180° to the direction of gas flow so that the flow "impacts" on the port or tube opening. In gas lines where the pressure within the line is greater than atmospheric, velocity head measurement is taken with a manometer by differential pressure between static pressure in the line and velocity pressure plus static pressure. Pitot tubes are common for such pressure measurement, in which case there is very small interference with flow due to insertion of the pitot.

Flow Calculation

Calculation for fluid flow can be made through the following formulas:

Velocity head (h) in feet of flowing fluid = $V^2/2g$
Velocity (V) = $\sqrt{(2gh)}$
Velocity head to Velocity = $18.3 \sqrt{(P_y/d)}$
Critical (Sonic) Velocity in gases = $\sqrt{[32.17 \, (R)}$ $(1543/M.W.) \, C_p/C_v]$ where $g = 32.17$
h = Velocity head in feet of flowing fluid
V = Velocity in ft./sec.
d = lbs. cu. ft.
R = Degrees rankine
$M.W.$ = Molecular weight
C_p/C_v = Ratio of Specific Heats
weight/cubic foot of 28.97 M.W. gas (std. cond.) = .0763.

The formula data provided is for fluid flow but fluids vary in their characteristics in that gas (a fluid) is compressible but that liquids (also fluids) are not compressible except to very small degrees. Therefore, in the study of liquid flow there is no need for pressure correction of density or weight per cubic foot of the flowing liquid at ordinary pressures. There is a need for temperature correction of density or weight at the flowing condition for liquids.

In the study of flow conditions in gases there must be density or weight/cu. ft. correction for both pressure and temperature with the correction made in keeping with the following formulation:

weight/cubic foot = $0.0763 \, (M.W./28.97)$

$$(P+14.7/14.7) \, (460$$

$$+60/T + 460)$$

where:

$M.W.$ = Molecular weight
P = Gage pressure at flowing condition
T = Temperature at flowing condition

A normal point for insertion of velocity-head measurement in pipes should be approximately 50 pipe diameters downstream from elbows, valves or other sources of flow disturbance. Flow in cross-sectional areas of the pipe will vary according to whether the flow is in the streamline state, typical of low-line velocity, or in the turbulent flow state, typical of greater line velocity, with greater difference present in streamline flow. There is always appreciable difference in velocity in the cross-sectional areas. If the venturi is located at the center of the pipe, the velocity-head indication will be highest but greater than the average velocity condition in the pipe. Superior accuracy is possible if the venturi can be moved radially from the center of the pipe to points near the inner surface to permit calculation of average velocity.

Velocity Head Energy

As an excellent example of the significance of velocity head consider a case in which air is being delivered into a plenum or wind box at 100 ft./sec. when the static pressure in the plenum or wind box is 2.00-in. W.C. as designed. The velocity-head pressure of air at 100 ft./sec. is quite close to 2.25-in. W.C. As the entering air meets the wall of the wind box, after entry and release from the entering duct, a portion of the velocity-head pressure is expressed as impact pressure to approximately double the static pressure in the area of the impact. Thus, in one area of the wind box, the static pressure can be substantially 4.00-in. W.C. while in areas near the entry of air the pressure is close to the design condition of 2.00-in. W.C. Air flowing from the plenum or wind box in the 4.00-in. W.C. pressure zone would be (in volume) approximately 1.415 times as great as the volume across an equal area in the 2.00-in. W.C. pressure

area. There is very serious upset in air delivery from the plenum because of the velocity head of the entering air. If equal air delivery from the wind box or plenum is required in all discharge areas, there must be a means for dissipation of the velocity-head energy at entry so that the velocity energy does not upset the state of flow from the plenum.

Lack of uniform flow from a plenum is very frequently observed in applications of forced draft for burner operation or in split flow of a process fluid or in flow from a manifold.

Where only a single fluid is to flow within a pipe or duct, there is no reason for consideration of the state of homogeneity as the fluid flows. A state of homogeneity of a mixture of two fluids which separately enter a pipe or duct can be of utmost significance. The theory that when flow within a pipe or duct is in the turbulent range a homogeneous mixture will exist after flow through a stated length of pipe or duct is simply not true as has clearly been shown in numerous cases.

Any postulation to the effect that a state of turbulent flow in pipes or ducts is *not* capable of creating a state of homogeneous mixture in fluid flow deviates greatly from present day theory and academic teaching. However, process experience over the years will teach with certainty that according to how the separate fluids are introduced to a common pipe or duct for combined flow there may or may not be creation of a condition of homogeneous mixture of the separate fluids in turbulent flow over very significant flow distances. This is clearly shown in a master's thesis (Bimal C. Narayan, University of Tulsa, 1971) where tiny variations in the supply pressures for the separate gases as they entered the common duct for combined movement at Reynold's numbers exceeding 50,000 for hundreds of pipe diameters produced wide fluctuations in the condition of mixture. Alteration of mixture condition went from best to worst cyclically at intervals of approximately 0.10 sec. There are actually "slugs" of the separate gases moving along the pipe. Note that in Narayan's pipe for combined flow there were several ells and tees.

Narayan's findings show a need for better definition of a state of turbulent flow. It is reasonably postulated that there is turbulent flow when flow velocity is essentially unchanged in a wall-to-wall traverse of a pipe, and turbulent flow is not a condition of wild gyration in the course of movement but is a condition of rhythmic pressure alteration within the body of the confined fluid as it flows linearly within the tube or duct. Lack of gyration in turbulence explains the lack of abrupt increase in pressure drop in transition from laminar to turbulent flow.

The function of resonance which is not uncommonly found in gaseous flow at significant velocity (in ducts particularly) can result from a condition in which pressure variations due to turbulence occur at a frequency which, in some manner, matches the resonant frequency characteristics of the confining flow passageway. Here velocity and viscosity govern with temperature a factor in each; thus resonance can be cancelled by appropriate temperature change if need be.

It can be suggested, then, that turbulent flow may well be defined as vibratory flow with the amplitude of vibration governed by the condition of energy which causes the vibration. The energy is due to two factors: linear velocity and viscosity at flow conditions of temperature; thus the term *Reynolds number* is used in fluid flow. In gases the effect of temperature increase is both increase of flow velocity and increase in viscosity. In liquids there is lesser increase in velocity but *decrease* in viscosity. A reference for Reynolds number derivation is found on pages 5-15, Perry's *Chemical Engineers'* Handbook, 4th Edition (McGraw-Hill). In the case of proprietary (and thus unreported) research in which a pressure transducer was inserted just through the wall of a tube for flowing gases at controllable velocity and constant temperature, no internal pressure excursions were found in laminar flow conditions. But immediately at the onset of turbulent flow there were cyclic variations in pressure; also as flow velocity was increased the cyclic pressure variations persisted at the same frequency but at greater amplitude.

Repeated experience in consultation has confirmed that failure of turbulent flow to create homogeneity of fluid mixture can and does lead to process failure to greater or lesser degree and at times quite seriously whether the fluids be gases or liquids. It is not to be questioned that a condition of turbulent flow makes better use of pipe or duct flow area, but reliance on turbulent flow for creation of homogeneity of mixture can produce serious errors in process.

Energy Required for Mixture

If, as two fluids come together, there is not enough inertial energy expressed to create a state of homogeneity in the mixture of the fluids, there is reason to believe that a state of even reasonable homogeneity cannot exist in the absence of lengthy mechanical mixing.

Mixture between two fluids occurs because of differential velocities as they meet. Within the pipe or duct, the two fluids are moving at identical velocities. It is reasonable to say that in such a case there can be no state of homogeneity within the pipe or duct. This has been shown in the movement of gas through more than 100 mi. of pipeline that the flow within the line was well within the turbulent range. It has also been clearly shown in the movement of liquids in pipes or ducts.

In process work, where two fluids are combined for production of useful products and where a state of reaction between the fluids is a function of the homogeneity of the mixture or the degree with which mixture is obtained, the state of mixture or of homogeneity is very significant. Neglecting this factor can result in process failure to greater or lesser degree.

Steam reforming of hydrocarbons for hydrogen production involves process considerations such that homogeneity of a mixture of steam and hydrocarbon at entry to the area of the catalyst where there is application of heat to promote the reactions can be extremely significant.

Beneficial effects of steps to obtain a more homogeneous mixture of steam and hydrocarbon at entry to the catalyst area are

1. Sharp reduction of fuel fired per pound of hydrogen produced
2. Sharp reduction in volume of steam demanded for the reaction
3. Elimination of carbon deposition on the catalyst
4. Better hydrocarbon conversion.

These benefits occur because as the reactive molecules reach a state where reaction can occur the conditions of reaction will depend largely on the relative proximity of reactive molecules.

Reaction According to Molecular Proximity

It follows then that the molecular proximity in a mixture of fluids, whether they be gaseous or liquid, depends on the homogeneity of the mixture as the mixture is made and immediately at the point where the fluids come together. Again, mixture in fluids occurs because of differential velocity and if the differential velocity for homogeneity does not exist as the fluids come together the state of mixture in normal conditions is always questionable. Complete evidence of this is to be found in the case of a single transmission line for separate hydrocarbons in liquid phase. The different hydrocarbons are separated by short water "pads" for hundreds of miles of turbulent flow in the pipeline without any mixture of the separate hydrocarbons as they travel. In this case, one liquid is water while the other is hydrocarbon. These are not miscible but are capable of emulsification. In view of the state of Reynolds numbers in the average transport pipeline, there is ample opportunity for emulsification to occur—but it does not occur to any appreciable degree.

Further evidence of failure of line turbulence to produce homogeneous mixtures of miscible gases is to be found in a case where two gas streams were combined at a point in a gas line for travel at 150 ft/sec. and at 300 psig pressure for more than 100 mi. and through two compressor stations to emerge unmixed at the end of the line. This condition, authenticated through repeated tests, is significant because, where two or more

gases are combined for a particular chemical reaction, the desired reactions cannot occur if the gases are not homogeneously mixed because of lack of suitable proximity of reactive molecules at the proper time.

Fluid Flow Factors

Complete understanding of the flow of fluids is, perhaps, one of the most critical requirements for dealing with burners, with processes, with process design or fluid transport.

The term fluid describes a substance which will with complete uniformity fill all areas and spaces within its container without any expression of external energy to cause the uniform filling.

According to this definition, both gases and liquids are considered as fluids, but there is further difference between them. Gases are readily compressible but liquids are not, except for micrometric changes with very high pressure. In the usual engineering sense, liquids are considered incompressible. Therefore, in the usual engineering application the flow characteristics of gases and liquids must be considered separately, despite the fact that both are fluids.

Both gases and liquids have characteristic viscosities which are measurable. The viscosities of gases increase as the temperature rises but the viscosities of liquids decrease as temperature rises. Viscosity may be largely defined as resistance to flow in the case of a fluid. The viscosities of gases are so very small as to be inconsequential in most plant operations. However, the viscosities of liquids are most significant because they are so much greater. Neglect of viscosity in liquid flow over any distance can be a serious error.

Viscosity Standards

Viscosity is measured by establishing flow through a relatively long capillary tube where the internal resistance of the fluid being checked can exercise influence on the quantity of flow through the capillary tube at standard conditions of pressure and temperature. The viscosity of the fluid is measured against the time required for a standard

Table 7-2
Representative Viscosities of Gases and Liquids

Gas	Temp. °F	Viscosity, Micropoises	Liquid	Temp. °F	Viscosity, Centipoises
Air	64	183	Glycerine	68	1486
Air	104	190	Glycerine	86	625
Hydrogen	32	83	No.6 Fuel Oil	140	220
Hydrogen	68	87	No.6 Fuel Oil	188	76
Methane	32	102	Light Lube	59	115
Methane	66	108	Light Lube	98	36
Oxygen	32	190	Octane	59	0.583
Oxygen	68	202	Octane	66	0.551

volume of the fluid to flow at standard conditions. In the United States, the standard viscosity systems for liquids in petroleum products are as Seconds Saybolt Universal (SSU); for the heavier oils, the system is Seconds Saybolt Furol (SSF). Some representative viscosities of gases and liquids are given in Table 7-2.

In chemical engineering, absolute or dynamic viscosity is generally defined as the resistance of fluids to the relative motion of their parts. In this system, the unit of viscosity is the poise, after Poiseuille. The poise is too large a unit for general use and the centipoise (poise/100) is usually more convenient. The viscosity of water at 68.4° F is 1 centipoise. This system is being used more and more widely in the petroleum industries.

Much work has been done toward establishing viscosity systems in Europe and in other parts of the world where viscosity is of interest; there are at least four additional recognized viscosity standards: Redwood, Redwood Admiralty, Engler and Barbey.

It is frequently desirable to convert from one American system to one of the other two. Table 7-3 is provided for this purpose.

In the flow of liquids across an orifice or through a piping system where viscosity is un-changed, there is constant increase in velocity with an increase in pressure drop. The relationship of flow velocity to pressure drop is not fixed on changing temperature because the velocity is governed by the state of viscosity which is governed by temperature. Since velocity of flow through a fixed cross-sectional area determines flow quantity, at pressure drop the quantity is also governed by viscosity factors.

Problems associated with movement of viscous fluids involve the state of viscosity as pumped, the rate of flow and relative pump capacity as well as pressure drop and power consumption. For these factors, there is no easy and ready solution except that it is at once evident that velocity of flow and viscosity as pumped must both be kept low.

It is interesting that the viscosity at 31 SSU is the viscosity of water at 68.4° F. While the effect of viscosity is quite significant, there is no correlation of viscosity with pressure drop if constant flow velocity (quantity) is maintained.

In fuel oils (No. 6 is typical) the viscosity as pumped is normally close to 237 SSU. If significant line pressure drop is to be avoided, the line velocity in pumping should not greatly exceed 3.00 ft./sec. and is best in the order of 2.00-2.50

Table 7-3
Viscosity Conversion Table

(The following table will give a comparison of various viscosity ratings so that if the viscosity is given in terms other than Saybolt Universal, it can be translated quickly by following horizontally to the Saybolt Universal column.)

Kinematic Viscosity Centipoises K	Seconds Saybolt Universal	Seconds Saybolt Furol	Seconds Redwood	Seconds Redwood Admiralty	Degrees Engler	Degrees Barbey
1.00	31		29		1.00	6200
2.56	35		32.1		1.16	2420
4.30	40		36.2	5.10	1.31	1440
5.90	45		40.3	5.52	1.46	1050
7.40	50		44.3	5.83	1.58	838
8.83	55		48.5	6.35	1.73	702
10.20	60		52.3	6.77	1.88	618
11.53	65		56.7	7.17	2.03	538
12.83	70	12.95	60.9	7.60	2.17	483
14.10	75	13.33	65.0	8.00	2.31	440
15.35	80	13.70	69.2	8.44	2.45	404
16.58	85	14.10	73.3	8.86	2.59	374
17.80	90	14.44	77.6	9.30	2.73	348
19.00	95	14.85	81.5	9.70	2.88	326
20.20	100	15.24	85.6	10.12	3.02	307
31.80	150	19.3	128	14.48	4.48	195
43.10	200	23.5	170	18.90	5.92	144
54.30	250	28.0	212	23.45	7.35	114
65.40	300	32.5	254	28.0	8.79	95
76.50	350	35.1	296	32.5	10.25	81
87.60	400	41.9	338	37.1	11.70	70.8
98.60	450	46.8	381	41.7	13.15	62.9
110	500	51.6	423	46.2	14.60	56.4
121	550	56.6	465	50.8	16.05	51.3
132	600	61.4	508	55.4	17.50	47.0
143	650	66.2	550	60.1	19.00	43.4
154	700	71.1	592	64.6	20.45	40.3
165	750	76.0	635	69.2	21.90	37.6
176	,800	81.0	677	73.8	23.35	35.2
187	850	86.0	719	78.4	24.80	33.2
198	900	91.0	762	83.0	26.30	31.3
209	950	95.8	804	87.6	27.70	29.7
220	1000	100.7	846	92.2	29.20	28.2
330	1500	150	1270	138.2	43.80	18.7
440	2000	200	1690	184.2	58.40	14.1
550	2500	250	2120	230	73.00	11.3
660	3000	300	2540	276	87.60	9.4
770	3500	350	2960	322	100.20	8.05
880	4000	400	3380	368	117.00	7.05
990	4500	450	3810	414	131.50	6.26
1100	5000	500	4230	461	146.00	5.64
1210	5500	550	4650	507	160.50	5.13
1320	6000	600	5080	553	175.00	4.70
1430	6500	650	5500	559	190.00	4.34
1540	7000	700	5920	645	204.50	4.03
1650	7500	750	6350	691	219.00	3.76
1760	8000	800	6770	737	233.50	3.52
1870	8500	850	7190	783	248.00	3.32
1980	9000	900	7620	829	263.00	3.13
2090	9500	950	8040	875	277.00	2.97
2200	10000	1000	8460	921	292.00	2.82

The viscosity is often expressed in terms of viscosimeters other than the Saybolt Universal. The formulas for the various viscosimeters are as follows:

Redwood $\quad$ K $\quad$ .261 - $\dfrac{188}{1}$ $\quad$ (British) $\qquad$ Saybolt Universal $\quad$ K = .22 1 - $\dfrac{180}{1}$ $\quad$ (American)

Redwood Admiralty $\quad$ K $\quad$ 2.396 - $\dfrac{40.3}{1}$ $\quad$ (British) $\qquad$ Saybolt Furol $\quad$ K = 2.2 1 - $\dfrac{203}{1}$ $\quad$ (American)

$\qquad\qquad\qquad\qquad\qquad\qquad\qquad\qquad\qquad$ Engler $\quad$ K = .147 1- $\dfrac{374}{1}$ $\quad$ (German)

$\qquad\qquad\qquad\qquad\qquad$ l = Engler Degress X 51 3

The Barbey measures the quantity of flow per hour under constant head instead of the time for a definite quantity under varying head as do the others. The Saybolt Furol and Redwood Admiralty are especially designed for measuring the more viscous oils and give a reading in seconds approximately one-tenth of that given for the same oil by the Saybolt Universal and Redwood respectively. If viscosity is given at any two temperatures, the viscosity at any other temperature can be obtained by plotting the viscosity against temperature in degrees Fahrenheit on special cross section paper. The points for a given oil lie in a straight line against temperature in degrees Fahrenheit on special cross section paper. The points for a given oil lie in a straight line.

ft./sec. As the line fouls, the pressure drop across a given length of line will increase. If the pump is capable of a greater discharge pressure, there is a correction for the increased pressure drop but at the expense of greater power cost for pumping.

With some oils there is very marked increase in viscosity as there is loss of temperature due to inadequate insulation. As line viscosity rises, there is marked increase in pressure drop within areas downstream of the point of heat loss. Fuel-oil system insulation excellence is fully as important as that of any insulation within the plant.

Varying Flow States

Because liquid is essentially incompressible, the shape of a stream flowing from an orifice is not necessarily predictable. Since there is no compression, the liquid does not expand at release from pressure through the orifice. In a precisely machined orifice, the stream of liquid may assume the appearance of a solid rod having a cross-sectional area equal to the area of the orifice times the orifice coefficient. Thus, the stream diameter is less than the orifice diameter if the rod-like flow exists. In other orifices such as a poorly machined long-channel orifice, energy factors may cause the liquid flow to "broom-tail" and assume the appearance of a cone of very coarse spray (large drops) at a low included angle. In any case, the velocity at the least diameter in flow across the orifice and before the spray is created is $V = \sqrt{(2gh)}$ where V is velocity; $2g$ is 2 (32.17) and h is head in feet of fluid. The h factor must include the approach energy of the liquid which is $V^2/2g$.

Through an orifice or at entry to piping, the contour over which the liquid flows as it enters the smaller passage of the inside diameter has a marked effect on the quantity of flow at a specific head or pressure drop. If the orifice is sharp edged, the flow coefficient is in the order of 0.61 unless (due to imperfections) the flow becomes broom-tailed, in which case the flow coefficient becomes 0.82. This state can exist only with heads of 40 ft. or less, which for water will be approximately 17.50 psig. With heads of more than 40 ft., the flow is rodlike and the orifice coefficient is 0.61.

If the approach to the orifice is rounded so that the radius of the rounding is as much as 10% of the orifice diameter or the round entrance to a pipe, the flow coefficient becomes 0.85 as a fixed factor. If the entrance to the orifice is machined as a paraboloid curve with the flat part of the curve fairing into the inside diameter of the orifice, the flow coefficient may be increased to in excess of 0.95. Thus, through proper care for the nature of the orifice or piping entrance the pressure drop at entry for a stated quantity of flow can be very markedly controlled. Overall pressure drop can be controlled and a system can deliver a greater quantity of liquid within the limits of overall pressure drop.

Fuel Oil Pressure Drop

The ideal system for delivering liquid from a supply source to a point of use will have no elbows, tees, valves or fittings, since these all add to the effective line length and increase the overall pressure drop. Data are readily available for precise effect of fittings in increasing the effective length of the line if precision is required. Where there are no globe valves in the line, a very good basis for estimation is to multiply the actual linear distance by 1.30 for the effective distance and base linear pressure drop calculation on the effective distance the liquid must travel in lines from 1 through 6 in. In the normal line there will be small error with the procedure.

Two-Phase Flow Considerations

Due to high vapor pressure or low line pressure where the liquid being pumped carries gases in solution, it is always possible for vapor to be present within the line, causing erratic flow conditions because of two-phase flow. The usual corrective measures include elevation of line pressure or a drop in flowing temperature. It is quite common for such conditions to exist at the upstream or suction side of pumps. The symptoms of such a condition may be erratic pressure, chattering or noisy pump operation, interruption of flow or shock discharge of gas along with liquid. When there is two-phase flow at a point of discharge or at a point of regulation such as a valve, the slugs of liquid are moving at velocities which may be very high and considerable damage may result from the high velocity energy of the slugs of liquid.

Valve Action in Liquid Transport

In any line transporting liquid where there are valves capable of stopping the flow, the valves should be designed for slow rather than abrupt closure. In such a line, when a valve is too abruptly closed (even in lines where the flowing velocity is low) a pressure wave is developed due to the flow energy of the fluid up to the point where the closure is made. A hammering effect is produced as a result of the shock pressure. The pressure is not concentrated at the valve but damage to the valve or the immediate area is probably due to the fact that the pressure wave strikes first in this area and is partially spent in expansion of the line in movement at from 1,500 ft./sec. to more than 3,000 ft./sec. opposite to the normal flow direction.

Serious damage is possible if the hammering is great enough. Slow closing valves have been found to be a most satisfactory means for avoiding the hammer-induced increase in internal pressure which is greater in lines of small internal diameter than in larger lines. The pressure can be as great as 60 plf of interrupted velocity in smaller lines and approximately 40-50 plf in larger lines. When as much as 300 lbs. adds to the normal line pressure, the line and its fittings may be stressed to the bursting point. Also, the speed of the pressure wave adds to the hazard at a tee or an elbow.

When liquid is discharged, as from an orifice or a pipe into a larger chamber such as a tank, a bubble tower or any vessel, the inertial energy of the liquid stream at some velocity should be taken into account in point of the upset in level or flow condition which may result. In many cases, there may be need for baffling or some means for distributing or redirecting the flow to avoid the upset. In this sense, inertia denotes energy of movement and this factor can, at times, seriously interfere with an effect or condition which may be either desired or required.

In measuring liquid flow as in a line there is always the problem of pressure drop due to insertion of the means for measurement. Typical of such devices are the orifice meter or a positive-displacement meter. With either of these devices, the pressure drop is quite significant. An alternative means for liquid-volume measurement is a well-designed and calibrated venturi meter which is quite reasonably accurate in liquid measurement at markedly less pressure drop. The flow coefficient of the venturi meter is given variously as from 0.95 to 0.99. Such loss of static head as is noted is said to be due to internal energy loss where there is careful machining of the meter, as would be the case with such a meter which is calibrated for service.

One of the most completely comprehensive and accurate works dealing with the flow of liquids is to be found in the *Engineering Data Book*, published by the Natural Gasoline Supply Men's Association, Tulsa, Oklahoma.

Compressible Fluid Flow Characteristics

Flow of gases, whether at an orifice or in passage through a line, is quite different than the flow of liquids (despite the fact that both are fluids) because of very great difference in viscosities, because gases are compressible, because there is very great difference in the mass per cubic foot, and because the ratio of specific heats enters gaseous flow calculations. Because of lack of compressibility in liquid flow, there is an increase in velocity as long as there is an increase in pressure drop when viscosity remains constant.

In gaseous flow, there is an increase in flow velocity with an increase in pressure drop only until the absolute pressure upstream of the cause for the pressure drop becomes approximately twice the absolute pressure downstream. When this state of pressures is reached, the flow velocity becomes critical or the velocity of sound is reached in that particular gas at its flowing temperature. There can be no increase in flow velocity. Thus, when the pressure upstream in discharge to atmosphere at sea level reaches 14.696 psig or 29.392 psia when the absolute pressure of the atmosphere

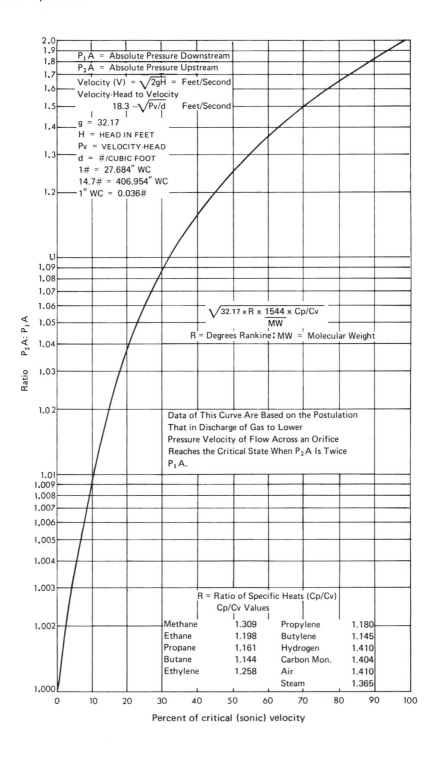

Figure 7-1. Critical flow velocity for gases.

is 14.696 psia, critical velocity will exist at the point of maximum acceleration due to upstream pressure. The empirical 2: 1 absolute pressure ratio for creation of sonic velocity is relative since the pressure required is slightly less according to the ratio of specific heats for the particular gas as it flows. It is possible to calculate critical velocity for any gas at any temperature through use of the following formula (see Figure 7-1):

$$\text{Sonic Velocity} = \sqrt{[32.17 \ (R) \ (1544/MW)} \ (C_p/C_v] \text{, in ft./sec.}$$

where:

R = Rankine Temperature of Gas (460 + °F)

MW = Molecular weight

C_p/C_v = Ratio of specific heats

From the formula, the factors 32.17 (g), molecular weight and Cp/Cv are fixed. Temperature is the only variable. Thus, sonic velocity must be defined at the observed temperature level. The absolute pressure upstream of an orifice which, in discharge to atmosphere, is capable of creating critical flow or sonic velocity at the orifice, is also correlated with the Cp/Cv of the gas and can be calculated through use of the following formula:

$$P_2 = P_1/(2/1 + R)^{(R/R - 1)}$$

P_2 = Upstream pressure, Absolute

P_1 = Downstream pressure, Absolute

R = Ratio of Specific Heats, (C_p/C_v)

Specific Heat Ratio Change

There is a decrease in the ratio of specific heats as the temperature rises but these factors are usually based on standard conditions of temperature (60° F and 14.696 psia). See Table 7-4. As the absolute pressure upstream of the orifice becomes twice the absolute pressure downstream of

Table 7-4

Absolute Pressure Upstream of an Orifice Required to Create Critical (Sonic) Velocity in Flow across the Orifice when P_1 = 14.7 psia (based on 60°F.)

Gas	Absolute Pressure	Gage Pressure
Air–68F-824F	27.65	12.95
Air–68F-1472F	27.55	12.85
Ammonia 73F-212F	27.15	12.45
Carbon dioxide 52F-417F	26.85	12.15
Carbon monoxide 79F-338Fz	27.75	13.05
Hydrogen 70F-212F	27.95	13.25
Hydrogen sulfide 68F-403F	27.10	12.40
Methane 64F-406F	27.00	12.30
Ethane 60F	26.00	11.30
Propane 60F	25.80	11.10
Butane 60F	25.70	11.00
Pentane 60F	25.30	10.60
Ethylene 60F	26.50	11.80
Propylene 60F	25.95	11.25
Butylene 60F	25.60	10.90
Water vapor 32F	26.65	11.95
Water vapor 212F	27.25	12.55
Water vapor 356F	26.90	12.20

the orifice, critical velocity exists and a number of standard cubic flow units at that velocity exists in any time period. If the absolute pressure downstream of the orifice is decreased so that the ratio of absolute pressures upstream and downstream exceeds the 2: 1 ratio, there is no change in the flow of gas across the orifice because the flow is at critical velocity prior to the drop in the downstream pressure. There can be no further velocity increase at the same temperature level. If, however, the drop in downstream pressure is accompanied by increased gas temperature, there is an increase in flow velocity because the critical velocity is increased as the temperature rises, but the temperature correction for flow in standard cubic feet across the orifice will cause the flow to be reduced.

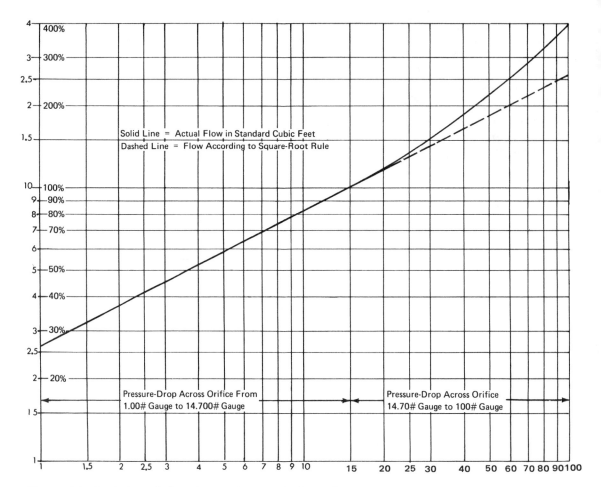

Figure 7-2. Deviation of flow in standard cubic feet of gas across an orifice from the square root relationship for flow when the pressure upstream of the orifice is greater than the pressure which can cause critical velocity of flow to exist.

It becomes evident that in the flow of gases, any velocity figure cannot be accepted as valid until the temperature level at which the velocity occurs is stated. The formula for use in calculating orifice area for gas temperatures other than 60° F is:

$$\sqrt{[(T + 460)/(60 + 460)]}$$

where T is flowing temperature,°F.

Flowing Temperature Correction

The net flow across an orifice for a change in temperature of the gas can be calculated with the formula:

$$\sqrt{[(T\text{-}1+460)/(T\text{-}2+460)]}$$

where:

T-1 = Initial temperature,°F

T-2 = New temperature,°F

In conditions up to the pressure capable of creating critical velocity in flow across an orifice, the flow across the orifice varies as the square root of the pressure drop in the passage of standard cubic feet. As the pressure upstream of the orifice is increased beyond that pressure which can cause critical velocity to occur, there is an increase in flow of standard cubic feet because the mass of gas flowing at the critical velocity is increased but the flow in standard cubic feet is greater than the square root of the pressure drop would indicate.

If we assume that critical velocity exists when the upstream pressure is 14.7 psig and if we increase the pressure drop to 30 psig, the square root of the ratio of 30.0/14.7 is 1.43. Thus, if flow followed the square root function, the flow would be 1.43 greater than the flow at 14.7 psig. But after the pressure for critical velocity is exceeded, correction for flow is on the basis of mass as based on relative absolute pressures. In this case, the mass correction is 44.7 psig (30 + 14.7) divided by 29.4 psig (14.7 + 14.7) equals 1.52. Thus, the flow in standard cubic feet is greater than the square root would indicate. The excess flow is the ratio of 1.52/ 1.43 is 1.06. At 50 psig pressure drop, the flow deviation from the square-root relationship is greater yet—1.19. As the pressure drop is further increased over 50 psig, the deviation becomes even greater. Deviation from the square-root relationship is calculable through the formula:

$$\frac{(P_2 + 14.7) / (P_1 + 14.7)}{\sqrt{(P_2 / P_1)}}$$

where:

P_1 = 14.7 pounds pressure drop across an orifice, psig.

P_2 = Measured pressure drop across orifice, psig.

When the ratio as per the formula equals or exceeds unity, the velocity across the orifice is critical or sonic and the degree of deviation will be revealed as the ratio exceeds 1.00 because of the absolute pressure correction, which is linear. This

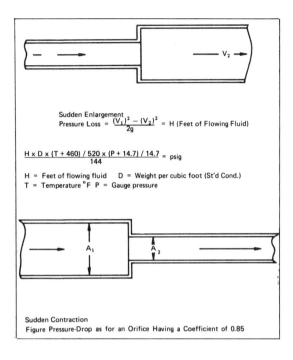

Sudden Enlargement
Pressure Loss = $\frac{(V_1)^2 - (V_2)^2}{2g}$ = H (Feet of Flowing Fluid)

$\frac{H \times D \times (T + 460) / 520 \times (P + 14.7) / 14.7}{144}$ = psig

H = Feet of flowing fluid   D = Weight per cubic foot (St'd Cond.)
T = Temperature °F   P = Gauge pressure

Sudden Contraction
Figure Pressure-Drop as for an Orifice Having a Coefficient of 0.85

Figure 7-3. Pressure loss in change of line size.

is very typical of burner operation discharging to atmosphere. (See Figure 7-2.)

Line Diameter

When gas flowing in a smaller line is abruptly delivered into a larger line as through a bushing or a reducer, there is a pressure loss which is quite close to the difference in the relative velocity heads. (See Figure 7-3). While there is usually some recovery of velocity-head energy, the amount of recovery is hardly predictable. Thus the error in assuming total loss is not significant. As an example, consider 29 MW gas flowing at 200 ft./sec. in 2-in. pipe with abrupt entry to 3-in. pipe where the loss at entry to the 3-in. pipe would be 0.266 psig without absolute pressure correction for the weight per cubic foot of the 29 MW gas as it flows. If the flowing pressure should be 100 psig, the pressure loss would be 2.07 psig. While such losses in static pressure may not necessarily be significant, the loss may be 98% cancelled if

Table 7-5
Capacity of Orifices in Cubic Feet per Hour
Based on 1.0 Coefficient of Discharge (Specific Gravity –.55)

PRESSURE—LBS. PER SQUARE INCH

MTD Size	Diam. Inches	Area Square Inches	1	2	3	4	5	6	7	8	9	10	12	14	15	16	18	20	25	30
80	.0135	.000143	1.7	2.3	2.9	3.4	3.8	4.1	4.5	4.8	5.	5.4	5.8	6.3	6.5	6.7	7.2	7.5	8.4	9.3
79	.0145	.000165	2.0	2.8	3.4	3.8	4.3	4.8	5.2	5.5	5.8	6.2	6.7	7.3	7.5	7.8	8.2	8.7	9.7	10.8
1/64 :	.0156	.00019	2.2	3.2	3.9	4.5	5.0	5.5	6.0	6.3	6.7	7.2	7.8	8.4	8.7	9.	9.2	10.	11.2	12.4
78	.016	.00020	2.4	3.3	4.1	4.7	5.3	5.8	6.2	6.7	7.1	7.5	8.2	8.8	9.2	9.4	10.	10.5	11.8	13.
77	.018	.00025	3.0	4.2	5.1	5.9	6.6	7.2	7.8	8.3	8.8	9.4	10.2	11.	11.4	11.8	12.5	13.2	14.8	16.3
76	.020	.00031	3.7	5.2	6.3	7.3	8.2	9.0	9.7	10.3	11.	11.6	12.7	13.7	14.2	14.6	15.5	16.4	18.3	20
75	.021	.00035	4.1	5.9	7.1	8.3	9.3	10.1	11.	11.7	12.4	13.1	14.3	15.4	16	16.5	17.5	18.5	20.6	23
74	.0225	.00040	4.7	6.7	8.2	9.4	10.6	11.5	12.5	13.3	14.1	15.0	16.4	17.6	18.3	19.	20.	21.	24.	26
73	.024	.00045	5.3	7.5	9.2	10.6	11.8	13.0	14.	15.	15.9	17.0	18.4	19.7	20.6	21.	22.5	24.	27.	29
72	.025	.00049	5.8	8.2	10.0	11.5	13.0	14.1	15.2	16.3	17.3	18.4	20.	22.	22.	23.	25.	26.	29.	32
71	.026	.00053	6.3	8.8	10.8	12.5	14.0	15.3	16.5	17.6	18.7	20.	22	23	24	25	27	28	31	34
70	.028	.00062	7.3	10.4	12.5	14.6	16.4	17.9	19.3	20.6	22	23	25	27	28	29	31	33	37	40
69	.0292	.00067	7.9	11.3	13.6	15.8	17.6	19.3	21	22	24	25	27	29	31	32	34	35	40	44
68	.030	.00075	8.9	12.5	15.3	17.6	19.8	21.6	23	25	26	28	31	33	34	35	37	40	44	49
1/32 :	.0312	.00076	9.0	12.7	15.5	18	20.0	21.9	24	25	27	28.5	31	33	35	36	38	40	45	50
67	.032	.00080	9.5	13.4	16.4	19	21.0	23.0	25	27	28	30	33	35	37	38	40	42	47	52
66	.033	.00086	10.2	14.2	17.6	20	23	25.0	27	29	30	32	35	38	39	40	43	45	50	56
65	.035	.00096	11.3	16.0	19.6	23	25	28	30	32	34	36	39	42	44	45	48	51	56	62
64	.036	.00102	12.1	17.0	20.6	24	27	30	32	34	36	38	42	45	47	48	51	54	60	66
63	.037	.00108	12.7	18	22.0	25	28	31	34	36	38	40	44	47	49	51	54	57	64	70
62	.038	.00113	13.3	19	23	27	30	33	35	38	40	42	46	50	52	53	57	60	66	74
61	.039	.00119	14	20	24	28	31	34	37	40	42	45	49	52	54	56	60	63	70	78
60	.040	.00126	15	21	26	30	33	36	38	42	44	47	53	55	58	59	63	66	74	82
59	.041	.00132	15.6	22	27	31	35	38	41	44	47	50	54	57	60	62	66	70	78	86
58	.042	.00138	16.4	23	28	33	36	40	43	46	49	52	56	61	63	65	69	73	81	90
57	.043	.00145	17.1	24	30	34	38	42	45	48	51	55	59	64	66	68	72	76	85	93
56	.0465	.00170	20.0	28	35	40	45	49	53	57	60	64	69	75	78	80	85	90	100	110
3/64 :	.0469	.00173	20.4	29	35	41	46	50	54	58	61	65	71	76	79	81	86	91	102	112
55	.0520	.00210	25	35	43	50	55	60	65	70	74	79	86	92	96	99	105	111	124	135
54	.0550	.0023	27	38	47	54	61	66	72	77	81	86	94	101	105	108	115	121	136	148
53	.0595	.0028	33	47	57	66	74	81	87	93	99	105	114	123	128	132	140	148	165	181
1/16 :	.0625	.0031	37	52	63	73	82	90	97	103	110	116	127	136	142	146	155	163	183	200
52	.0635	.0032	38	53	65	76	84	92	100	107	113	120	131	141	146	151	160	169	189	206
51	.0670	.0035	41	58	71	83	92	101	109	117	123	131	143	154	160	165	175	184	207	226
50	.070	.0038	45	63	78	90	100	110	119	126	134	143	155	167	174	178	190	200	225	245
49	.073	.0042	50	70	86	99	111	121	131	140	148	158	172	185	192	198	210	222	248	271
48	.076	.0043	51	72	88	101	113	124	134	143	152	161	176	189	196	203	215	227	254	278

Size	No.																					
5/64	:	.0781	.0048	57	80	98	113	127	139	150	160	170	180	196	212	220	226	240	253	283	310
	47	.0785	.0049	58	82	100	116	129	142	153	163	173	184	200	216	224	230	245	258	288	316
	46	.081	.0051	60	85	104	120	135	147	159	170	180	192	208	225	233	240	255	269	300	329
	45	.082	.0053	63	89	108	125	140	153	165	176	187	200	217	234	242	250	265	280	312	342
	44	.086	.0058	69	97	118	137	153	168	181	193	205	218	238	256	265	273	290	306	342	375
	43	.089	.0062	73	103	126	146	163	179	194	207	219	233	254	273	283	292	310	328	366	400
	42	.0935	.0069	82	115	141	163	182	199	215	230	244	259	282	304	316	325	345	364	406	445
3/32	:	.0937	.0069	82	115	141	163	182	199	215	230	244	259	282	304	316	325	345	364	406	445
	41	.096	.0072	85	120	147	170	190	208	225	240	254	270	294	318	329	339	360	380	425	465
	40	.098	.0075	88	125	153	177	198	217	234	250	265	282	307	330	342	354	375	396	442	483
	39	.0995	.0078	92	130	159	184	206	225	244	260	276	293	320	344	356	368	390	411	460	503
	38	.1015	.0081	96	135	165	191	214	234	253	270	286	304	331	358	370	382	405	428	478	522
	37	.104	.0085	100	142	173	200	224	246	265	283	300	318	348	374	388	400	425	449	500	547
	36	.1065	.0090	106	150	183	212	238	260	283	300	318	340	370	396	411	425	450	475	530	580
7/84	:	.1093	.0094	111	157	192	222	248	271	293	312	332	354	385	414	430	443	470	496	555	606
	35	.110	.0095	112	159	194	224	250	275	297	316	336	357	388	419	434	448	475	501	560	612
	34	.111	.0097	115	162	198	228	256	280	303	323	343	364	396	428	444	458	485	511	572	625
	33	.113	.0100	118	167	204	236	264	289	312	333	354	376	409	441	457	471	500	528	590	645
	32	.116	.0106	125	177	216	250	280	306	331	353	385	400	434	467	485	500	530	560	625	685
	31	.120	.0113	133	189	230	267	298	326	355	376	400	425	462	497	526	534	565	596	676	728
1/8	:	.125	.0123	145	205	250	290	325	356	384	410	435	462	503	521	563	580	615	650	725	793
	30	.1285	.0130	153	217	265	307	344	376	405	433	460	490	532	574	595	614	650	686	767	840
	29	.136	.0145	171	242	296	342	383	419	452	482	513	545	594	640	663	685	725	765	838	935
	28	.1405	.0155	183	259	316	367	410	447	485	516	547	582	635	683	709	730	775	818	915	1000
3/64	:	.1406	.0156	184	262	318	368	412	450	488	520	552	588	638	687	714	736	780	823	920	1005
	27	.144	.0163	192	272	332	385	430	470	509	542	576	614	667	718	745	770	815	860	960	1050
	26	.147	.0174	205	290	353	410	460	502	543	580	615	655	712	765	790	820	870	918	1025	1122
	25	.1495	.0175	207	292	357	413	462	505	547	582	620	658	717	770	800	825	875	924	1030	1130
	24	.152	.0181	214	302	370	428	478	522	565	602	640	681	742	797	830	853	905	955	1068	1170
	23	.154	.0186	219	310	380	440	491	538	580	620	657	700	760	820	850	877	912	980	1095	1200
5/32	:	.1562	.0192	226	321	391	443	507	555	600	640	680	721	785	846	879	906	960	1012	1130	1240
	22	.157	.0193	228	322	394	455	510	556	602	642	683	726	790	851	883	910	965	1014	1140	1242
	21	.159	.0198	234	332	405	468	525	572	619	660	700	745	810	872	906	935	995	1043	1170	1278
	20	.161	.0203	240	340	414	480	535	586	634	676	718	763	830	894	928	960	1015	1070	1200	1310
	19	.166	.0216	255	361	440	510	570	625	674	720	764	814	882	950	987	1020	1080	1140	1275	1390
	18	.1695	.0226	267	368	460	534	595	654	705	752	800	850	925	995	1030	1065	1130	1190	1330	1457
11/84	:	.1719	.0232	274	388	473	548	614	670	725	772	820	874	950	1020	1060	1093	1160	1223	1370	1495
	17	.175	.0235	278	392	480	555	620	678	734	782	830	885	961	1033	1075	1109	1175	1240	1385	1520
	16	.177	.0246	290	412	502	580	650	710	768	820	870	925	1005	1082	1123	1160	1230	1292	1450	1590
	15	.180	.0254	300	445	518	600	670	735	792	845	900	955	1040	1120	1160	1200	1270	1340	1500	1640
	14	.182	.0260	307	435	530	615	687	750	810	865	920	980	1062	1142	1190	1225	1300	1360	1530	1680
	13	.185	.0269	318	450	548	635	710	776	838	895	950	1010	1100	1182	1230	1268	1345	1420	1590	1732
3/16	:	.1875	.0276	326	460	564	650	728	797	860	920	975	1040	1130	1215	1260	1300	1380	1465	1630	1780

Reprinted courtesy of Eclipse Fuel and Engineering Co., Aurora, Ill.

Table 7-6
Capacity of Orifices in Cubic Feet per Hour
Based on 1.0 Coefficient of Discharge (Specific Gravity –.55)

Inch MTD Dia.	Size	Diam. Inches	Area Square Inches	1	2	3	4	5	6	7	8	9	10	12	14	15	16	18	20	25	30
	12	.189	.02805	330	467	573	664	742	810	875	935	990	1045	1145	1238	1281	1320	1403	1483	1650	1810
	11	.191	.02865	342	479	586	675	758	827	893	955	1012	1070	1170	1262	1310	1350	1430	1513	1690	1850
	10	.1935	.0294	347	490	600	695	775	846	916	980	1040	1095	1200	1295	1343	1382	1470	1550	1732	1920
	9	.196	.0303	356	504	617	712	795	870	941	1005	1070	1125	1235	1330	1380	1420	1510	1592	1781	1945
	8	.199	.0311	366	519	635	734	820	895	970	1035	1100	1160	1270	1370	1420	1461	1552	1643	1835	2000
	7	.201	.0316	373	527	646	745	833	910	985	1050	1118	1180	1290	1390	1442	1485	1580	1670	1865	2040
18/64	..	.2031	.0324	383	541	664	765	855	935	1010	1080	1145	1210	1325	1430	1480	1520	1620	1710	1910	2090
	6	.204	.0327	386	545	668	771	860	940	1025	1090	1155	1218	1335	1440	1493	1535	1632	1730	1930	2105
	5	.2055	.0332	392	554	678	782	875	960	1040	1105	1175	1238	1356	1460	1517	1560	1660	1752	1960	2140
	4	.209	.0343	404	571	700	810	905	961	1065	1142	1212	1278	1400	1510	1568	1610	1715	1810	2020	2210
	3	.213	.0356	420	583	725	840	940	1025	1113	1185	1260	1325	1455	1570	1628	1675	1780	1880	2100	2300
7/32	..	.2187	.0376	443	626	766	886	995	1085	1178	1250	1330	1400	1535	1656	1720	1765	1880	1985	2220	2420
	2	.221	.0384	452	640	684	905	1011	1110	1202	1280	1360	1430	1570	1690	1752	1805	1920	2030	2265	2480
	1	.228	.0409	482	680	835	965	1080	1180	1280	1361	1448	1522	1675	1800	1870	1920	2045	2160	2415	2640
	A	.234	.0430	506	716	880	1015	1135	1240	1348	1430	1520	1600	1755	1898	1965	2020	2200	2270	2540	2770
15/64	..	.2343	.0431	509	718	883	1018	1138	1270	1350	1432	1521	1605	1760	1900	1970	2025	2205	2275	2550	2780
	B	.238	.0444	524	740	905	1048	1170	1280	1390	1480	1570	1652	1810	1955	2030	2090	2220	2342	2620	2860
	C	.242	.0460	542	766	940	1082	1210	1325	1440	1530	1628	1713	1880	2030	2100	2160	2300	2430	2720	2960
	D	.246	.0475	560	792	970	1120	1252	1370	1490	1581	1680	1770	1940	2095	2170	2185	2375	2510	2800	3060
1/4	E	.250	.0491	579	820	1000	1160	1300	1418	1540	1635	1736	1830	2000	2160	2240	2310	2455	2595	2890	3180
	F	.257	.0519	610	864	1060	1226	1370	1500	1625	1730	1835	1930	2120	2290	2370	2440	2590	2690	3060	3240
	G	.261	.0535	630	895	1095	1260	1410	1540	1675	1780	1890	1995	2190	2360	2440	2520	2670	2815	3160	3450
17/64	..	.2656	.0554	654	925	1132	1309	1465	1600	1735	1848	1960	2065	2260	2440	2530	2600	2770	2930	3270	3570
	H	.266	.0556	658	930	1138	1312	1470	1602	1738	1850	1963	2075	2275	2450	2540	2610	2780	2940	3280	3590
	I	.272	.0580	683	965	1185	1370	1530	1670	1816	1931	2050	2160	2370	2560	2650	2730	2900	3060	3420	3740
	J	.277	.0601	709	1000	1230	1415	1590	1732	1880	2000	2120	2240	2450	2650	2742	2830	3000	3180	3540	3880
	K	.281	.0620	730	1030	1270	1461	1630	1785	1940	2060	2190	2310	2530	2740	2830	2920	3101	3270	3660	4000
9/32	..	.2812	.0621	735	1040	1275	1462	1640	1790	1945	2070	2200	2320	2540	2760	2840	2930	3110	3280	3665	4005
	L	.290	.0660	777	1095	1350	1565	1740	1900	2065	2200	2338	2460	2700	2910	3020	3100	3300	3480	3890	4250
	M	.295	.0683	805	1140	1395	1610	1800	1970	2140	2280	2420	2545	2790	3010	3120	3180	3410	3600	4030	4400
19/64	..	.2968	.0692	816	1152	1412	1630	1830	2000	2165	2300	2450	2580	2830	3050	3160	3260	3460	3660	4080	4460
	N	.302	.0716	840	1192	1460	1690	1880	2060	2240	2390	2530	2670	2930	3150	3270	3370	3580	3770	4220	4610
5/16	..	.3125	.0767	905	1280	1568	1790	2020	2210	2400	2560	2710	2860	3140	3380	3500	3610	3830	4050	4520	5000
	O	.316	.0784	922	1310	1600	1850	2070	2260	2460	2610	2780	2920	3210	3450	3580	3690	3920	4140	4620	5050
	P	.323	.0820	968	1370	1680	1930	2160	2360	2570	2740	2900	3060	3350	3620	3750	3860	4100	4330	4830	5300

PRESSURE—LBS. PER SQUARE INCH

21/64		.3281	.0846	1000	1412	1730	2000	2240	2440	2650	2820	2990	3160	3460	3730	3870	3980	4230	4460	5000	5450
	Q	.332	.0866	1020	1445	1770	2040	2290	2500	2710	2880	3060	3230	3540	3820	3960	4070	4340	4580	5100	5590
	R	.339	.0901	1060	1500	1840	2130	2380	2580	2820	3000	3190	3360	3690	3970	4120	4240	4500	4760	5310	5800
11/32		.3437	.0928	1094	1550	1890	2190	2450	2680	2890	3100	3280	3460	3800	4090	4240	4370	4640	4890	5570	5980
	S	.348	.0950	1121	1585	1950	2240	2500	2740	2960	3160	3360	3550	3890	4190	4340	4470	4750	5010	5600	6120
	T	.358	.1005	1185	1675	2060	2370	2650	2900	3140	3350	3560	3750	4120	4440	4590	4730	5020	5300	5930	6480
23/64		.3593	.1014	1200	1695	2080	2400	2680	2930	3160	3380	3600	3795	4150	4480	4640	4790	5090	5350	5980	6550
	U	.368	.1063	1255	1780	2170	2510	2810	3070	3320	3540	3770	3970	4350	4700	4860	5000	5420	5620	6300	6850
3/8		.375	.1104	1300	1840	2260	2610	2920	3180	3450	3680	3900	4120	4520	4870	5050	5200	5510	5830	6520	7120
	V	.377	.1116	1315	1860	2280	2640	2940	3250	3480	3710	3950	4160	4560	4910	5100	5250	5590	5900	6580	7200
	W	.386	.1170	1380	1950	2390	2760	3090	3380	3650	3900	4140	4360	4790	5150	5350	5500	5850	6180	6900	7550
25/64		.3906	.1198	1412	2000	2450	2830	3160	3450	3740	4000	4240	4470	4900	5290	5480	5630	5980	6320	7080	7750
	X	.397	.1236	1450	2060	2520	2910	3260	3560	3860	4120	4370	4600	5050	5440	5645	5810	6180	6520	7300	7960
	Y	.404	.1278	1505	2090	2610	3020	3380	3690	3990	4260	4520	4770	5210	5625	5840	6020	6390	6750	7540	8250
13/32		.4062	.1296	1530	2160	2650	3060	3420	3740	4040	4320	4590	4840	5300	5700	5920	6100	6460	6840	7650	8350
	Z	.413	.1340	1580	2240	2740	3160	3540	3870	4180	4460	4740	5000	5490	5900	6120	6300	6700	7080	7900	8650
7/16		.4375	.1503	1775	2510	3070	3550	3960	4340	4700	5010	5320	5600	6150	6620	6870	7100	7540	7950	8860	9700
29/64		.4531	.1613	1890	2690	3300	3800	4250	4650	5030	5380	5800	6020	6600	7120	7370	7600	8060	8530	9530	10400
15/32		.4687	.1726	2040	2970	3520	4060	4550	4970	5390	5750	6100	6430	7050	7600	7890	8120	8610	9100	10180	11120
31/64		.4843	.1843	2170	3070	3760	4350	4860	5310	5750	6140	6500	6870	7630	8130	8450	8690	9200	9750	10900	11860
1/2		.5000	.1963	2320	3280	4000	4640	5180	5660	6130	6550	6950	7320	8050	8650	8980	9250	9800	10350	11600	12650
33/64		.5156	.2088	2460	3480	4260	4920	5500	6030	6500	6960	7300	7780	8550	9200	9550	9850	10420	11000	12300	13500
17/32		.5312	.2217	2610	3690	4510	5220	5840	6400	6900	7400	7830	8250	9060	9750	10100	10400	11090	11700	13100	14300
35/64		.5468	.2349	2770	3920	4800	5560	6200	6780	7320	7500	8300	8750	9600	10300	10720	11100	11750	12400	13850	15180
9/16		.5625	.2485	2930	4150	5080	5860	6550	7160	7750	8270	8780	9270	10180	10950	11360	11700	12400	13100	14650	16000
37/64		.5781	.2625	3100	4370	5360	6200	7200	7560	8190	8750	9280	9800	10720	11550	12000	12310	13100	13850	15500	16800
19/32		.5937	.2769	3270	4410	5650	6540	7300	8000	8640	9230	9800	10310	11320	12200	12650	13000	13820	14600	16300	17850
39/64		.6093	.2916	3440	4850	5950	6900	7700	8400	9100	9700	10300	10850	11900	12820	13300	13700	14550	15400	17200	18800
5/8		.625	.3068	3720	5200	6160	7240	8100	8850	9570	10210	10820	11420	12550	13500	14000	14400	15320	16200	18100	19800
41/64		.6406	.3223	3800	5370	6570	7600	8500	9300	10050	10750	11400	12000	13200	13750	14700	15150	16100	17000	19000	20800
21/32		.6562	.3382	4000	5640	6900	7980	8940	9750	10550	11300	11950	12600	13850	14900	15400	15900	16900	17850	19900	21850
43/64		.6718	.3545	4200	5900	7240	8350	9350	10250	11050	11700	12520	13200	14500	15600	16200	16700	17700	18700	20900	22900
11/16		.6875	.3712	4370	6160	7560	8750	9800	10700	11580	12400	13100	13800	15200	16300	16900	17450	18500	19600	21900	23900
45/64		.7031	.3883	4600	6500	7950	9150	10250	11200	12100	12950	13750	14500	15900	17100	17700	18300	19400	20500	22900	25100
23/32		.7187	.4057	4800	6750	8300	9550	10700	11700	12680	13500	14350	15100	16600	17850	18500	19100	20300	21450	23900	26200
47/64		.7343	.4236	5060	7060	8650	10000	11150	12200	13200	14100	14950	15800	17300	18650	19500	19900	21100	22350	25000	27300
3/4		.750	.4418	5230	7400	9050	10400	11670	12700	13800	14700	15600	16500	18000	19400	20200	20800	22000	23300	26000	28500
49/64		.7656	.4604	5430	7650	9360	10900	12200	13300	14400	15350	16300	17100	18800	20300	21000	21700	23000	24300	27200	29700
25/32		.7812	.4794	5680	8000	9800	11300	12620	13800	14950	15900	16900	17900	19600	21100	21900	22700	23900	25300	28200	30900
51/64		.7968	.4987	5900	8300	10200	11780	13150	14300	15500	16600	17600	18600	20400	22000	22800	23500	24800	26900	29400	32100
13/16		.8125	.5185	6110	8650	10600	12220	13680	14950	16180	17300	18300	19300	21200	22800	23600	24400	25900	27400	30600	33400
53/64		.8281	.5386	6350	8950	10950	12700	14200	15500	16800	17900	19000	20000	22000	23700	24600	25300	26900	28400	31800	34700
27/32		.8437	.5591	6600	9300	11400	13200	14720	16100	17400	18650	19750	20800	22900	24600	25500	26300	28000	29500	33000	36100
55/64		.8593	.5800	6840	9650	11820	13700	15030	16600	18100	19300	20500	21600	23800	25100	26300	27300	29000	30600	34200	37400
7/8		.875	.6013	7120	10000	12300	14200	15850	17300	18750	20000	21300	22500	24600	26500	27500	28300	30000	31800	35400	38800

Reprinted courtesy of Eclipse Fuel and Engineering Co., Aurora, Ill.

expansion from the smaller to the larger line can be as an elongated section with smooth and straight walls tapering at an included angle of 7° (3 1/2° on each side of the center-line). This is as the venturi meter where the flow coefficient is 0.98 in conversion of velocity head to static head.

When the flowing fluid is as a gas, its density or weight per cubic foot is subject to correction for both absolute pressure and absolute temperature at the flowing condition for pressure drop calculation. In liquid flow, because liquids expand only slightly in normal temperature ranges and also because liquids are largely incompressible, correction is not necessarily required except for extreme accuracy, which is hardly justified here.

The loss of pressure is due to failure to convert velocity head to static head. If the pressure loss is quite critical in abrupt expansion and must be avoided, the initial velocity head can be almost quantitatively converted to static head.

Orifice Area Calculations

Calculation of orifice area for passage of a fixed quantity of gas is a tremendous exercise in higher mathematics and fraught with potential judgment error. Therefore, except for orifice meter service where the orifice is machined with utmost precision, the sizing calculation is usually based on published flows for gas of a specific molecular weight (specific gravity) with the orifice coefficient as 1.00 and the temperature at 60° F for flows at pressures from 1 psig to at least 30 psig. Tables 7-5 and 7-6 provide for orifice diameters from 1/64 in. to 7/8 in.

Orifice Calculation Data

$$V = Q/C \cdot \sqrt{(MW/16)} \cdot \sqrt{[(T + 460)/(520)]} \cdot \sqrt{(14.7/P)}.$$

where:

Q = Gas quantity required in scfh
V = Flow in scfh at pressure drop from Table 7-3
C = Orifice coefficient
MW = Molecular weight of flowing gas
T = Flowing gas temperature, °F
P = Job site atmospheric pressure

C Factors

L/D = Thin-edge   as 0.68
L/D = 0.5   as 0.80
L/D = 0.75 - 3.0   as 0.85

Correction must then be made for the actual orifice coefficient, for the actual molecular weight (specific gravity), for the flowing temperature of the gas and if the discharge is not to atmospheric pressure there must be an absolute pressure correction. Note that the accuracy of such calculation and the orifice diameter it provides will usually fall somewhere between plus or minus 5%, thus, such orifices are suitable for burners but are not intended as metering devices.

Critical Factors for Orifices

If the orifice can be perfectly machined to within 0.0001 in. and if the approach contour to the minimum diameter of the orifice is perfect, the coefficient of the orifice will be micrometrically close to 1.00 and prediction of its flow characteristics is excellent. But such orifices are prohibitively expensive, particularly in smaller sizes. In the usual orifice meter, the machining tolerance is equally close but the orifice is machined in a thin plate with no special approach contour and with machining of the downstream face at a high included angle, forming a typical thin-edged orifice as a straight section which is a very small fraction of the diameter. Exquisite care must be taken to avoid forming of a burr at the upstream face to provide a flow coefficient very close to 0.61 in most orifice meters as a predictable factor. Such orifices are quite difficult to make if the diameter is less than 1/2 in. The coefficient is governed by the beta ratio of orifice diameter to pipe diameter. The average burner orifice for passage of gas fuel at pressure is usually from 1/16 to 1/2 in. in diameter in most cases, with larger orifices required at times for larger gas flows or for low gas pressure conditions. Burner orifices are usually square-edged holes which are drilled with standard Morse-Taper Drill sizes as calculated or as close to the required diameter as standard drill sizes will permit. Obviously a cost of $10.00 or more per orifice when there may be 100 or more orifices per burner increases burner costs prohibitively.

It is virtually impossible to drill an orifice to specific size because the hole will always be larger than the drill which made it. It is impossible to put a 0.250 in. drill into a precisely drilled 0.250 in. hole. If a hole is drilled in a steel plate with a drill having a diameter of 0.250 in., the diameter of the hole will be (as a very minimum) 5/10,000 of an inch larger in very careful machining with a new drill. If the drill has been reground, the hole may have a diameter of 0.252 in. or even larger. Thus, the orifice area may be as much as 1.63% greater than the 0.049-sq. in. area of a 1/4 in. port as calculated. In larger orifices enlargement is still greater. A further hazard for accuracy in sizing burner orifices is in the temperature level of the orifice site as well as a possible gas-temperature increase in flow up to the orifice. In both cases, there is reduction in flow of standard cubic feet of gas because a gas orifice as drilled is much smaller than the part in which it is drilled. The orifice gets smaller as the temperature level rises, and the flow of gas is reduced as the square root of the absolute temperature ratio. There are thus two sources of reduced flow in higher temperature levels. Some significant error can creep in due to these effects.

We must be aware, then, in burner orifice drilling that there are numerous hazards in applying calculations to derive suitable orifice sizing. The greatest problem is the flow coefficient of the orifice as drilled, since this factor must be estimated for a drilled orifice which is typical of burner practice. The next problem is the actual temperature of the gas as it flows across the orifice, and calculation here must be as reasonable as possible in view of the application. The flow coefficient may be as low as 0.79 and it may be as high as 0.90, but a safe mean is 0.85 for a drilled ori-

fice. The temperature as the gas flows should be presumed to be 100° F unless there is some source of added temperature level due to burner design. It is impossible to anticipate gas temperature changes due to weather or other effects, but the orifice should be based on a reasonably high temperature level to ensure sufficient gas flow at a stated pressure drop where the gas temperature is 100° F as delivered up to the orifice.

Common practice among burner manufacturers provides orifice drilling in a precision drill press using special jigs or fixtures to establish the centerline of the orifice being drilled in relation to other orifices as to both included angle and divergent angle or as to concentricity with the threads of the spud, or removable orifice piece. It is virtually impossible to drill a satisfactory orifice with a portable electric or air drill.

Services Performed by Orifices

An orifice for the passage of fluid serves many purposes, all of which are vital to satisfactory burner functioning. The first purpose is establishment of a satisfactory flow condition of a fluid fuel in terms of the quantity required at a specific limiting pressure drop. The second purpose is the establishment of a flow path for the fuel such that the burner can perform as it should. A third purpose is the establishment of a proper energy profile as the fluid fuel flows with kinetic energy available through discharge of the fuel from gage pressure.

Bernoulli teaches that when a stream of fluid of finite shape is moving forward from an orifice at a velocity based on the pressure from which it has been discharged, the pressure within the stream is lower than the pressure in the atmosphere through which the stream is moving. The atmosphere is then drawn into and mixed with the stream with violence and to a degree based on the stream velocity. If the atmosphere surrounding the stream of fuel is air, a condition of air-fuel mixture occurs and the excellence of this mixture is governed by the quantity of energy as well as the effectiveness with which the energy is used. A

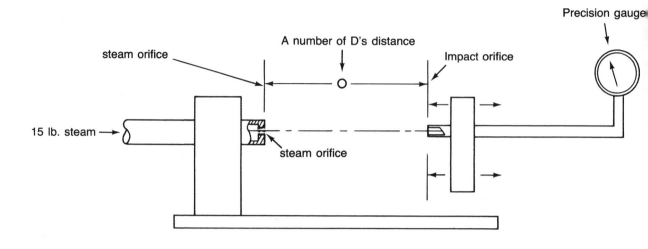

Figure 7-4. Residual gaseous flow energy after critical velocity flow of steam.

prime requisite for suitable fuel burning is excellence of the air-fuel mixture and improperly drilled or oriented orifices can seriously interfere with the use of the energy, causing improper fuel burning.

Minor imperfections in orifice drilling can seriously interfere with the performance of the burner. Improperly ground drills cause much of the trouble. If adjacent ports are producing gas streams which flow too closely to each other, the low pressures within each of the streams cause the streams to depart from the direction in which they were drilled and to coalesce or collapse and flow together. A port drilling at 120° total included angle may make a flame having an included angle of less than 70° due to this effect. In premix burners, deviation of as little as 5° from the proper centerline can cause loss of as much as 10% of the gas energy. It may be said that the drilling of fuel orifices in any manner other than with suitable jigs, tools and equipment involves a condition of calculated risk of poor burner performance, and only emergency justifies such procedure. The flow

of gases following their discharge from pressure cannot be predicted if the travel is for more than 20 diameters. Relatively tiny energies distort and divert the flow and prediction of the tiny energies is impossible.

Supersonic Flow

Supersonic gaseous flow factors are well known in relation to turbine steam nozzles and jet engines, but it is not common knowledge that a supersonic condition exists immediately downstream of any orifice gaseous discharge if the pressure upstream is great enough. It is postulated that the flow across an orifice reaches "sonic" or "critical" speed when the absolute pressure upstream of the orifice becomes twice the absolute pressure downstream of the orifice. While this is not actually a correct postulation according to the Cp/Cv ratio, it is certain that the sonic flow speed in feet per second *does* exist when the pressure ratio reaches 2/1. However, despite the fact that when the 2/1 pressure ratio exists and the ratio is increased, there is increased flow despite the sonic flow state. (See Figure 7-2.) However, the increased flow condition departs from square-root functions relating to flow caused by pressure drop. In absolute pressures up to the 2/1 ratio flow in scfh or lb/hr. follows the square-root relationship. But after the 2/1 ratio of absolute pressures is exceeded there is greater flow than the square-root functions would predict. The reason is that mass (density) correction, is linear and not a $\sqrt{}$ factor.

If, in flow across an orifice, gases have been accelerated to sonic (critical) speeds and if the mass of the gases is greater than would be the case as sonic velocity is reached, there would be secondary expansion immediately downstream of the orifice. If the velocity is sonic as the secondary expansion occurs in the moving stream of gases, the flow state becomes supersonic (supercritical) as the expansion occurs. Flow data of Figure 7-2 are metered for actual flow and the data of the curve were plotted to establish better steam orifice sizing for gauge pressures greater than 50 psi.

The following data are research-derived for residual flow energy for discharge of steam from a 15 lb gauge orifice into air as measured downstream of the orifice. The orifice diameter is "D" and, at selected downstream distance, the residual energy is based on a number of "D's."

4.00 D's	83.20%
5.33 D's	79.90%
8.00 D's	53.30%
9.33 D's	38.60%
10.66 D's	29.30%
12.00 D's	24.00%
13.33 D's	23.30%
16.00 D's	15.40%
18.66 D's	10.60%

Energy measurement was taken as impact pressure on a ¼" orifice with the apparatus shown in Figure 7-4. Impact pressure has been converted to velocity, and by $MV^2/2$ to foot-pounds.

8

Fuels and Fuel Systems

Fuel supplies for chemical process plants and refineries may truly be said to range literally from alpha to omega in their physical diversities, their calorific values and their burning characteristics. Yet to be profitable, such plants must burn fuels in manners best suited to their operations because most of the heat demand for process must be realized through burning fuels which are produced by the processes. If it should not be possible to burn such residual products in a gaseous state, in a liquid state, in a solid state and as they are produced, many very vital chemical and petroleum processes could not be profitably operated because the added cost of purchased fuel supplies would be too high.

Some of the compounds and elements which may be present in the fuel supply are paraffins, olefins, diolefins, aromatics, carbon as coke, hydrogen, mercaptans, organic sulfides, ammonia, hydrogen sulfide, carbon monoxide, carbonyl sulfide, alcohols, phenols, esters, acids, waxes, oils of many natures and others far too numerous to mention. Each of the compounds or elements has separate burning characteristics. If any single compound should be fuel, the problems for firing process heaters and the like would be relatively easy. But the fuel for a particular facility must be supplied according to the fuels produced by the various processes involved plus make-up through admissions of natural gas, through vaporization of propane into the fuel system, or through the burning of oil if the quantity of made-fuel is not sufficient for all firing services. There are a few—a very few—process heaters which are fired preferentially and with a single fuel such as natural gas because of some operational condition which requires this handling of fuel. But, by and large, heaters in a process plant must burn fuels as produced and the firing equipment must be capable of accepting changes in the fuel supply without requiring attention as the fuels change. Requirements for meeting this condition must dictate the choice of burners and control equipment because, if the burners and the controls are not chosen according to the fuel variation, operation of the heater cannot be satisfactory. If the fuel supply to an existing heater is to be changed to any great degree, there should be very careful checking of both burners and controls to see that they are suitable for the new conditions.

Fuel Sources and Mixture

In the average process plant there are many fuel sources, with some of them as gases, some as liquids and some as solids. It is not usual for a process unit to produce its entire fuel supply; therefore, the fuels as made are delivered to a common point such as a mix drum where make-up fuel is added and the mixture is then delivered to the various heaters when the fuels are gases. This presumes that the fuel supply as withdrawn from the mix drum is a fairly homogeneous mixture of the various gases delivered to the drum.

This presumption is usually quite erroneous because the mixture is far from homogeneous in all except a very few cases. It has been shown clearly that if, as two gases come together, there is not an expenditure of energy adequate for forcing homogeneous mixture of the gases it is very difficult to obtain a later state of homogeneity.

If we take the case of mix-drum operation where the calorific value of gases ranges from 500 to 1,400 Btu/cu. ft., and if we take instantaneous gas samples from the line leading from the mix drum to the burners of a heater, we will find the calorific values of the instantaneous samples from the fuel line to the heater varying almost as greatly as those of the separate gases at entry to the mix drum. It has been further shown by experiments that the calorific value of the fuel gas to the heater changes almost instantly, and unless the burners and controls as well as the process being served by the varying fuel can tolerate such changes in fuel characteristics there is simply no heater control and operation is virtually impossible if specification product is to be made. If the calorific value of the fuel changes instantaneously from about 500 Btu/cu. ft. to approximately 1,400 Btu/cu. ft., controls constantly hunt for a stabilization point and the variation in coil outlet temperature is much greater than is tolerable.

Better Fuels Mixture

This completely undesirable condition can be partially eliminated if it is possible to take a pres-sure drop of 10 psig or more from each of the make-gas supply sources to the pressure of the mix drum and immediately at the entry to the mix drum so that the velocity as established by pressure drop at 10 psig to the atmosphere of the mix drum can supply the energy required to reasonably mix the entering gas with the atmosphere of the drum. Experimentation has shown that if the pressure drop as suggested can be taken to the atmosphere of the mix drum, the variation in the fuel gas supply at exit from the mix drum can be largely eliminated and heater control can be obtained.

Control Problems

It is quite interesting to note that the cause of such a condition of lack of control is seldom recognized. Therefore, instrument people spend many hours trying to solve a problem which is really not theirs, because if controls are to function properly, there must be stabilization of the fuel supply both as to pressure and calorific value. However, if the fuel supply characteristics are held constant, the reverse is true and the problem is within the province of controls.

In a plant where some relatively heavy hydrocarbons such as butane and pentane may be present in the fuel gas, there may still be control difficulty in cold weather but not at all in warm or hot weather. The difficulty is caused when the heavier hydrocarbons in the fuel are at pressures and temperatures capable of driving the heavier components to the dew point. (See Figure 8-1.) If dew point occurs, the hydrocarbons are no longer present as gases but are found as liquids which may either accumulate to slug the burners with liquid rather than gaseous fuel or may be carried by the gas stream as micron-size droplets of liquid hydrocarbon.

In either case, there is considerable difference in the specific volumes of a hydrocarbon as a gas and the same hydrocarbon as a liquid and since gas burners are designed for passage of gas at X Btu/cu. ft., they are hardly suitable for passage of the hydrocarbon as a liquid with tremendously increased calorific value per cubic foot. The liquid

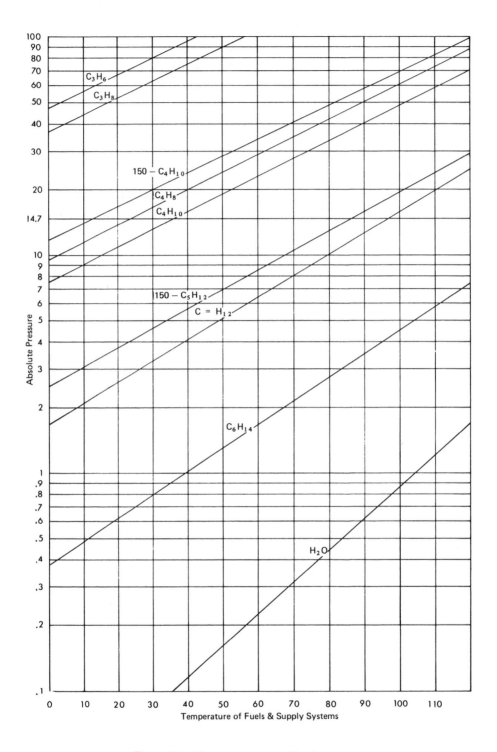

Figure 8-1. Vapor pressures of hydrocarbons.

hydrocarbon results in very greatly increased heat release at a specific pressure drop, whether the burner is slugged with liquid or whether the liquid is present as micron-size droplets. In such condition, control becomes impossible. There is frequently black smoke at the stack. The heater puffs violently, in some cases, or there may be aggravated plugging or coking of burner parts.

Liquid Hydrocarbons in Gas Fuels

A very serious offender from the standpoint of liquid hydrocarbon in the gas fuel system can (in many cases) be an absorber which, when inadequately designed or in conditions of overload, can deliver a mist of absorber oil along with the overhead gas to the fuel system. This oil is particularly bad in that it cokes more readily than lighter fractions. This source of liquid should always be suspected since, in one case, where gas fuel was being purchased from a commercial supplier at a point more than a hundred miles from the last absorber, there was severe difficulty with coking of burners due to the presence of a mist of absorber oil in the gas.

Fuel gases may or may not reach the dew point according to the fuel pressure, the minimum temperature the fuel can reach and the partial pressures of the various hydrocarbons in the fuel. Heaviest hydrocarbons should be checked first. If a check of the high molecular weight components reveals no danger, no steps to prevent difficulty due to liquid are required. If there is danger of liquid hydrocarbon, it must not be allowed to reach the fuel burning equipment as a liquid.

Liquid Hydrocarbon Removal

It is common to install knock-out pots in fuel lines. Because of design inadequacy and because of their locations, most knock-out pots are of small value. To be effective the knock-out pot must remove not only slugs of liquid but must also remove most of the fog or mist of dew point hydrocarbons carried by the gas stream. Numerous demisters are commercially available and one of these, in addition to means of trapping all the separated liquid, should be present.

The location of the means for liquid removal is important. One large pot in the main fuel supply line is not to be considered adequate because there can be additional condensation in the line between the single pot and the point where the fuel is admitted to the burner. An ideal arrangement would include a knock-out pot at each point where fuel is to be used, provided that the pots be designed for as complete removal of liquid as possible.

Fixed investment in pots for each point of fuel used and where they may be required can be amortized on the basis of labor saving in avoiding repair of badly coked burner equipment as well as on the basis of recovery of valuable higher boiling point hydrocarbons plus improved operation of burners to produce better firing control and less fuel loss.

Determination of dew-point temperature for a fuel mixture is quite simple through the use of vapor-pressure curves for hydrocarbons as in Figure 8-1. As an example, consider a case in which a fuel of the following analysis by mol-percent (volume percent) is being burned:

CH_4	75%
C_2H_6	8%
C_3H_8	4%
C_4H_{10}	8%
C_5H_{12}	5%
	100%

Calorific value = 1,331 Btu/cu. ft., LHV
Supply pressure = 60 psig (74.70 psia)
Minimum possible temperature level = 0°F

In a mixture of gases, the total pressure is the sum of the partial pressures of the gases in the mixture. The partial pressures of the component gases are the same as their mol-percentages. Partial pressures are as absolute pressures. Therefore, in this example, the partial pressures of the components are as follows:

$$CH_4 = 0.75 (74.70) = 56.025 \text{ psia}$$
$$C_2H_6 = 0.08 (74.70) = 5.976 \text{ psia}$$
$$C_3H_8 = 0.04 (74.70) = 2.988 \text{ psia}$$
$$C_4H_{10} = 0.08 (74.70) = 5.976 \text{ psia}$$
$$C_5H_{12} = 0.05 (74.70) = \underline{3.735} \text{ psia}$$
$$74.700 \text{ psia}$$

Reference to the vapor-pressure data of Figure 8-1 shows that for methane, ethane and propane vapor pressures are significantly greater than the partial pressures for these gases at $0°$ F and there is no danger of dew point for these gases. However, the partial pressure for butane at 5.976 psia is quite close to the vapor pressure of butane at $0°$ F and it is evident that a drop in temperature of approximately $10°$ F could drive the butane to dew point. But in this case, with the minimum temperature fixed at $0°$ F, the butane must be presumed to be in a gaseous phase. The pentane partial pressure at 3.735 psia, is considerably greater than the vapor pressure of pentane at $0°$ F. Thus, the pentane is driven to dew point and is present as a liquid.

It has been suggested that the liquid hydrocarbon must not be allowed to reach the burners and is to be extracted as a liquid by some means. The calorific value of the gas with the pentane in a gaseous phase is 1,331 Btu/cu. ft. LHV, but if the pentane goes to dew point and is removed from the gas as a liquid the calorific value of the gas falls to less than 1,300 Btu/cu. ft. LHV and a greater volume of gas must be supplied to maintain heat release at desired levels. If the greater volume of gas is available there is a small problem in maintaining heat release through slightly higher gas pressure; but if the additional volume of gas is not available, there is no solution in gas firing other than providing means for heating the gas supply to a temperature which at the fuel-supply pressure will not allow dew point to occur. The safe temperature is at least $20°$ F. above the dew-point temperature. However, in this case the heat supplied to the gas fuel appears within the furnace as sensible heat and is at least partially recovered.

Water Vapor in Fuel Gases

The vapor-pressure data of Figure 8-1 show the characteristics of water vapor. If there are even small quantities such as less than 1% of water vapor in the gas fuel the water vapor must also be checked for dew-point characteristics. If the water vapor reaches the dew point, there is danger of frost stoppage of lines or even freezing and bursting of lines due to water within them. Either condition is serious but the danger of fire from burst gas lines requires serious thought and precautions for avoiding it.

As an example, if there should be only 1,500 ppm of water vapor present in a gas supplied at 74.70 psia, this small quantity of water vapor (0.15% by volume) would have a partial pressure at 74.70 (0.0015) equaling 0.112 psia. It would reach the dew point when the temperature dropped to approximately $38°$ F, causing water as a liquid to be present in the line. If the temperature should drop below $32°$ F, it would freeze, causing valves to stick and, if there should be any significant accumulation, bursting the line as it freezes.

The operator of a plant in such a condition would have alternate preventive choices. He can install dehydration equipment to reduce the dew-point temperature through removal of the water vapor. But he is still confronted with the danger of dew point in the heavy hydrocarbons in the fuel gas. If his fuel supply is not adequate to compensate for removal of the heavy hydrocarbons as liquids, in keeping with earlier discussion concerning calorific value of gas fuel, he has no choice but to heat and insulate his gas fuel lines to ensure suitable cold weather operation. There is a demand for steam as a heat source for the heating, with insulation over steam tracing being one preferred procedure. Exhaust steam can be used for this service if the exhaust steam supply pressure is great enough to drive it through the tracing tubes.

The fuel gas temperature should be elevated to at least $20°$ F above the lowest dew-point temperature if the tracing and insulation are carried to within 6 ft. of the burner with insulation recommended to the burner. If the distance between the

Table 8-1
Heat Loss from Insulated Lines
(at 0° F with wind at 10 mph)

Gas Temperature (0°F)	Heat Loss (Btu/sq. ft./hr.)
40	50
50	70
60	94
70	102
80	128

insulation, tracing and the burner is significantly greater than 6 ft. or if the gas line is bare, an increase of 40° F over the lowest dew-point temperature is recommended. Heat loss from insulated lines at 0° F and exposed to wind at 10 mph at various gas temperatures are shown in Table 8-1.

These heat loss figures, which are seen to be significant, will be correct for temperature at the surface of the insulation. Note that due to its thickness, the insulation adds significantly to line area. Heat loss must be added to the fuel-gas heat demand to establish heat supply for safe temperatures.

Heat demand for the gases burned as fuel can be estimated with the specific heats in Btu/lb./° F for the separate components of the gas stream, which are given in Table 8-2.

Steam Tracing Factors

Steam charge to the tracing should be at such a rate that there is minimal blow of steam from the tube discharge to avoid excessive use of steam, but there should be appreciable blow of steam along with steam condensate discharge to assure delivery of adequate heat. The tracing tube can be operated at full steam pressure up to the traps if steam usage must be kept at a minimum. However, in very cold weather, the trap should not be allowed to become inactive or there is danger of freezing.

Heating of the gas fuel lines serves the very useful function of keeping all fuel components in the vapor phase if there are no hydrocarbons heavier than pentane or very small mol-percentages of hexane present. If there is a mist of absorber oil in the gas stream, there will still be difficulty with the bad effects of liquid fuel delivery. There is considerable difficulty with absorber oil in gas fuel. If it is present, there must be means for its removal; because of the high boiling point of such oils, normal preheating is of no benefit in this respect. Note that the normal knock-out pot is of some small benefit for removing absorber oil. But if this oil is satisfactorily removed, it will be necessary to install a properly designed mist extractor system, if absorber malfunction cannot be corrected.

Absorber Operation Difficulties

Evidence of the presence of absorber oil in the gas system can be observed if opening a bleeder valve in the gas system reveals a discharge of oil which is not volatile, which has a slightly oily feel (typical of light gas-oil or kerosene) and which is relatively dark in color. Further evidence is to be found when the interior of gas lines are oily, when

Table 8-2
Specific Heat (in Btu/lb./°F)

Gas Components	Specific Heat
CH4	0.527
C2H6	0.409
C3H8	0.388
C4H10	0.397
Hydrogen	3.408
Ethylene	0.362
Propylene	0.354
Butylene	0.370
Carbon monoxide	0.248
Hydrogen sulfide	0.254
Pentane	0.397

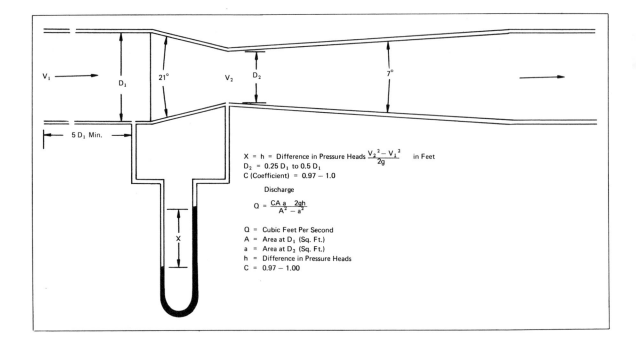

The following equations appear in the figure:

$$X = h = \text{Difference in Pressure Heads} \ \frac{V_2{}^2 - V_1{}^2}{2g} \ \text{in Feet}$$
$$D_2 = 0.25\,D_1 \text{ to } 0.5\,D_1$$
$$C \ (\text{Coefficient}) = 0.97 - 1.0$$

Discharge

$$Q = \frac{CA\,a \quad 2gh}{A^2 - a^2}$$

Q = Cubic Feet Per Second
A = Area at D_1 (Sq. Ft.)
a = Area at D_2 (Sq. Ft.)
h = Difference in Pressure Heads
C = 0.97 − 1.00

Figure 8-2. Gas flow measurement with least pressure loss.

a deposit of oil appears at the primary air aspirators (mixers), or when there is an accumulation of oily dust in, on and about the aspirators.

Ample gas-fuel supply pressure is vital to proper operation of any process facility. Often, the pressure on the gas fuel at its source may be low. But in any case, plant operation is severely handicapped by a fuel distribution system which is not adequate for the delivery of fuel to the points of use with enough pressure to permit the best operation. Operation of heaters at the present time needs a minimum of 25 psig gas pressure at the burners, and after all regulation and control pressure at 35 psig is preferred at the burners. It may be said that burner performance is proportional to the square root of the maximum gas pressure which can be applied to the burners because energy for mixture of air with fuel is also largely proportional to the square root of the gas pressure.

High maximum fuel pressure is particularly important to good operation where there is a relatively wide range of calorific values for the gas fuel as delivered for burning, because the burner equipment must be designed for maximum heat release with the lowest calorific value gas at the maximum pressure available at the job site. When the calorific value of the gas rises, fewer standard cubic feet of gas are required for release of a stated quantity of heat and the gas pressure falls. (See Figure 8-3.) If the drop in pressure is too great, because of greatly increased calorific value of the fuel, the burner performance falls off—at times seriously.

Burner Capability in Fuel Changes

It is a rare process plant in which the fuel is available at even reasonably fixed calorific value because of variation in the value of gases as they

These typical examples of burner fuel gas pressures and variation of pressures as calorific value of gas fuel changes are based on full firing when the lowest calorific value gas is being used.

Condition #1

Heat release required   — 5,000,000 Btu/hr. LHV
Maximum gas pressure — 30 psig
First fuel   — 700 Btu/cu. ft. and 11.6 MW
Second fuel   — 1400 Btu/cu. ft. and 25.8 MW
Third fuel   — 2100 Btu/cu. ft. and 42.6 MW

$5,000,000/700 \cdot (1/0.85) \cdot \sqrt{11.6/16}$ = 30 psig on 3/8 in.
$5,000,000/1400 \cdot (1/0.85) \cdot \sqrt{25.8/16}$ = 17 lb. on 3/8 in. orifice
$5,000,000/2100 \cdot (1/0.85) \cdot \sqrt{42.6/16}$ = 12 lb. on 3/8 in. orifice

Condition #2

Heat release required   — 5,000,000 Btu/hr. LHV
Maximum gas pressure — 15 psig
Fuels   — As for condition #1

$5,000,000/700 \cdot (1/0.85) \cdot \sqrt{11.6/16}$ = 15 psig on 29/64 in.
$5,000,000/1400 \cdot (1/0.85) \cdot \sqrt{25.8/16}$ = 8 psig on 29/64 in. orifice
$5,000,000/2100 \cdot (1/0.85) \cdot \sqrt{42.6/16}$ = 5 psig on 29/64 in. orifice

Varying pressure data are based on full-scale heat release, but control requires reduction in heat release. A typical control range is 2/1 or from design release to 50% of design release. In this case pressures at 50% of release would be about 1/4 of the pressure at 100% of release.

Figure 8-3. Comparative pressure data.

are produced by the process as well as variation in the quantity of gases as the process conditions vary. This condition can at times dictate the type of fuel burning equipment chosen for a particular service. The fuel burning equipment must be suitable for the change in calorific value of the fuel as it may be available.

Where the burner equipment is designed to use no secondary air at all and is of the sealed-port type, the variation in calorific value of the fuel cannot exceed 10% if there is to be an adequate air supply for the highest calorific value gas. Burners designed for 100% premix operation but with provisions for entry of secondary air, based on approximately 10% excess air with the lowest calorific value gas, can accept variation in calorific value of as much as 40-50% with enough air for the highest calorific value but at quite close to zero excess air.

Other premix burners designed for greater quantities of secondary air can accept and burn gases where the heating values of the gases vary as much as 150%. Gas burners designed for use of no primary air, where there is no premixture of air and gas, can satisfactorily burn gases which vary as much as 250% or more if the available gas pressure is approximately 35 psig for the use of the lowest heating value fuel so that the pressure with the highest heating value gas is 10 psig or more for great enough turbulence and mixture to provide satisfactory burning.

Undersized gas lines and the resulting pressure drop are responsible for much undesirable burner operation. The gas-fuel system must be capable of delivering the required fuel quantity at minimal pressure drop; in this case, the use of one line size larger than that which will cause line gas velocity flowing at line pressure to exceed 100 ft./sec. may be considered a good investment, permitting operating excellence as well as allowing a maximum of operating flexibility. Line pressure drop between the source and the point of use subtracts from the pressure at the source. If the pressure at the source is high enough, subtraction of the line pressure drop is not serious, but where the pressure at the source is low, the line drop does, indeed, become serious.

Sizing of gas headers for groups of burners firing a heater should be based on maximum line velocity at not more than 50 ft./sec., if the pressure as established by the firing controls at entry to the header is to be presented to all burners so that each burner "sees" the same gas fuel pressure for uniform heat release in all areas under control.

Solid Matter in Gas Supply Systems

Only those who have seen the quantity and size of solid matter which can come from gas supply lines when they are new or even after years of use can understand why gas line strainers at each point of fuel use can save many times their cost by avoiding burner plugging and maintenance as well as difficulty with control of firing. Strainers with 1/8 in. mesh traps installed between the fuel supply system and the gas pressure regulator will entrap most of the solid matter; but trap mesh of 1/16 in. or less will be far more effective. If the

strainer pressure drop is a factor, parallel strainers are effective at reduced pressure drop.

Some relief from plugged burners can be had if the connection from the header to the burner is made in the top of the header; but smaller solids, suspended in the gas stream, will still get into burner orifices and plug them if the particle size is greater than the gas orifice diameter, which all too often is the case.

Design of fuel-oil systems is fully as critical as the design of gas-fuel systems but for quite different reasons such as the requirement for unvarying fuel-oil pressure at any point where oil is to be burned. (See Figure 8-4.) As fuel-oil systems are considered, one important factor is pumping cost as the system operates. Many times, steam drive for the pump is either preferred or is dictated by utility availability. Since turbine drive for rotary pumps may be quite expensive, in addition to the cost for a suitable rotary pump, a reciprocating steam pump is used as an alternative. Such pumps which produce pressure surges for each action of valves are not capable of producing the steady oil pressure demanded for reasonably close control of firing. Pressure surges in such systems can be as great as from 25 to 100 psig because oil, a liquid, is far from compressible. Oil burners fired from such a system are alternately flooded and starved. Flames balloon then may almost disappear. It is difficult to avoid smoking at the stack and fuel loss is inevitable.

Because the first cost of reciprocating pumps is low and since the operating cost is reasonable, there has been much effort to solve the pressure pulsation problem with such pumps. In all fairness, there has been certain success but at significantly added material and maintenance costs such that an original installation of suitable rotary pumps with required drive would have given far better firing, better control of firing for production of specification product and maintenance saving.

Sizing of lines for fuel-oil systems is difficult and tedious at best because of the many factors which must be considered. Where the effective length of the system exceeds 100 ft., line pressure drop becomes a factor because in addition to the

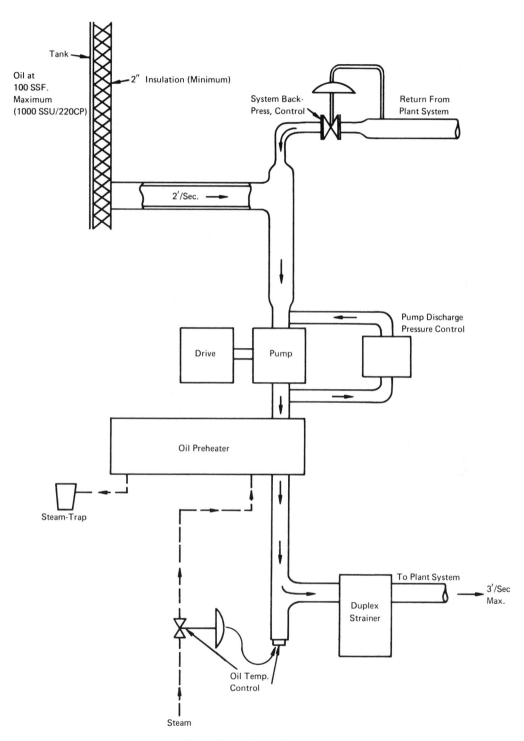

Figure 8-4. Fuel oil system.

requirement for lack of pressure pulsation on a cyclic basis, as from the reciprocating pump, there is a demand for pressure stabilization on an hour-to-hour basis. The term effective length is due for consideration because a point-to-point length in the physical sense is not the true length of the system (in point of system pressure drop) if there are elbows, tees and other fittings in the line.

Fuel Oil Line Length Factors

Each fitting adds to the effective length of the line and the addition to effective length is governed by the viscosity of the oil as it is pumped; fortunately, the effective length added decreases with an increase in viscosity. As an example, consider the case of a 2 in. line with oil movement at the rate of 20 gpm. At viscosity of 15 SSF (103 SSU), each elbow adds 4.30 ft. at 27 SSF (237 SSU), the addition is 3.90 ft. at 50 SSF (475 SSU), the addition is 2.60 ft. and at 95 SSF (950 SSU), only 1.40 ft. are to be added.

However if the effective length is 100 ft., the line pressure drop increases as the viscosity of the oil increases, as is shown clearly in the case of a 2 in. line again at 20 gpm as in the foregoing paragraph. With viscosity at 15 SSF, the pressure drop is approximately 0.86 psig; at 27 SSF it is approximately 1.28 psig, and viscosity at 50 SSF increases the pressure drop to approximately 3 psig while viscosity at 95 SSF produces a drop at 6 psig. Because of these data, the velocity of flow of fuel oil in the line and as pumped should not exceed 3 ft./sec. Thus, while effective length of fittings decreases with an increase in viscosity, the drop through the line increases quite markedly with an increase in viscosity to make pumping viscosity a source of concern in line sizing. The viscosity for any particular oil is governed by the temperature of the oil, but here we encounter a most unfortunate condition. There is no relationship of viscosity with API gravity or specific gravity in oils; neither are the viscosity indices of oils in any firm or fixed relationship. In some oils a rise of 50° F may reduce viscosity from hundreds of seconds Furol to 20 seconds Furol, and in a corresponding drop in temperature, the viscosity may

increase from 20 seconds to hundreds of seconds. In other oils a change of 50° F may have but relatively small effect on viscosities.

If viscosity-temperature data are available for the oil which is to be burned, the oil as pumped should be at a temperature which will produce suitable viscosity to avoid unnecessary line pressure drop as well as increased pumping cost. A suitable viscosity for oil as delivered to the fuel-oil system is suggested as from 15-20 SSF. (Refer to Table 7-3.)

Fuel Oil Line Insulation

Fuel-oil line insulation is very important for maintenance of line temperature, line viscosity and suitable viscosity for oil burning. All too frequently this factor is neglected, producing the undesirable results of high pressure drop, increased pumping cost and delivery of cold oil to burning equipment. This result was shown clearly in one case where oil, as it left the heating and pumping set, was at 215° F but as it arrived at the burning equipment 400 ft. away, its temperature was less than 90° F, the oil fires were full of "fireflies," there was black smoke at the stack, and firing of the heater was virtually impossible. It is true that the atmospheric temperature was near zero to produce such very undesirable conditions, but the firing conditions at higher atmospheric temperatures were anything but good. This condition is all too common.

It may be said without qualification that where fuel oil firing is essential to the operation of a process facility, no insulation in the plant is more important than that which avoids heat loss from the fuel-oil system. The added pumping costs due to increased viscosity are literally of no consequence as they are compared to increased operation cost, due to poor burner operation, poor firing conditions, loss of throughput and fuel loss caused by delivery of cold oil to burning equipment. The burning equipment cannot possibly function as it should if the fuel-oil viscosity is too high.

With industry turning to vacuum residual oils which are within the tar range and are taken directly from the tower bottom at high temperature for fuel, there is greater demand for excellent insulation of fuel-oil lines as well as steam tracing inside the insulation to avoid freezing the tar as circulation slows or stops. However, the steam tracing should not be in operation during normal circulation since the tar is usually considerably hotter than the steam which is available. In many cases, there is a provision for flushing the tar line with a lighter and less viscous oil if the tar flow stops or is discontinued for any reason. It is to be noted that such tars are excellent fuels only as long as their temperature is kept high and the viscosity at burning temperature is low enough for the burning equipment.

Solids in Fuel Oil

One of the more distressing factors involved in the firing of oil as fuel is the quantity of solid matter it carries in suspension. The solid matter may be coke, line scale, catalyst fines in decanted oils or polymers formed in the oil as well as sand and small rocks which have gotten into the system. The problem of solids which cause stoppage is always present.

The solids problem is made more acute because the solids are present in particles ranging from as large as 1/4 in. to micron size. The large particles can be removed through suitable strainers, but it is virtually impossible to remove all solids. Thus they must be lived with. The small particles make ordinary valves useless for control of oil flow if the valve is to operate in nearly closed position. Valving based on the vee-port principle must be used to avoid slow stoppage of flow with the valves throttling to any degree. This applies to firing valves for individual fuel burning units as well as to any flow control valve; but note that there are numerous approaches to the vee-port principle according to various manufacturers.

Residual oils from catalytic cracking operations at times carry with them certain quantities of catalyst fines. In such oils very severe erosion is to be expected, particularly in the tips and atomizers of fuel-burning equipment but also in other parts of the fuel system because of the great abrasive capability of the catalyst fines. At this writing there is little that can be done to counter the abrasive action which can destroy atomizers and tips of fuel-burning equipment in as little as two weeks with ordinary metallurgy and in a month or less with hardened parts made of especially heat-treated alloys. If the design of the oil-burning parts will permit it, certain relief from this abrasion can be had through the use of special alloy burner parts, but the state of relief hardly justifies the cost.

A further problem with solids is that some fuel oils tend to polymerize if their temperature level is too high for too long, which would happen if the fuel oil tank were held at high temperature for long periods while the contents of the tank are being withdrawn for burning. The polymer solids are not present as the oil is charged to the tank; they form while it is held in the tank. While this solid matter is not extremely hard, it is still capable of interfering with oil flow through stoppage of passages.

A solution for this problem is to maintain a storage tank heat level just adequate for removal by pumping plus separation of the tank's contents from excess oil returned hot from the burning system. A suggested system is shown in Figure 8-4. This system permits suitable heating of the fuel oil for burning as it is used so that the oil is at a high temperature level for only a short time prior to burning. In addition to relief of the polymerization problem, this system is distinctly economical in the use of preheat steam because the oil, once heated, is held within the burning circuit and does not lose any great proportion of heat whereas if the hot oil should be returned to the tank, the greater portion of its heat content is lost while contained in the tank waiting to be picked up again by the fuel-oil pump. The system should circulate more oil than the maximum quantity which is to be burned. The quantity circulated should be in the order of 1 1/2 times the quantity to be burned, for uniform temperature on the fuel oil around the system as well as better control of temperature, since even with the best insulation there will be some heat loss as the oil circulates. Tank temperature should be held just high enough to permit the pump to hold suction.

Fuel Oil Calorific Values

A good average lower heating value for No. 6 fuel oil is 146,000 Btu/gallon, 17,500 Btu/lb. or 6,150,000 Btu/barrel. This presumes an API gravity in the order of 10 or a specific gravity in the order of 1.00 and is reasonably close estimating the amount of fuel oil needed to provide specified quantities of heat. (See Figure 6-2.)

Always take very great care to avoid water entry to the fuel-oil system with the water either as a liquid or as steam, which is used for preheat or purging of burners as they are taken out of service. Where there is provision for steam purging of burners, the purge valves should be checked for tightness and assurance of no leakage from the steam system to the oil system, or in cases where the oil pressure is greater than the steam pressure, that there is no leakage of oil to the steam system. Oil storage tank roofs should always be very tight and there must be no steam leakage from the tank heating coils.

Fuel Oil—Water Mixtures

When water is mixed with oil it tends to emulsify. An oil-water emulsion is difficult to burn with any degree of satisfaction. When burners which have been properly performing suddenly begin to misbehave, the operator should check for water in the oil. Steam leaks are usually the culprits but finding them may be difficult. A sample of the fuel checked for BS&W to show higher than normal water is a good indication of the trouble source. If the high-water content is present at the connection to the tank, the tank heater is suspect. Leaky purge valves are hard to find, and because of this the selection of purge valving should be made carefully for its ability to provide a bubble-tight seal.

In some oil burner designs, steam is capable of lifting oil or pulling a vacuum on the oil supply. If the burners in service are of this general type, oil temperature must be controlled closely to avoid flashing or vaporization of the fuel en route to the burner. If flashing or vaporization happen, the burner is apt to sound like a gasoline engine running at low speed and the flame from the burner looks bad.

Fuel Oil Flashing to Vapor

Such flashing or vaporization can occur in other basic oil burner designs if the oil temperature gets too high and particularly at turn-down condition in operation of the burner. The symptoms of vaporization of fuel are as just described. It is rare to find this condition with typical No. 6 residual oils but it can occur with lighter fuels such as No. 2 or No. 3 and where there is improper preheat control.

In the burning of fuel oil, it is difficult to make a mistake quite as great as to establish a dead-end fuel supply system where small oil flow in the absence of steam tracing can cause very bad burner operation because of oil which is too cold to burn properly. If it is necessary to use the dead-end header system for any reason, it should (by all means) be steam traced. The insulation must be excellent if the oil is not heavier than typical No. 6. If the oil is in the tar range, a circulating system must be used.

Fuel Oil System Heat Loss

The best header system is of no value if the individual take-off connection from the header to the burner is long and is poorly insulated because its oil content may either freeze or become very viscous. Insulation here is fully as important as on the header and steam tracing is indicated for best operation in all conditions of firing. It is interesting that a drop of more than 50° F in oil temperature has been observed in a take-off connection 5 1/2-ft. long to a burner releasing 3,000,000 Btu/hr. to make the burner perform very badly.

Take-off connections for burners should be made at the top of the header rather than the side or the bottom so that solid matter can be carried past the burner rather than delivered to it. The solid matter here is larger than micron size but small enough to pass through such strainers as may be in service. Particles in this size range, in addition to being hard to remove, are responsible for most difficulty with plugging of burner parts, valves and oil lines through slow accumulation. A procedure which has been found to be decidedly advantageous is that of thoroughly flushing fuel-oil supply lines at regular intervals to remove accumulations of such small solids.

Fuel Oil Atomization Principles

In the use of liquid fuels for heat production, it is necessary to convert the liquid fuel to the gaseous phase before there can be mixture with air in preparation for burning. There are several means for satisfactory conversion of oil as a liquid to oil as vapor, but with average commercial fuel oil some sort of an atomizer is used. The term atomizer is a misnomer since its action is to break up the oil liquid into droplets which are not in the atom size range but are in the micron size range. Since the atomizer designer is aware that larger drops or droplets of oil make sparks or "fireflies" in the oil flame, judgment of atomization excellence must be based on the presence or absence of sparks and fireflies.

In the process of converting the oil liquid to thousands of micron-size droplets, the ratio of surface-to-mass in the oil increases so tremendously that when the tiny droplets of oil are exposed to heat, there is instant conversion of the liquid oil to oil as vapor. In vapor phase the oil readily mixes with air and burns, as would gaseous fuel, because both the air and the fuel are in the gaseous state and can therefore mix. If the droplets are too large, there is not enough time for vaporization before escape from the flame and the burning continues to cause either sparks or fireflies to appear. If the droplets are much too large (a result of poor atomization), there can be deposition of coke within the furnace and on tubes, floor and wall as well as deposition of oil. In this case, it

would be difficult if not impossible to avoid black smoke at the stack at any condition of excess air or firing adjustment.

Atomizer Design Variation

Atomization is obtained through expenditure of energy. The energy may be steam suitably injected to the oil or it may be high oil pressure plus discharge of oil through tangential orifices to a spinning chamber and then to the furnace for burning as a conical spray. The former is steam atomization and the latter is mechanical or pressure atomization. In some oil burner designs the oil is admitted to a rapidly spinning rotary cup to escape from the lip of the cup as spray. This rotary-cup atomization is used quite widely in so-called package boilers.

In any of the atomization systems, the viscosity of the oil as atomized is critical to excellence of atomization. The systems vary quite widely as to their tolerance for viscosity of oil as atomized. A great tolerance for viscosity is a characteristic of steam atomization, with 30 SSF being considered ideal, but with acceptable burning with viscosity as great as 150 SSF. Pressure or mechanical atomizers do not perform at all well if the viscosity greatly exceeds 10 SSF.

One system designed for light distillate oils such as kerosene and No. 2 oils uses low-pressure air for atomization, but the ability to produce more than minor heat release (such as from one to two million Btu) is somewhat limited since the quantity of air for atomization is approximately 10% of the theoretical air for burning and must be supplied by blowers or as compressed air.

Steam atomizing burners are of two distinctly different types. One type is for inside mixing of steam and oil while the other is for outside mixing. In the former, the oil and steam are brought together inside the body of the atomizer and the mixture is then discharged through ports or slots for burning. The opposite is true for the outside-mix design which produces mixture of steam and oil outside the body of the atomizer. Inside-mix burners are far more economical in point of steam for atomization, with steam demand ranging upward from 0.10 lbs. of steam per lb. of oil to approximately 0.3 lbs. per lb. while the outside-mix variety will demand steam at from 0.5 lbs. per lb. up to as much or more than 1 lb. per lb. with all variations in steam demand governed by burner design.

Atomization with steam is not too difficult. There are many designs of steam atomizers and all work reasonably well. Choice should be based on demonstrated excellence of atomization at minimal steam demand which is also demonstrated or substantiated along with satisfactory flame pattern and length in combination with ability to alter flame shape by other than air-register control.

Draft for Fuel Oil Burning

Steam atomized burners can produce a satisfactory flame condition when the draft loss or air pressure drop across them is 0.10 in. or less with 0.25 in. a good average air pressure drop in natural draft service.

Thus, oil burning in low-draft heaters is practical and literally hundreds of burners are in such service and in automatic control of firing. However, it must be pointed out that excellence in oil burning is governed by the state of the air pressure drop across them because of greater turbulence with increase in air pressure drop. Improved firing is related to the square root of the air pressure drop, but the relationship is not necessarily direct. At times, this alone is the deciding factor for installation of forced draft for critical firing service or to allow the use of a smaller furnace structure such as a boiler or steam generator for releases which are quite large. It is accepted as factual that higher air pressure drops across the burners, even up to as much as 15-in. W.C., greatly accelerate and improve the burning of fuels whether they be liquid or gaseous.

However, the improvement and speeding of burning occurs only if the burner design takes as much pressure drop as possible across the burner throat and little pressure drop across the burner air register, which is in the wide-open position. Burner sizing should be adequate for the required release of heat at the maximum possible air pressure drop, with all air registers in the wide-open position. The benefits of the high air pressure drop are substantially lost if the burner is oversized for the required heat release because in this case the air pressure-drop would occur in passage across the air register and not at the throat.

Atomizing Steam Factors

A most important portion of the fuel system is the means to supply steam for atomization to the various points where steam is to be used for atomization of the oil as burned. The atomizing steam system must deliver dry steam to the burners at constant pressure to hold suitable control of firing in the absence of the sparky fire which is characteristic of most steam atomizing burner oil guns with wet steam.

Dry steam at the burner requires excellent insulation of the steam line plus adequate trapping of condensate, which may form in the steam system, even with the best insulation. If there is pressure variation in the supply system due to sudden use of large quantities of steam at points along the system the steam pressure to the burners should be regulated to hold constant pressure up to the burner control valving to avoid firing irregularities.

Velocity of steam in the supply system to burners, should not exceed 100 ft./sec. A formula for quick calculation of the square inches of flow area at 100 ft./sec. follows:

$$\frac{[W(380/18)\ (P_1/P_2+P_1)\ (T+460/520)}{3600 \times 100} \text{ x } 144 = \text{sq. in.}$$

where:

W = Total pounds of steam per hr.
P_1 = 14.7 psia
P_2 = Steam pressure, psig
T = Steam temperature, °F

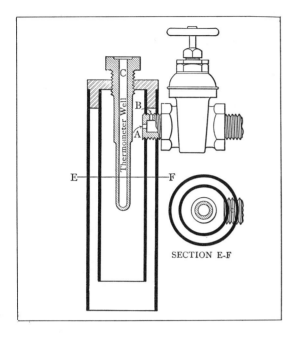

SECTION E-F

Figure 8-5. Compact throttling calorimeter. Reprinted from Steam, *courtesy of Babcock & Wilcox.*

All too frequently the system for steam generation and distribution in the process plant fails to receive careful consideration, which is typical of the process units for the simple reason that generation and distribution of steam will be based on factors so well time proven. This can be a serious error. In a large refinery which used more than a million pounds of steam per hour, steam generation was reduced more than 5% as the result of a program of checking steam traps and packings such as valves, rods, and the like as well as for leaky steam valves and gaskets in the entire plant steam system.

In this plant, the cost of steam was based on 50¢/1,000 lbs. Thus, the quick economy due to the 50,000 lbs./hr. reduction in steam generation is real at $25/hr. to justify the cost of the program which required the services of two men for the greater part of a month as well as several thousands of dollars worth of equipment and supplies.

Moisture in Steam

It is quite common to purchase steam generating equipment based on certain minimum steam quality or moisture content at the boiler nozzle. As the test runs are made in acceptance of the boiler, it is typical to run throttling-calorimeter checks of the steam to determine what the quality of the steam may be to ensure guaranty conditions are being met. However, these checks are usually made under carefully maintained operating conditions and the results obtained are not necessarily typical of conditions during continued operation. (See Figures 8-5 and 8-6.)

Operating conditions are largely associated with feed water supply and treatment as well as the amount of dissolved solids and the pH of the boiler water as the boiler operates. All these factors influence the tendency for the boiler to foam or prime, and the results of these phenomena increase the amount of unevaporated water in the steam more or less seriously, causing the steam quality at the boiler outlet to change or causing rapid departure of water from the boiler. In most cases, the rate of blow down can control the tendency for foaming or priming, and careful checking of dissolved solids or the pH of the boiler water (not the feedwater) establishes the blow down rate required for maintenance of steam quality. If steam quality is to be maintained, the boiler must be operated as nearly at the specified conditions as possible.

If moisture escapes the boiler with the steam, it must be withdrawn from the steam system because there is no further application of heat with saturated steam; therefore, there will be no heat for evaporation of the moisture. All boilers are equipped with steam scrubbers which are capable of maintaining steam quality at specified conditions within the boiler water. But such scrubbers are seldom over-designed to the degree which will permit departure from specified water conditions. Removal of the moisture is typically through steam traps in which accumulated moisture due to carry over as well as heat loss from the lines is removed. For the system through which saturated

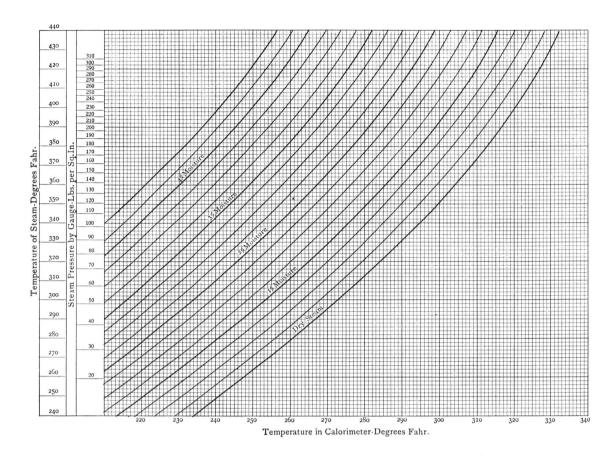

Figure 8-6. Graphic method of determining moisture contained in steam from calorimeter readings. Reprinted from Steam, *courtesy of Babcock & Wilcox.*

steam is to be delivered to points of use, there must be steam traps or some means for removing accumulated water. It is to be noted that if steam traps are not carefully maintained, they are sources of very great steam loss regardless of design because they are mechanical devices and as such are subject to mechanical failure.

All saturated steam carries some moisture according to the effectiveness with which the steam drum internals perform. It is only in superheated steam that the steam trap burden becomes eased and then only in respect to the effectiveness of insulation on the line between the boiler or gener-

ator and the point of steam use. If the heat loss from the lines exceeds the quantity of superheat, water as a liquid will be present and must be removed.

The reasons for removal of water from the steam supply are many; but some of them are avoidance of serious water hammer, avoidance of wire drawing valves and orifices, avoidance of other erosion (such as on turbine blades), avoidance of shocks in the steam system due to a sudden slug of water in the steam flow at 100 ft./sec. or so, avoidance of bad oil burner operation among others.

As has been noted, there will be some moisture in all saturated steam, but modern specifications for boiler or generator performance are quite rigid as they limit carry over of moisture to a few parts per million under test or specified conditions. If the moisture content of the steam is as specified, there is small cause to be concerned, and steam trap operation should be quite rare if the steam lines are well insulated.

If the moisture content of the steam is measured in parts per million, there is a great advantage in that the heat loss as sensible heat in the moisture is so small as to be negligible, but this is true only when a few parts per million of moisture are present. If, due to departure from specified conditions for operation, the moisture content of the steam should rise to 0.25% or 99.75% quality steam, the heat loss due to the unevaporated moisture in the steam begins to be a factor deserving attention. As the moisture content rises further, the heat loss becomes proportionally more serious. A table is provided for steam pressures and moisture contents to more clearly convey the seriousness of the heat loss; but it is to be noted that in terms of *fuel* loss, the heat loss as specified is to be divided by the thermal efficiency of the boiler or generator.

It can be an error of considerable magnitude to presume that because a boiler or generator has been purchased and tested for acceptance with moisture in parts per million, it will continue to so operate. Unanticipated changes in feed water or in blow down rate can cause the moisture content of the steam to rise to a point where the carry over of boiler water can become serious and the steam quality will fall. The definition of steam quality is the percentage of steam in a steam-moisture mixture; thus, if there is 1% moisture in the steam, the steam quality is 99%.

The quality of steam can be measured within the limits of accuracy of pressure and temperature measurement through the use of a throttling calorimeter. Steam at gage pressure is dropped to atmospheric pressure within the calorimeter and the temperature of the steam at atmospheric pressure is indicated by measurement. The temperature indication will be high or low according to the moisture content of the steam.

There are many variables in estimating heat loss from insulated steam lines and it is possible to calculate the loss accurately if necessary. A very good assumption is that the loss from the steam line minimum will be 75 Btu/sq. ft./hr. and maximum 150 Btu/sq. ft./hr. based on the diameter of the insulation covering the pipe. From these figures it is possible to estimate the heat loss from a properly insulated steam line. Assuming the heat loss as latent heat, it is then possible to estimate the quantity of moisture which will condense in the line due to unpreventable loss of heat; in all cases where the steam is saturated, the quality of steam will decrease as the steam travels through the steam line. If the steam should be superheated, the loss is as superheat, and if the heat loss does not exceed the superheat, there will be no dew point or condensation of water.

If, in the case of entry of superheated steam to the line, it is discovered that the steam quality is less than 100% at some point along the system, there is serious failure of the insulation to cause the heat loss to be too great and demands immediate correction.

If the steam to the line is saturated at entry, it is possible to calculate the heat loss from the line and estimate the expected decrease in quality at points along the line. If calorimetric checks show that the decrease in quality is greater than is to be expected due to normal heat loss, there is excellent reason to check and repair the insulation of the line. In one plant, it was discovered that monthly calorimetric checks produce very nice annual savings with the checks carried out on a plant wide basis as routine procedure.

Heat loss due to accumulation of moisture is much greater than the loss as sensible heat in the condensate discharged by traps because in each operation of a steam trap which is in good repair there is always some discharge of steam. If the steam trap is not in good condition and if it fails to shut off the steam as the blow is completed, there is great additional loss of steam. This is a characteristic of the trap which, again, is a mechanical device and therefore subject to mechanical ills. But the steam trap is a very necessary device which, in common with other mechanical devices, must be kept in good repair or it can be very, very expensive.

If the steam traps are allowed to blow into the open air, continual discharge of steam is evidence of misoperation; but as is often the case, the discharge is to a closed gathering system for condensate recovery. This evidence is lacking and periodic checks are the only recourse. It can be a serious error to assume that steam trap operation is as it should be and leave the trap unchecked.

An effective plan to avoid loss of steam is one in which each employee of an operating facility is urged to be alert for steam leakage such as poorly packed valve stems, leaking gaskets, improperly closed valves and steam traps which need repair. If steam loss is observed, it must be immediately reported to a central agency which can arrange for repairs.

Distribution of steam at required pressure and with from 50-100° superheat as it leaves the generator has proven to be economically superior to distribution of steam at the same pressure and saturated as it leaves the generator because the superheat tends to avoid the presence of moisture in the system and there is less need for constant trap drainage.

Since rising pressure on the steam supply increases the enthalpy or total heat content of the steam, it is often very advantageous to distribute steam at high pressure to points of usage along the system where the steam pressure is dropped from supply pressure to the required pressure. If the pressure is dropped from 500 psig to 150 psig as required service pressure, the extra heat content of the steam at 500 psig causes the steam at 150 psig to be slightly superheated and thus quite dry, or at least of higher quality than the 500 psig steam.

9

Theory

Research relating to combustion processes and reactions has been carried out for the better part of two centuries. The findings have been reported in the literature, but, quite distressingly, there is small agreement in findings as they pertain to a specific function.

This state of affairs, which is completely atypical of scientific pursuits, generally has been the source of much confusion and debate as the postulations—all set forth by people of standing in the scientific and industrial communities—are studied and applied. Of course, science and industry are not necessarily related because one seeks discovery and the other seeks to benefit through discovery; but if reported discovery fails to produce benefit there is, rightfully enough, great tendency to criticize the discoverer for publishing data which cannot be verified in industrial operation. This happens despite the fact that as the discovery is applied to industry there are almost certainly deviations from the specific research conditons; however, it may be considered the researcher's responsibility to carefully point out all limiting conditions which justify his findings.

The Importance of Research

Utter importance of fuel research to industry is quite understandable since fuel is a major portion of operation cost. This is particularly true of petroleum refining but also of chemicals, petro-chemicals and metals production and power generation.

Fuel research can become almost fantastically complex because there are literally hundreds of fuels—each of which has its own composition and burning characteristics. In addition, the state of burning for each fuel can be controlled. Control of burning for each of the hundred of fuels, will more than quadruple the research effort. It is an active and diligent researcher who properly examines the separate characteristics of more than five fuels!

The research is further burdened because he must take his data as based on a specific set of conditions, with such techniques as he may elect and within the limits of accuracy of the chosen instrumentation with which data are taken. In reporting data, instrument error is an inescapable hazard which must be minimized as instrumentation is chosen; thus, there is partial control of this source of error. However, a great source of error lies in the specific conditions of air supply, air pressure, fuel-air mixture procedure, fuel condition as to pressure, temperature and chemical purity and the partial pressure of water vapor in the fuel-air mixtures, as well as the true state of fuel-air mixture homogeneity.

Literature Disagreement

Published data seldom provide the full picture which can be depended upon for study. A typical example of this is the case of a well-known and respected chemical handbook which, in one place, lists the autoignition temperature of methane (CH_4) as $999°F$ and another place states the auto-ignition temperature of methane as ranging from $1,202°F$ to $1,382°F$. This state of confusion and contradiction, rather than being an isolated case is instead typical of the literature pertaining to combustion. It is not unreasonable to think that a very serious accident might occur if one of the lower autoignition temperatures were applied even after diligent reference to authority. It is further to be noted that all three figures are correct, if the partial pressure of water vapor in the fuel-air mixture is taken into account!

Potential error in connection with autoignition temperature is but one of the significant hazards. It is quite common to find disagreement between authorities—and respected authorities—as to the calorific values of fuels which are in daily use.

Study of theoretical combustion for any particular fuel must delve into the varying states of chemistry, reaction, endothermic and exothermic states, gross and net heating value per pound or per cubic foot, ultimate flame temperature and other factors. However, it is when there is an attempt to delineate the steps in the chemistry of burning (either on a theoretical or an observed basis) that the state of divergence of educated opin-

ion becomes truly obvious. As an example, there was heated debate for years as to which hydrocarbon fuel component burned first—the hydrogen or the carbon. This was typical of earlier fuel burning research but the debate continues, with learned papers in support of the divergent views.

Potential Research Reporting Errors

The earlier researches considered hydrogen and carbon separately, in point of burning, and the segment of the scientific community concerned with the burning of carbon set up their own debate as to whether CO_2 or CO was the initial product. Angus Smith (1863) found that when moist oxygen was adsorbed by charcoal at $10°F$, it evolved as CO_2 upon elevation of temperature to $212°F$. Sir Lowthian Bell (1872) challenged prior production of CO_2 in carbon burning by sampling gases from just above the tuyeres of a blast furnace to find 1% CO_2 and more than 37% CO, with the remainder of the sample as N_2, and promptly declared himself as favoring the CO school of thought, despite the fact that in the blast furnace there is an ideal condition for the reaction $C + CO_2 - 2CO$ to support the conclusion research all too frequently proves a point rather than discovers what is happening and how.

Experiments with Carbon Oxidation

A further work found that when diamond was strongly heated in air CO_2 was produced, but we are left to wonder what the strongly heated temperature might have been. This work and the work of Smith intrigued C.J. Baker (1887) and H.B. Baker (1888). H.B. Baker found that when carbon was heated in a closed chamber filled with anhydrous oxygen the carbon did not glow as it did with moist oxygen and that the gases in the chamber contained both CO and CO_2 despite the presence of excess oxygen. C.J. Baker repeated Smith's experiment with moist oxygen to verify the evolution of CO_2, but when he repeated it with anhydrous oxygen the gaseous evolution did not occur at $212°F$ and it was necessary to drive the temperature level to a reported $842°F$ to obtain gaseous evolution. At that temperature the gas is CO rather than CO_2. It is to be noted that the C.J. Baker research is one of the first if not actually the first reference to the role of water vapor in oxidation of fuel. But neither Baker nor others who have read his report became aware of its significance as a possible, catalytic agent in combustion reactions.

Burning carbon for the production of useful heat is much better understood at this writing; however, there is still brisk debate as to whether CO or CO_2 is the initial product because of the many variables to be considered in the burning of carbon in its solid state whether the carbon is a lump of coke or graphite or carbon derived through dissociation of hydrocarbons to produce a typical yellow flame in gas or oil burning. Chemistries, routes or manners in which carbon is converted to its oxides either endothermically or exothermically can vary quite considerably, accounting for the peculiar burning characteristics.

Possible Carbon Oxidation Chemistries

If it is presumed that the temperature is adequate for them, the reactions can be as follows and either singly or with all reactions simultaneously (within a few microseconds).

$$C + O_2 = CO_2$$
$$2C + O_2 = 2CO$$
$$C + CO_2 = 2CO$$
$$CO + \tfrac{1}{2}O_2 = CO_2$$
$$C + H_2O = CO + H_2$$
$$C + 2H_2O = CO_2 + 2H_2$$
$$CO + H_2O = CO_2 + H_2$$

With the number of states of reaction possible and in view of the necessity for microsecond sampling, it is small wonder that debate continues as to which is first produced—CO_2 or CO. However, the resolution of this particular debate is distinctly within the realm of pure science and not necessarily pertinent in the burning of fuels except that the *final* oxide of carbon must be CO_2 if fuel cost is minimized. Since carbon, as such, is a solid, oxidation occurs through surface attack and not through diffusion, as is the case with gaseous fuels.

Carbon has another characteristic which causes it to be the problem child of fuel burning. Because of its great loss of heat by radiation due to its emissivity near 1.00 and the endothermic C + CO_2 = 2CO reaction, there is greater heat lost than heat produced as it burns. Heat loss results in cessation of burning because the carbon temperature falls below its kindling temperature, unless the burning is proceeding in an atmosphere at a temperature which is capable of causing continued burning to complete oxidation. If the carbon content of the fuel does not burn, the unburned carbon will appear as black smoke at the expense of greater fuel demand since the heat value of the carbon is not recovered.

This characteristic of carbon is easily proven in the typical home barbecue in which charcoal briquettes are used as fuel. It is common knowledge that a suitable state of burning requires that the briquettes be in a rather neat pile such that each burning briquette is "looking" at other burning briquettes, which are equally hot, to minimize heat radiation loss and permit continued burning. Each burning briquette will then glow brightly because it is producing more heat than it is losing. But if one brightly glowing briquette is taken from the pile and placed off to one side, permitting unrestricted radiation heat loss, it will promptly cease to burn.

The "Three T's" of Combustion

A state of required temperature thus becomes a factor in fuel burning, first to initiate burning or kindling and secondly to determine the subsequent rate of burning. But temperature is only one of the "Three T's." Temperature, time and turbulence all govern the speed and chemistry of burning after its initiation. Here enters still another factor. There are two—not one—thermal states directly related to fuel burning. The initial state is endothermic before the final exothermic state can exist because the mixture of fuel with an adequate supply of air as a source of oxygen must be driven to a temperature adequate for kindling or igniting the fuel before the exothermic state of burning can begin and the temperature level can rise. Temperature level, following initiation of temperature rise, directly governs the speed or time of burning if all other factors are fixed and in very close relationship with Arrhenius's equations for the effect of temperature on the velocity of chemical reactions. The effect of temperature is fixed in a constant state of turbulence, but if this state is increased as the burning reactions progress, the burning reactions speed up in keeping with the increase in turbulence. Thus, the burning of fuels progresses at a speed and according to the effects of Three T's of combustion.

Water Vapor and Combustion

However, there is still another factor which merits consideration—the role of water vapor in the burning of fuels. In this respect, there are many effects which escape consideration. It is now accepted that the very great deviation in autoignition temperatures, as postulated by respected authority, is principally due to lack of consideration of the partial pressures of water vapor in the gas-air mixtures as they were checked for ignition temperature; checks of the identical hydrocarbons, in ranges from the anhydrous condition to saturation at 70°F, show that the anhydrous ignition temperature can be as much as 70% higher than the saturation ignition temperature. Repeated checks at identical partial pressures of water vapor show very close correlation and are, in fact, well within the limits of accuracy of the temperature instrumentation. Also, it has been shown through re-research of speeds of flame propagation that the speed of flame propagation is always greater in saturated air-fuel mixtures and that, at times, the speed of flame propagation in a saturated mixture is twice as great as in a dry mixture. As an example of potential error, it is noted that one international authority lists the flame speed in a hydrogen-air mixture as 9.60 ft./sec., while another equally respected authority says such a flame speed is 16.00 ft./sec. These data were taken in 1 in. tubes in each case, but most references show marked increase in flame speed as the diameter of the tube in which it is checked is increased. As a matter of perhaps passing interest is the observa-

tion based on more than 33 years experience in design and operation of gas burners that there are relatively few instances there where speed of flame propagation was a governing or limiting condition as such in the normal function of burners for hydrocarbon fuels.

There are repeated observations of shorter flame and more rapid burning of fuel when the relative humidity is high than when it is low. For identical heat release, the steam-atomized oil flame is less than half as long and much brighter and crisper than the pressure-atomized or mechanical-atomized flame. The fireman who hand stoked a coal-fired boiler knew that when he sprayed his coal with water prior to scooping it into the furnace, his fire was hotter, made less smoke and he burned less coal per 1,000 lbs. of steam. All these observations add up to evidence that water vapor materially aids the processes of combustion, whether by catalytic action or otherwise, yet typical studies of fuels burning seldom take this into account. There is reason to believe that the effects of water vapor as just discussed are within the realm of catalysis, because while there is certain direct chemical combination of water vapor with hydrocarbons to form CO/CO_2 and release hydrogen, this chemistry is endothermic and tends to reduce the immediate temperature even though it does convert the carbon to CO, in one case, and always releases hydrogen and these gases burn with great rapidity. In the normal case, there is not enough water vapor present to cause this particular reaction to materially influence the speed of burning of the entire fuel mass. We thus note that the presence of water vapor speeds fuel burning and materially influences speed of flame propagation and, as is suggested, it would appear that the effect is due to some form of catalysis which is unexplained at this writing if, indeed, it is recognized by those of the scientific community pursuing their studies of fuel burning.

NOx Factors

Because typical burning of fuels, however they may be burned, results in the formation of oxides of nitrogen to greater or lesser degree, a pollution-imposed limitation now burdens all heat-energy production derived through fuels usage in industry. Reason is that NOx is a significant generator of "smog" through complex reactions about which much has been written following researches by many capable people. The limiting result of research finding is that various environmentally concerned agencies have promulgated rules (which are well equipped with "teeth" for enforcement) to limit NOx emission to atmosphere wherever and however fuels are burned.

Formation of NOx in the course of combustion can be considered a somewhat puzzling factor for a number of reasons; and, as is typical of combustion generally, there is considerable disagreement in research findings as published as to what may be done to secure reduction in NOx emission. The fact that NOx generation is typically and initially as NO (nitric oxide) which demands 21.6 K Cal/gram-mol of endothermal heat, directly suggests high temperature level for formation. One school of thought insists that the high temperature level must exist in both the flame and in the combustion chamber while another is sure that *either* high furnace temperature or high flame temperature results in excessive NOx generation with small difference resulting from *either* condition separately. Current research findings which have been carefully verified cast doubt on the temperature factor for either flame or furnace. Where flame/furnace cooling is obtained with CO_2 and H_2O containing recirculated cold flue gas, there is quite marked reduction in NOx emission, but equal cooling with other inert and non-reactive gases causes small reduction in NOx emission.

One widely held shibboleth holds that the presence of nitrogen bonded into the fuel molecule (such as NH_3, HCN) drastically increases NOx generation. A number of papers support this view and tests support the view, but there is failure to take into account the fact that NH_3 has been used as an NOx suppressant with great success.

Contradictory research findings, as properly considered, pointedly suggest either error in research techniques or error in observation of data, as well as need for an entirely new approach to the demanding problem of reduction in NOx emission.

Some groups, reasoning that all combustion reaction is chemical in nature, have adopted means for alteration of normal combustion chemistries with considerable success to secure emission of less than 50 ppm of NOx in normal fuels burning. Their findings confirm that the presence of either CO or H_2 within the reducing areas of the flame accomplishes marked reduction in NOx emission. Various techniques for promotion of such a condition are presently research objects including recirculation of relatively cool stack gases to the combustion zone to obtain both lowered flame temperature and alteration of burning chemistry as:

$$CH_4 + CO_2 = 2\text{-}CO + 2\text{-}H_2$$
$$H_2O + CH_4 = 2\text{-}CO + 2\text{-}H_2$$

Reaction as shown for CH_4-CO_2 and CH_4-H_2O is endothermal but experiments involving direct injection of H_2 to proper flame zones produces equal NOx reduction without significant flame-cooling action to lead to postulation that NOx reduction is essentially due to alteration of burning chemistry. The postulation is not confirmed beyond reasonable doubt and research continues for suitable means for reduced NOx emission.

Research toward further reduction in combustion-evolved NOx tends to be quite frustrating for those who wish to compute NOx production for a specific condition of fuel burning. This condition results because computation-predicted NOx evolution is rarely (if ever) even reasonably close to actual NOx measurement after burning. It is universal that the presence of bonded nitrogen in the fuel drastically increases NOx presence in flue gases whether the fuel is gaseous or liquid. Ammonia or gaseous amines (also liquid amines) are examples.

One apparently firm factor is that the bonded nitrogen must pass through the oxidation reactions if NOx production is to increase. This process takes place because of the presence of bonded nitrogen in the fuel. If the burning of the bonded nitrogen-bearing fuel is carried at sub-stoichiometric conditions for oxygen, and if ammonia is added to the hot gases after combustion, the NOx presence is sharply reduced. This practice, despite its expense, is not uncommon for NOx abatement.

As a matter of theoretical fact, the presence of NOx in combustion gases may be considered a baffling anomaly that is a serious problem in oil fuel burning. A paper which appeared in the December 1978 issue of *Chemical Engineering Progress* on page 59 (Reed and Martin) postulates a reason for the anomaly. In the presence of free radicals oxygen combines immediately with nitrogen at a more than 5,000°F (2,760°C) heat level. This heat level is characteristic of uncooled fuel-O_2 heat production such as fuel that is burned with pure oxygen where nitrogen does not perform its cooling function. In normal fuel burning the presence of excess air in the combustion zone governs NOx presence to a certain, small degree if the excess air is not great enough to have an undue cooling effect (such as from 5% to 20%). However, NOx is invariably present in any excess air, permitting stable burning well in excess of 100%.

A favored gesture toward fuel conservation is the use of preheated combustion air. Unfortunately, this procedure has been shown to repeatedly cause a significant increase in NOx flue gases shown by the air preheat temperature with higher temperatures. This condition increases NOx evolution, bringing fuel conservation and NOx abatement into conflict.

The conflict exists for burner equipment which does not produce NOx abatement or typical burners for either/both gas and oil fuels. Intense research in burner designs that will permit air preheat along with "legal" NOx production have been successful and were completed in 1979. Oxides of nitrogen in stack gases in excess of allowable concentrations has been a fuel-use problem in the burning of # 6 oil because of its bonded nitrogen content. Environmental rules prescribe 200 ppm of NOx as the maximum allowable, although in some old burners at oil-fired installations more than 300 ppm is common. With suitably designed burners, 150 ppm of NOx can be attained. However, the heat release per burner becomes significant, since it has been repeatedly shown that higher heat release per burner increases NOx evolution. A lower heat release per burner will decrease NOx with any fuel, but particularly with # 6 oil. The relative increase or decrease in oxides of nitrogen in heat release is not yet firm, but there is growing evidence that 10MM/Btu/hr/burner is a maximum figure.

The restriction on heat release per burner in avoidance of excessive NOx is a problem for steam generators where few burners deliver a large heat release per burner. The restriction is also a problem where operators prefer to reduce drastically the number of burners firing relatively large furnaces. There is no known relief for heat release restriction where NOx is a problem; however, the NOx emission from stacks has been held within acceptable limits, especially with steam-flood generators using heavy California oils where per-burner heat release is low.

Combustion reactions typical of carbon and hydrogen burning are given below, using methane as an example of hydrocarbon burning. Heats are expressed on a 60°F basis.

$$2\text{-}C + O_2 = 2\text{-}CO + 52,200 \text{ Btu/mol}$$
$$C + O_2 = CO_2 + 174,600 \text{ Btu/mol}$$
$$C + CO_2 = 2\text{-}CO - 70,200 \text{ Btu/mol}$$
$$C + H_2O = CO + H_2 - 70,900 \text{ Btu/mol}$$
$$C + 2\text{-}H_2O = CO_2 + 2\text{-}H_2 - 71,600 \text{ Btu/mol}$$
$$CH_4 + HEAT = C + 2\text{-}H_2 - 36,800 \text{ Btu/mol}$$
$$CH_4 + 2\text{-}O_2 = CO_2 + 2\text{-}H_2O + 384,000 \text{ Btu/mol}$$
$$2\text{-}CO + O_2 = 2\text{-}CO_2 + 122,000 \text{ Btu/mol}$$
$$2\text{-}H_2 + O_2 = 2\text{-}H_2O + 123,000 \text{ Btu/mol}$$
$$CO + H_2O = CO_2 + H_2 - 700 \text{ Btu/mol}$$
$$CH_4 + H_2O = CO + 3\text{-}H_2 - 88,635 \text{ Btu/mol}$$
$$CH_4 + 2\text{-}H_2O = CO_2 + 4\text{-}H_2 - 70,912 \text{ Btu/mol}$$
$$CH_4 + CO_2 = 2\text{-}CO + 2\text{-}H_2 - 106,358 \text{ Btu/mol}$$

Fuel Compositions and Burning Chemistries

Typical fuels, whether they be gaseous, liquid or solid, are composed principally of carbon and hydrogen in varying weight percentages from which are derived the H/C ratios, by weight; also, the fuel can be high purity hydrogen or high purity carbon, in isolated circumstances, which are not necessarily of interest here because such fuel is rarely used for commercial burning. As carbon and hydrogen burn the oxidation reactions are highly exothermic such that the lower heating value of hydrogen is approximately 51,500 Btu/lb. and the heating value of carbon is about 14,100 Btu/lb. Hydrogen burns extremely rapidly, producing a pale lavender flame which is difficult to see except against a dark background. Hydrogen burns as a gas while carbon burns slowly, very brightly and as a solid. This presumes that each burns separately and such is the case if the hydrocarbon fuel burns with a yellow flame; however, if the hydrocarbon burns with a blue or translucent flame, there is no separate burning and both hydrogen and carbon are combined and as distinct molecules until burning is completed. The final products of burning are CO_2 and H_2O. We are thus led to the postulation that the chemistries of yellow flame and blue flame burning are quite separate and distinct—and indeed they are. In the case of yellow luminous flame, the color is due to dissociation or cracking of the hydrocarbon to its carbon and hydrogen components followed by separate and very rapid burning of hydrogen and slow burning of carbon, which as it is heated by the burning hydrogen glows brightly at approximately the temperature of the hydrogen flame; but the pale lavender of the hydrogen flame is completely hidden in the bright yellow glow of the incandescent carbon.

Blue flame burning of the same hydrocarbon is due to a state of progressive oxygenation/reaction in which there are no dissociation reactions to allow uncombined carbon to be present in the flame envelope. Both yellow and blue flame produce the ultimate products of CO_2 and H_2O to denote the separate oxidation of hydrogen and carbon; thus, there is no significant difference in heat production whether the fuel burns with yellow or blue flame, which is contrary to widely held opinions. Since the identical fuel can be burned in either color flame, it is necessary to determine what is required for either flame color, since identical quantities of air and fuel can be present in either case. Here again we venture into the gray area of debate as to theoretical combustion; thus, there will be an effort to present both sides of the debate along with certain comments derived from personal research which will tend to favor one series of reactions. But the statement that yellow flame is the result of poor or inadequate air-gas mixture, in most cases, is a fundamental truth, according to the H/C ratio by weight of the fuel, with higher H/C values less prone to yellow flame burning than lower values. However, this statement is somewhat tempered by the specific state of turbulence as the fuel burns; but the state of turbulence governs the state of mixture at any point before or after burning starts.

It is widely thought that yellow flame burning occurs as a result of air deficiency, but this opinion is incorrect because yellow flame burning can exist in any condition of lack of air or with infinite excess air present. There is a tendency for yellow flame burning as the molecular weight of any fuel increases, when the separate hydrocarbons of the same series of compounds are being burned, which is to say that butane is much more prone to yellow flame than methane. Butane has a molecular weight of approximately 58 and methane has a molecular weight of approximately 16. Both are representative of the paraffin hydrocarbon series. But molecular weight alone is not a criterion for yellow flame, as there is movement from one hydrocarbon series to another, as is the case in ethane (paraffin) to ethylene (olefin) because here the molecular weight of ethane (30) is greater than that of ethylene (28), yet ethylene is very yellow-flame prone and ethane is relatively easy to burn without any yellow flame. Thus, some factor other than molecular weight must be sought. The answer is found in the weight ratio of hydrogen to carbon as the key factor in reference to fuel excellence as well as to the relative yellow-flame tendency. In all cases, the higher H/C ratio-by-weight is preferred. For example, methane, which can be described as the most preferable of fuels, has an H/C ratio of 0.33, ethane has an H/C ratio of 0.25, butane has a ratio of hydrogen weight to carbon weight of 0.208 and the H/C of ethylene is 0.166, which is typical of all olefins.

However, the difficulty with burning or decreasing excellence of fuel is not directly proportional to H/C ratio decrease. It can be generally said that if the H/C ratio exceeds 0.200, the fuel can be burned satisfactorily with suitable conditions of air mixture and turbulence, but at less than the 0.200 ratio there is considerable difficulty. As the weight ratio approaches 0.100, very difficult, expensive techniques and procedures are demanded to secure proper burning. Carbon is, indeed, the problem child of fuel burning.

When the separate elements carbon, hydrogen, oxygen and nitrogen are present in a zone where the state of thermal excitation can be considered magnificent, as the separate elements go through both rise and fall of temperature level, there is small wonder that there is little agreement in the scientific community as to the whats, whys and hows of fuel burning. It can be stated without equivocation that the burning may be as a yellow flame, as a blue flame and, at times, both yellow and blue flame due to specific fuel conditions, air presence, turbulence and air-gas mixture as well as temperature.

Blue Flame Burning

It now becomes of interest to study blue flame burning; but as we begin, it must be pointed out that controversy as to specific phenomena and states of reaction is generally typical of combustion studies. It must also be said that reasonable postulation by capable authority is usually correct; therefore, it might be intemperate to say that one specific procedure is correct and the remainder are incorrect, in total, and should be disregarded.

At this time, there are two general explanations of blue flame burning which seem to be acceptable and thus are generally adopted. One theory says that such burning is due to progressive oxygenation (or hydroxylation) of the hydrocarbon in a relatively small number of steps, while the

other presumes a greater number of steps and quite different states of reaction, but both processes produce identical final products. It is to be understood that in the choice of these separate processes, there is not delineation of all theory but discussion is considered adequate. The separate processes are as follows, with methane as the fuel in each case:

$$CH_4 + OH = CH_3 + H_2O$$
$$CH_3 + O_2 = OH + HCHO = HCO + H_2O$$
$$HCO + O_2 = CO + HO_2$$
$$HCHO + HO_2 = CO_2 + 3OH$$
$$2HCHO + O_2 = 2\text{-}CO + 2\text{-}H_2O$$
$$2CO + O_2 = 2CO_2$$

$$CH_4 + \tfrac{1}{2}O_2 = CH_3OH$$
$$CH_3OH + \tfrac{1}{2}O_2 = CHOH + H_2O$$
$$CHOH + H_2O + Heat = CO + H_2 + H_2O$$
$$CO + H_2 + H_2O + O_2 = CO_2 + 2H_2O$$

As the two processes are considered, note that the CH_3OH phase is completely neglected in one process. There is certain omission here because careful probing of a Bunsen flame with a chilled capillary tube clearly shows that CH_3OH is present despite theories that it cannot exist. If it cannot exist, why then is it found? In the procedures shown, vast over-simplification is highly probable because of the thermally induced state of potential reaction and additional chemistries which are not only possible but often occur. Some, but far from all, of the chemistries are as follows:

$$C + O_2 = CO_2$$
$$CO_2 + C = 2CO$$
$$2C + O_2 = 2CO$$
$$2CO + O_2 = 2CO_2$$
$$CH_4 + H_2O = CO + 3H_2$$
$$CH_4 + CO_2 = 2CO + 2H_2$$
$$2H_2 + O_2 = 2H_2O$$
$$C + H_2O = CO + H_2$$
$$C + 2H_2O = CO_2 + 2H_2$$
$$CO + H_2O = CO_2 + H_2$$
$$CH_4 + 2H_2O = CO_2 + 4H_2$$
$$CH_4 + HEAT = C + 2H_2$$

In both of the theoretical combustion processes shown for hydrocarbon burning and oxidation, the initial steps are satisfactorily exothermal, or heat productive, although the first suggested procedure involves direct combination of the OH radical (rather than oxygen) with the hydrocarbon, and the second or "hydroxylation" theory proposes partial oxydation. Neither is presented as a conclusive and correct procedure. The presentation here is to illustrate the degree of academic controversy in relation to combustion factors. Both procedures have been academically endorsed with enthusiasm.

It is interesting to note the effect of water vapor on flame propagation speed and ignition temperature. The flame speed is low when the fuel/air mixture is deficient in water vapor, high when it is saturated; and the ignition temperature is very high in water vapor deficiency and low in saturation. Water vapor, as a source of the OH radical, suggests validity for the first procedure, but the fact that ignition CAN occur in an anhydrous gas-air mixture suggests caution unless it is postulated that the ignition source provides the required water vapor. A further factor is added to the confusion and controversy because of the presence of CH_3OH in the methane-produced Bunsen flame as proposed by the hydroxylation postulation.

It must clear that while the alpha (fuel) and the omega (products) are quite firm and fixed, there are myriad paths between them or from beginning to end of the combustion processes; and while there is scientific debate as to the specific paths followed, this debate is to be considered of only minor interest to one who seeks to create profit through the burning of fuels, because his concern is essentially with what goes in and what comes out and making best use of the fuel.

He is concerned, however, with the nature of his fuels and how they will best serve their purpose in terms of cost, ease of burning, ease of control, satisfactory relation of fuel with the process and other factors. A suggestion has been made that methane (CH_4 with H/C ratio of 0.33) is considered the ideal fuel, as concerned with operational factors; and in an effort to show the effect of H/C as a fuel factor we will consider butadiene (C_4H_6

with H/C = 0.125). It is extremely difficult to get rapid, clear flame burning of butadiene with any typical burner configuration. But butadiene can be caused to burn with the excellence of methane if adequate partial pressure of water vapor is added before burning begins. The direct reaction of butadiene with water vapor is: $C_4H_6 + 4H_2O = 4CO + 7H_2$ However, it is not necessary or desirable to add four volumes of water vapor to each volume of butadiene as the reaction formula would indicate. It is necessary for the condition of reaction to proceed to a point where a combination of carbon as CO and release of H_2 has the required upgrading effect on the H/C ratio as the fuel burns and to retain the carbon in partial combination with oxygen until the final oxidation step is completed. This is but one of a number of procedures with which less desirable fuels can be made far less troublesome. Even impure acetylene (C_2H_2 with H/C = 0.083) can be made to behave as fuel in a much less troublesome manner!

This applies to any fuel; but as there is consideration of all fuels typical of the process plant and as it is understood that such fuels may be either gaseous or liquid, it is evident that special treatment for liquid fuel burning must exist for a comparable state of burning since all comment has been in reference to the gaseous phase for both fuels and oxygen source which is typically air. Gases cannot diffuse into liquids for mixture. In any case, there must be a fuel-air mixture, so obviously liquid fuels must first be converted to the gaseous phase before any reasonable state of burning can begin. For this function, all liquid fuel burners are equipped with atomizer devices. This term is misleading because its function is not to separate the liquid mass into atoms, as such, but to break the liquid mass up into micron-size droplets. This tremendously increases surface-to-mass ratio for extremely rapid oil heating for delivery of sensible and latent heat to the oil mass, converting it to vapor so that the air-fuel mixture can occur and rapid burning can begin presuming heat supply and temperature are adequate. This is a very large "if" and all liquid fuel burner designs must provide for it if the oil burner is to be satisfactory for firing. A further requirement is that the heat supply and the temperature must exist within inches of forward movement from the atomizer.

Thus, the burning of liquid fuel such as oil requires a means for breaking up the oil into micron-size droplets, instant conversion of liquid to vapor, instant mixture of part of the air for burning with the vaporized liquid and stable ignition, within a time interval which is for accuracy measured in microseconds. It may be said that the prime function in this critical series is the degree with which truly micronized droplets are produced by the atomizer. Many designs perform this service with varying degrees of burning excellence, which can be measured as speed of burning, presence or absence of sparklers or rapidly moving sparks emerging from the flame zone proper, fire flies or burning blobs of oil in the furnace and ability to operate without smoke at low excess air with very low demand for atomizing steam. Very low steam demand has been defined as 0.10 lbs. steam/lb. of oil; but as the technology of steam atomization improves, this figure is rapidly becoming obsolete. At this time, there are well-verified cases where measured steam for atomization is as low as 0.05 lbs./lb. of No.6 oil. While this will appeal to those with experience as a bit preposterous, it is documented by many carefully conducted tests. A wag has said, with tongue in cheek, "Lives there an engineer with soul so dead that upon contemplating an oil atomizer design cannot immediately design a better one?" However, and because there are literally hundreds of oil atomizer designs, the statement is not as waggish as it might seem.

Oil Burning Criteria

The buyer must have some means for predetermining the excellence of the atomizer-equipped oil burning unit he plans to purchase. In this respect, a number of points need examination prior to purchase.

1. What is the demand for atomizing steam for the heat release contemplated with the understanding that steam rates per pound of oil decrease markedly at higher heat release and increase as the heat release is reduced?

2. Does the atomizer/burner assembly produce a bright and clean fire at low excess air and at reasonable steam demand?

3. What is the turn-down ratio or what is the operating range of the assembly in point of maximum and minimum heat release?

4. How tolerant is the burner for continued good operation when changing fuel, for varying viscosity of fuel as delivered for burning, with what may be low-quality steam?

If it is felt that these factors might better be discussed under the heading of "Burners," it is pointed out that the factors pertain to the theoretical basis for fuels burning and are due for attention here.

How to Atomize Oils?

Other means for atomization, aside from steam techniques, exist. But the many advantages of steam make it most commonly used, so it alone will be considered here. Atomization of oil through the use of steam is due to two significant phenomena. First is the shearing action of high-energy, high-velocity steam streams. Second is the tendency for oils to foam or emulsify in contact with hot water vapor. Opinion is naturally divided as to which is more important because no means for proof exist when both are present. Basic phenomena which cause or permit the required high temperature/high heat density zone to exist are typical and are largely functions of simple physics, whatever the burner design configuration. There are at least 50 separate and distinct oil burner designs for the many firing services for oil fuels. All are reasonably satisfactory.

Fuel Oil Types

Typical oil fuels fall into general classifications: distillates and residual oil fuels. Each type has advantages and disadvantages of cost, burning characteristics, viscosity, preparation required for burning, costs for handling or oil stand-by, difficulty in handling and the H/C ratio-by-weight. Distillate fuels are, of course, produced through some distillation operation; however, they may range from propane to very heavy gas-oil. Residual fuels are generally the unevaporated components of a stream of oil charged to a distillation system of some sort. Distillates are generally composed of saturated hydrocarbons with mean H/C ratios which seldom fall as low as 0.178. The exceptions are the olefin-rich cat-cracker cycle stocks which, because of their low H/C ratio, cannot be sold as burning oil because of their soot and bad burning characteristics. Distillate fuels are preferred for burning since they can, if required, be burned with flames very similar to those from gas or only partly yellow luminous. Residual fuels burn with typical yellow oil flame because of low H/C ratios by weight and because their dissociation temperatures are so low.

In fuel burning, air is the oxygen source for the exothermic reactions. Therefore, air must be admitted in relatively measured manners for mixture with the fuels. As air for burning is considered, there are two states of air admission which are of interest. One refers to theoretical air or air required for chemically complete burning, while the other refers to theoretical plus excess air, which is the state of fuels burning in industry. The latter statement is true because laws of chemistry require an excess of one component involved in a state of reaction, if the reaction is to be driven to completion within a reasonable time.

Air may be considered, for all essential purposes, as a mixture of oxygen and nitrogen. Very dry air, rather than being such a simple mixture, is actually a mixture of many gases. A chemistry handbook which has worldwide acceptance provides us with the following analysis:

Nitrogen	78.024%	
Oxygen	20.946%	
Argon	0.934%	
Carbon Dioxide	0.033%	
Neon		18.180 ppm
Helium		5.240 ppm
Krypton		1.140 ppm
Xenon		.087 ppm
Hydrogen		.500 ppm
Methane		2.000 ppm
Oxides of Nitrogen		.500 ppm

In typical air, as checked in an industrial area, there would be microscopic traces of other gases such as SO_2, other oxides of nitrogen, ozone and others. However, air as the source of oxygen for fuel burning is to all intents and purposes oxygen and nitrogen. Here we speak of dry air and in nature, air in such a condition simply does not exist. Instead, air is humid, with water vapor content varying from the very low relative humidity of a desert to 100% relative humidity. It is a rare industrial area which does not, at times, experience 100% relative humidity. The air of such an area at $100°F$ carries with it close to 6.45% water vapor. If fuel burning with such an air supply is being carried out at very low excess air and in close volume control, there is no escape from periods of operation in oxygen deficiency and, accordingly, partial loss of unburned fuel as humidity changes. (See Figure 9-1).

Water Vapor in Humid Air

One of the fallacies of air supply calculations for fuel burning is neglect of the potential water vapor content of the air supply. With methane as fuel, it is quite easy to determine air supply on the basis of stoichiometric burning as.

$$CH_4 + 2O_2 + 7.6N_2 = CO_2 + 2H_2O + 7.6N_2.$$

This formulation, which is rounded for ease of handling with a volumetric error of 0.3%, shows that for each cubic foot (or 1 pound-mol) of methane, the oxygen demand is 2 cu. ft. (2 pounds-mol); and with the oxygen due to air supply, there are 7.60 cu. ft. (7.60 pounds-mol) of nitrogen. The air supply for methane is 9.60 cu. ft. per cubic foot (or 9.60 pounds-mol/mol). If 9.60 is multiplied by the excess air factor required, the air supply would seem to be established in either case. Not so! It has not been established because the

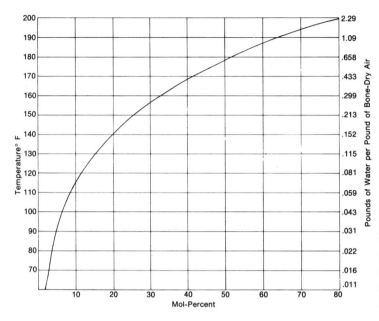

Figure 9-1. Data for mol-percentages of water vapor at 100% relative humidity (saturation) in mixtures of bone-dry air and water vapor as well as pounds of bone-dry air at atmospheric pressure.

basic calculation is as bone-dry air and the air actually used will contain varying percentages of water vapor as humid air. Therefore, if the volumetric ratio of 9.60/1 is used, there will not be enough oxygen to completely burn the fuel and fuel loss can result according to the excess air factor used. At saturation, the air can contain about 1.50% water vapor at 60°F and about 6.5% at 100°F. As has been stated, a temperature level of 100°F with 100% relative humidity is a distinct possibility at most job sites for many process furnaces.

Regardless of the excess air factor set up for air volume or weight calculation, if correction for water vapor content of admitted air is not taken into account, the operating excess air will be less than calculated. This factor, added to further potential error due to calculation at 60°F rather than 100°F, can further result in lack of O_2 and lead to serious error if the calculation is based on a low excess air factor initially. The water-vapor error plus the air temperature error can more than cancel a 10% excess air factor and result in incomplete fuel burning.

Combustion Air Calculation

Air quantity calculation for specific fuel burning can be quite easy, with minor error, which is always in the right direction for assured burning or it can be complex. The calculation is easier, in either case, if the dry rather than the humid basis is used and then corrected for the humidity factor as well as the temperature factor and the chosen excess air factor.

Simple procedure takes into account the fortunate circumstance created by the fact that 9.57 cu. ft. of dry air are theoretical air for 1,000 Btu higher heating value or 910 Btu lower heating value for paraffins, less than 6% excess air with olefins and less than 4% excess air with aromatics which are the fuel constituents of greatest interest within the process field. (See Figure 9-2.) Thus, if the higher heating value is being considered for total heat release and if the total heat release is divided by 1,000 then multiplied by 9.57, the *dry* theoretical air quantity for the expected heat release is available for humidity, temperature and excess air correction. If the lower heating value is

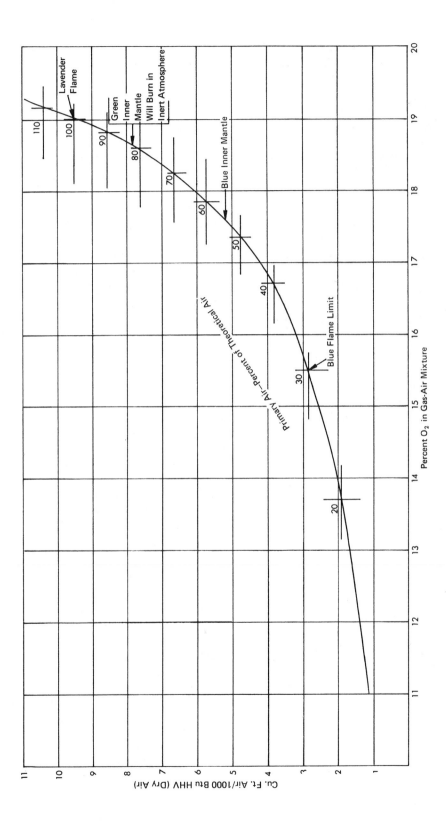

Figure 9-2.   Theoretical air data for natural gases.

used in establishing the total heat release, the division is by 910 rather than by 1,000. Through this procedure there will always be enough air with paraffin fuels and certain excess air for olefins and aromatics. In the case of the latter two fuels, the ancient and esteemed institution of the safety factor or, more properly, the ignorance factor comes into play to deviate some degree from precision, if precision can be said to apply to fuel burning generally.

Micrometric precision in oxidation of fuels is virtually impossible, no matter what the procedure for calculation may be, for excellent reasons:

1. The figure of 20.946% oxygen in air is a mean or average figure.
2. The perfect gas law postulates specific volume for the gram-mol or the pound-mol; but due to deviation from the perfect gas law it appears that no one is absolutely certain what the deviation may be for any specific gas.
3. Air temperature variation
4. Air humidity variation

It is true that in these variables both air weight and air volume are considered, but such consideration is required for air delivery pressure drop calculation. As a means for attempted precision calculation consider burning, for example, 4,000 lbs./hr. of ethane (C_2H_6) for establishment of the dry air requirement:

Fuel weight = 4,000 lbs.
Fuel molecular weight = 30.068
Carbon weight percent = 79.885
Hydrogen weight percent = 20.115
Carbon weight =
4,000 x 0.79885 = 3,195.4 lbs. = 266.061 mols
Hydrogen weight =
4,000 x 0.20115 = 804.6 lbs. = 399.107 mols
O_2 demand for carbon =
266.061 x 1.0 = 266.061 mols
O_2 demand for hydrogen =
399.107 x 0.5 = $\underline{199.553}$ mols
465.614 mols total

Dry air demand = 465.614/0.20946 = 2222.925 mols

Dry air demand, once calculated, must be corrected for temperature; for the excess-air factor; for altitude and for humidity with only altitude and the excess air as fixed numerical factors. But even here the effect of altitude is subject to variation in barometric pressure change. If the calculation should be based on 60°F and if the temperature should change to 100°F, volume change would be 1.0769 and for pressure drop the change would be 1.0377, which is typical.

Thus, temperature change within normal atmospheric ranges can clearly be quite significant. It is equally clear that a drop in temperature has a reverse effect. When pressure deviation is considered where the pressure change is based on barometric pressure changes of typical weather patterns of higher or lower pressure are of concern, the correction is usually a source for concern in precision operation. If, however, the job site is at a significant elevation above sea level (500 ft. or more), the absolute pressure at the job site will be less than that at sea level (14.696 psia) which is taken as 14.7 psia with very small error. In this case, the calculation for air quantity must take into account the less than standard atmospheric pressure at the job site whether the quantity is as mols or standard cubic feet. At standard pressure and temperature 1,000 cu. ft. of air weighs approximately 76.33 lbs. or 0.0763 lbs./cu. ft. with standard pressure as 14.7 psia. If, due to elevation above sea level, the absolute pressure is 11.7 psia, the air is less dense in the ratio of 11.7/14.7 = 0.7959/1.0000. Therefore, the number of cubic feet at 11.7 psia must be increased by 14.7/11.7 = 1.2564 to obtain the oxygen quantity equal to atmospheric pressure at sea level (absolute pressure). Note that if the mols of air are taken as 28.966 lbs. rather than as the volume of a lb./mol, the number of *pounds* of air will be unchanged, but it is still subject to the density correction for altitude or atmospheric pressure at the job site. A greater volume of air will be demanded at the reduced absolute pressure at the job site.

At the equivalent pressure drop for flow, as at altitude, the flow area must be increased to compensate for altitude. Since all flow is based on the area at the pressure drop for the required flow, the area correction is taken as the square root of the absolute pressure ratio. In this case, the square root of 14.7/11.7 = 1.1215 times the area for operation at sea level. This area correction must be applied to burners, ducts, fans or any portion of the air flow system.

It is highly unusual for natural-draft firing of fuels to require any calculation of air-for-combustion, since the burner designer will have considered furnace draft conditions as he sizes burners. Nature, in the form of draft (or less-than-atmospheric pressure) within the furnace, provides the pressure decrease for delivery of adequate air for combustion across the burner air-register. But forced-draft firing is another condition. Computation of air quantity is demanded for blower delivery of air whether there is, or is not, air preheat for fuel conservation as a part of the facility. Air computation for combustion can be a tedious procedure if the fuel analysis is based on pounds of carbon and pounds of hydrogen, "Btu's/cubic foot" of gases, or the Btu's/pound of either gases or oils.

A much simpler and less error-prone procedure is to determine air demand on the basis of per million Btu's as a total figure. This procedure is more efficient because the theoretical air demand for methane per million Btu's is 27.9 mols, and the theoretical air demand for # 6 oil is 27.79 mols. The difference in air demand for either methane or # 6 oil is less than 1%. Therefore, the adequate air for methane combustion will be adequate air for any process fuel in the range between methane and # 6 oil. Air calculation based on methane is a proper and safe procedure for process firing or steam generation.

The presence of either CO or free H_2 in gaseous fuels produces a certain reduction in air demand, but because the CO or H_2 concentrations are subject to variation, and because the "start-up" fuel is usually a hydrocarbon in the methane-to-# 6 oil range, computation of air demand on a methane basis will assure adequate air for combustion. The designer's cardinal sin is insufficient air supply from a blower for a target

process condition. The air pressure capability of the blower must provide for selected windbox pressure, duct and air heater pressure drops, and a suggested "ignorance factor" of at least 1.10.

An error common in computation of air for combustion is the use of handbook air analysis data as mol (or weight) percentages. The handbook air analytical data are for bone-dry air—atmospheric air is invariably humid to some degree. Atmospheric air is the forced-draft blower air supply, and saturated air at 100°F (37.77°C) contains 6.45% water vapor as a dilutant that reduces the oxygen mol-percentage from a handbook-stated 20.95% to 19.68%. Saturation at 100°F (37.77°C) is possible at the vast majority of process sites. Air volume correction for water vapor content is required. In addition, the laws of chemistry provide that if a chemical reaction is to move to completion in a "reasonable" time, there must be an excess of one or another reaction components. In combustion the reaction components are fuel and air, and the "reasonable" time may be defined as milliseconds, or as rapidly as possible. The component excess is taken as air in excess of the theoretical quantity for the combustion reaction sought. Any computation should never presume less than 10% excess air (theoretical air X 1.10).

Computation of combustion air demand should first establish theoretical air as scfh for Q total heat release in millions of Btu's per hour. Methane has a HHV of approximately 1,000 Btu's/cf, and a LHV of 910 Btu's/cf. On the HHV basis, theoretical air is Q/1,000 X 9.6, and on the LHV basis theoretical air is Q/910 X 9.6 with all volumes as scfh. When this computation is done, the computed volumes must be corrected for water vapor content and for excess air:

HHV — (Q/1,000 X 9.6) X 1.0645 X 1.10
= scfh of saturated air/hr at 10% excess air

LHV — (Q/910 X 9.6) X 1.0645 X 1.10 = scfh
of saturated air/hr at 10% excess air

Volumes derived are, again, at scfh of saturated air for blower delivery, but the blower manufacturer must make his own correction for blower air delivery so that the air temperature is 100°F (37.77°C) rather than 60°F (15.55°C). The procedure as suggested has been very satisfactorily used in hundreds of cases, and for all process fuels over many years. Note: the 1.10 "ignorance" factor does not appear here because it is *suggested* as a hedge against improper calculation of pressure drop and not required.

Combustion Air Fundamentals

It is, perhaps, in order to summarize certain factors in relation to air and the burning of fuels. These factors are

1. Some quantity of excess air (oxygen) is demanded.
2. Air must always be considered as humid.
3. Flame color and excess air are not related.
4. Excess air is the fundamental temperature control means for any furnace and any operation involving the burning of fuels.

Because of lack of knowledge of point three above, in reference to flame color, the technical service group of one of the world's largest refineries wasted 5% of the fuel for a 500,000,000 Btu/hr. furnace through improper burner adjustment for more than a year. Error was shown when lightening struck the stack of the heater after dark to create a very long plume of blue flame off the stack! If burner design is adequate for proper firing of the heater, the burner flame will continue to be short, clear and blue when there is as little as 85% of theoretical air present in the burning zone with a predominantly methane fuel, but at a decrease in air supply to less than 85% theoretical air, the burner flame is extinguished. The products of incomplete combustion are aldehydes, hydrogen and carbon monoxide, which cannot be seen as they exit from the stack. Thus, there is no alarm

through the presence of black smoke, in this case. However, with lower H/C ratio-by-weight fuels, such as oils or heavier gases, there is potential alarm through black smoke production in misadjustment, as the H/C ratio of the fuel falls.

A flame such as is produced in the burning of fuel can be seen, has definite proportions, shape and size and has other interesting characteristics such as color and temperature. But as we speak of a flame we might ask just what a flame is. A flame is simply an area within which there is an extremely active series of chemical reactions in the gaseous phase or, if you please, a state of ionization the progress of which can be noted through the visible light produced. Light color is according to the nature of ionization and such light may range in color from pale lavender, light blue, deeper blue, pale apple-green to darker green for the gaseous phase and from red, orange, yellow to white for free carbon contained in the flame zone. Proof of the state of ionization is found in that the gases of the flame conduct electricity to a quite appreciable degree but at quite high resistance. That the state of ionization ceases at the flame boundary can also be shown in that at a point half an inch beyond the flame boundary, there is infinite resistance to flow of electricity.

Physicists tell us that the light emission is due to bond severance in which there is disturbance of the normal orbits of electrons involved. Another state of light emission from the flame can exist when there is ionized mineral matter present such as sodium with its yellow ionization characteristic, calcium with its orangy color, copper with its blue to green color and lithium or strontium with their reddish colors.

These colors are often due to the presence of wind-blown dusts and are not at all related to combustion. Such flames can be seen on a windy day or when there is disturbance of the dust within a wind box or air duct. There is frequent and needless alarm because when the mineral matter is present, the flame will become much larger, but the effect is due to the fact that there is continued ionization of the mineral far beyond the point normal to the combustion reactions and there is no projection of a true flame. Sodium, for example, will continue to ionize out to the 1,800-2,000°F boundary about the flame when the temperature of the flame proper may be at 2,500-2,800°F.

Flame Temperature

Flame temperature in any specific application of fuel burning is governed by many factors, most of which are quite finite but several of which are considered empirical; some are much more significant than others. Nine of these factors are:

1. The quantity of excess air present,
2. The chemistry of combustion,
3. Heat loss from the flame by radiation,
4. Furnace mean temperature,
5. Degree of dissociation of H_2O,
6. Degree of dissociation of CO_2,
7. Degree of dissociation of fuel,
8. State of hydrocarbon-H_2O reaction,
9. Cooling of flame through mixture with furnace gases.

Clearly, with these variables the true state of flame temperature is largely a matter of speculation. (See Figure 9-3.) For purposes of estimation, there have been numerous tabulations of ultimate flame temperatures in which there is typical disagreement as to what the temperatures may be. Thus, the delineating of any specific data for flame temperatures is fraught with contradiction. A typical tabulation is as follows:

Hydrogen	4,010°F
Carbon monoxide	4,475°F
Methane	3,650°F
Ethane	3,820°F
Propane	3,840°F
Butane	3,870°F
Ethylene	4,250°F
Propylene	4,090°F

Butylene	4,030°F
Acetylene	4,770°F
Benzene	4,110°F
Toluene	4,050°F
Xylene	4,010°F
Naphthalene	4,100°F

A total of nine conditions that influence flame temperature have been tabulated. Combustion is normally considered as an exothermal process to provide a reason for erratic flame temperature data. This consideration is an error that is varingly significant in particular cases because the procedure of combustion chemistries can be either exothermal or endothermal at various stages. The onset of dissociation of water vapor, or carbon dioxide, occurs minutely at 2,600°F (1,427°C). However, as temperature increases, the dissociation reactions become more rapid and comprehensive—largely in keeping with Arrhenius' teachings (*Chemical Engineers' Handbook,* McGraw-Hill Book Company, Fifth edition). The dissociation reaction is endothermal and can be based on heats of formation for H_2O and/or CO_2. But the degree of dissociation defies computation and can best be described as a "guesstimate."

Water vapor can be present because of hydrogen burning or because of its presence in humid air for combustion, and CO_2 is a small, variable component of the same air. There is further endothermal reaction from hydrocarbon/water vapor reaction such as $CH_4 + H_2O = CO + 3H_2$ at temperatures typical of the flame. Endothermal reactions play a significant role in combustion chemistry, and their required heat subtracts from heat produced by fuel component oxidation in an exothermal manner. There is less heat to elevate the temperature of gaseous evolution components that determine flame temperature. No one can be certain of the extent of endothermal reaction. It is true that the hydrocarbon/water vapor reaction speeds burning because of much greater burning speed for CO and H_2, but the endothermal reaction heat is eternally lost to temperature elevation.

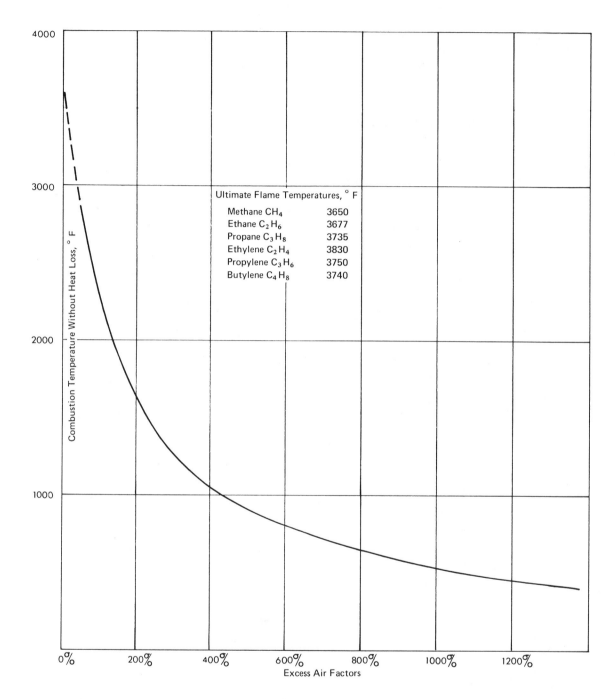

Figure 9-3. Data for combustion (flame) temperature where there is no loss of heat from the burning zone based on typical natural gas. For other fuels curves, data are corrected as the ratio of their ultimate flame-temperature to the ultimate flame temperature of methane. Such correction produces minor error. Data for dashed portion are not necessarily correct because the state of dissociation of H_2O and CO_2 is not determinable.

Furnace Temperature Control by Excess Air

The prime flame-temperature control means is excess air as admitted. In the operation of process furnaces (heaters), it is the sole applicable control means since excess air acts as a readily controllable heat sink. In air-heater design, the degree of heat sink of excess air establishes the air demand for a specific outlet temperature to within approximately 5%, but where there are tubes or other absorptive sources, the actual flame temperature is difficult to establish to within as much as 20-30% because the true state of absorption is questionable, as is radiant heat loss from the furnace structure and other variables. A further empirical factor is the state of burning with any fixed quantity of excess air, as influenced by the state of turbulence in and through the combustion zone. While this is a function of burner design as chosen, it is clear that the speed of burning is a function of turbulence. As an example, consider the separate and careful (as well as slow) introduction of stoichiometric quantities of methane and air to a flask so that the mixture results from diffusion. As the introduction is completed and if the ignition source should be in either the air or the methane, there would be neither burning nor explosion. This state would persist until diffusion had created a burnable or explosive mixture at the ignition source. All components for burning are present within a specific space or volume; but because there is only diffusion for mixture, there is a great delay in burning. If there is a relatively violent state of turbulence or mixture and if there is a spark or other ignition source, burning to completion would occur in milliseconds.

Reaction According to Molecular Proximity

This is to say that in gases, which are to be reacted, the speed of reaction will be in proportion to proximity of reactive molecules and the preferred condition of molecular proximity exists in a homogeneous mixture of the gases where, within any volume of the mixture, there are numbers of molecules of each gas in direct proportion to the volumes of the separate gases as they are mixed. In a stoichiometric mixture of methane and air, molecules of methane would be present as in multiples of 1, molecules of oxygen as in multiples of 2, and molecules of nitrogen in multiples of 7.6 or in that proportion, to establish the preferred molecular dispersion. Since reaction occurs according to molecular proximity and since a rise in pressure reduces volume, pressing molecules closer and closer together, a rise in combustion pressure increases the speed of the combustion reactions at any specific temperature because the space between the molecules is being reduced, increasing molecular proximity. There is evidence that doubling of absolute pressure doubles the rate of reaction or substantially produces half the flame volume; but at this time and to the best of knowledge, there has been no definitive research to either confirm or refute this. However, the speed of burning of fuels at the reduced absolute pressures typical of significant altitudes in increase of flame volume (as the absolute pressure is reduced) tends to confirm the postulation that speed of burning is in keeping with the state of absolute pressure.

Speed of Burning

Speed of burning of fuel can vary widely according to conditions which can and do influence speed. A quite reasonable assumption is that methane in a stoichiometric mixture with air will burn in approximately 10 milliseconds at 14.7 psia pressure. In such a mixture, there would be (proportionally) 1 cu. ft. of methane, 2 cu. ft. of oxygen and 7.6 cu. ft. of nitrogen. The partial pressures of the three gases would be in keeping with the mol (volume) percentages. Therefore, the partial pressure of oxygen is 0.1886 of the total pressure. With this partial pressure of oxygen, in an otherwise undiluted stoichiometric mixture of air and fuel, the burning time is, again, 10 milliseconds. But if the fuel has been diluted by inert matter, the burning is markedly slower at the same stoichiometrical condition of mixture because the added inert gas increases the volume of the mixture to reduce the partial pressure of oxygen.

In burning a fuel which is 10% methane and 90% nitrogen the stoichiometric mixture would be:

$$(CH_4 + 9N_2) + 2O_2 + 7.6N_2$$

In this case, the partial pressure of O_2 is only 0.1020, which reflects the nitrogen dilution. Observing the state of burning of this mixture shows that the burning speed is only 30% (approximately), of the speed of the undiluted stoichiometric mixture. If we presume that the partial pressure of O_2 is the governing factor in the speed of burning, the ratio of the partial pressures of O_2 does not correlate with repeatedly observed burning speeds. If we pursue the theorem and take the ratio of the squares of the partial pressures of O_2' we strike pay dirt; 0.1020 squared divided by 0.1886 squared is 0.293, which very closely correlates with observed burning speed. Thus, we can say that the burning speed will vary inversely as the ratio of the squares of the partial pressures. The burning time will vary directly as the ratio of the squares or as:

    0.1886 squared = 0.0355
    0.1020 squared = 0.0104
    Speed = 0.0104/0.0355 = 0.293
    Time = 0.0355/0.104 = 3.409

From these suggested data, it is possible (with minor error) to say that the burning speed is 29.3% or that the time required for burning is 3.409 times as great in the case of a 10% CH_4-90% N_2 fuel compared with the time/speed for undiluted methane also in a stoichiometric mixture with air. Calculations for other fuels in a diluted state follow the same procedure; but it is clear that according to the state of dilution the dilute fuel may not be capable of stable burning as is and may require maintenance of temperatures suitable for burning from another source. It should also be understood that the procedure outlined is not for precision but is for quite reasonable estimation.

There has been discussion of mixture and turbulence as key factors for satisfactory fuel burning. Both are products of some expression of energy. The burner designer or the fuel consumer, confronted with necessity for fuel burning in a manner suited to the service to be performed, finds it necessary to make the best use of the energies available. There are two sources of energy. First, his greatest source is made available from the discharge of fuel from gage pressures to the substantially atmospheric pressure of the typical process furnace or the fuel pressure drop at or just prior to burning. Second is air pressure drop across the burner structure. Pressure drop in fluid flow sets up the velocity of flow. Velocity of flow is proportional to the square root of the pressure drop. With compressible fluids such as gases there is an increase in velocity as the pressure drop is increased until critical or sonic velocity is reached. Even though the pressure drop is further increased there can be no increase in velocity. Sonic or critical velocity is reached approximately as the absolute pressure upstream of the orifice becomes twice the absolute pressure downstream of the orifice.

Critical (Sonic) Velocity Calculations

Critical velocity for any gas at any temperature can be calculated as:

$$\sqrt{\frac{32.17 \times (R) \times (1544) \times (Cp/Cv)}{MW}} = \text{critical velocity ft/sec}$$

where:

    R = Rankine temperature (absolute)
    MW = Molecular weight
    Cp/Cv = Ratio of specific heats

Since the energy produced in fluid flow is measured as $MV_2/2$ it is clear that velocity is the governing factor in the energy equation since the velocity is squared and the mass is both linear and fixed by the heat release required. Therefore, a maximum velocity is preferable for production of maximum energy.

After critical (sonic) velocity has been created in flow across the orifice through an increase in pressure, a further increase in pressure can cause no increase in velocity, but the flow of gas across the orifice in standard cubic feet becomes greater than the square root of the pressure drop would indicate because as the pressure is increased the *mass* flowing at critical velocity increases and the mass correction is linear to add to the square root correction. A curve for gas flow to atmospheric pressure will illustrate the degree of deviation, which is minor up to approximately 25 psig pressure, is substantially 4% at 30 psig and increases quite rapidly by a further pressure increase. (See Figure 7-2.) This effect can, at times, be quite significant.

Burner Fuel Pressure

Since at critical velocity the velocity factor becomes optimum, it would appear that operating pressure (for gas fuel) might well be that pressure capable of creating critical velocity, but this is not true for two reasons. The first is that the burner operating range is based on gas pressure because gas flow varies largely as the square root of the applied gas pressure. Thus, an operating range from 100 to 25% of duty will force a reduction in gas pressure at design (100%) of 24 psig to 1.50 psig at 25% of design. At 12½% of design, the gas pressure becomes 0.375 psig. If the gas pressure for design firing is, say, 16 psig, the gas pressure for 25% of firing becomes 1.00 psig, and at 12½% the gas pressure is 0.218 psig. It is largely true that the operating gas pressure for a burner should not fall much below 1 psig for best operation. Premix burners are most sensitive to gas pressure reduction while raw-gas burners are much less sensitive.

The second reason for higher gas pressure is that while velocity does become maximum as critical flow is established, there is a certain energy increase at greater gas pressure because the mass flowing at critical velocity is increased. Greater applied gas pressure becomes valuable.

Bernoulli teaches that in velocity increment there is a drop in pressure; therefore, as gas is discharges at critical velocity to atmospheric pressure, the pressure immediately adjacent to the gas stream approaches 0.5 psia to create a state of violent entry to and mixture of air with gas at this point. But because there is a great expenditure of energy, the energy of the gas stream is (in the order of 90%) spent in the movement of approximately nine orifice diameters forward of the orifice. Therefore, there is greatest mixture and turbulence immediately at the orifice, but the end effect of this expression of energy is to cause extremely rapid mixture of air with gas. Because of the violence of the induction of air, there is also a great state of turbulence. If the gas can be caused to begin burning quite close to the orifice and in a great state of turbulence, the burning is rapid. If, however, the burning does not begin immediately at the orifice due to lack of suitable ignition or kindling effect the turbulence is not effective and burning is delayed. The flame for specific heat release gets longer and of greater volume and unsatisfactory burning results to such a degree that there may be incomplete burning in even a quite hot furnace.

Unstable Burning Effects

The effect is unstable burning in which there is danger of ignition loss. The furnace pants or puffs even with excess air present and continued operation under such conditions is quite dangerous. It is the burner manufacturer's responsibility to supply burners which are stable in their burning characteristics. However, panting or puffing in the course of operation can also be due to inadequate air supply, which is not a function of burner design. There is treatment elsewhere of this phenomenon. Much speculation exists about the chemistries of burning/reaction when the air supply is inadequate.

Unusual Fuel Characteristics

Some fuels have characteristics which depart from those of hydrocarbons as they burn in that they are directly reactive with oxygen. Such fuels are H_2 and CO. Their states of burning are so rapid that they preempt the oxygen in the zone of greatest turbulence to cause hydrocarbons to move into a less turbulent zone to find oxygen and thus delay burning and produce greater flame volume/length according to the mol-percentage of H_2-CO present. For example, in a 50-50 mixture of CH_4 and H_2, the flame length/volume is much greater than for CH_4 alone. When there is 85% H_2 and 15% CH_4, the flame proportions will be much the same as for CH_4 alone so rapid burning of the H_2 compensates for the delay in burning of the CH_4. A further increase in H_2 causes shortening of the flame.

Some rarely found fuels such as NH_3 have a further peculiar characteristic. They must dissociate endothermically before they can begin to burn and flame length/burning problems can arise if the mol-percentage of NH_3 in the fuel rises unduly. This is reflected as the quite high ignition temperature for ammonia is considered and some authorities show more than 1,400°F for it. In fact, the burning of any significant quantity of ammonia requires a special design and special piloting, but stable burning is typical if the burning arrangements are satisfactory.

Sulfur compounds such as H_2S, COS, organic sulfides and mercaptans have significant value as fuels but the products formed as they burn can be very troublesome. Chemistry teaches that as sulfur burns the product formed is SO_2 unless there is catalysis in some manner to reoxidize SO_2 to SO_3. In the manufacture of sulfuric acid, the catalyst of choice is V_2O_5 (vanadium pentoxide) for creating SO_3 as the anhydride of sulfuric acid from SO_2. However, privately conducted research gives striking evidence that other substances accomplish the catalysis quite capably if not to the degree of vanadium pentoxide. The research was based on all standard fuels such as coal, coke, oils and gases where there was an appreciable weight percentage of sulfur in the various fuels and interesting data have emerged in confirmation of catalysis.

The first serious problem which required a solution before definitive data could be taken was that of analysis for SO_3 in the gases produced in burning in an accurate and repeatable manner. A suitable solution was found for collecting SO_3 and avoiding dew point in the sample en route to analysis by R.R. Martin (Doctoral Dissertation, University of Tulsa). Failure in this respect accounts for much erratic SO_3 data derived from prior research.

The finding of the research is that from 3-5 weight-percent of the total sulfur burned appears at the stack as SO_3, with the remainder as SO_2. The lower weight-percentage was found where low H/C fuels were burned and the higher weight percentage with higher H/C ratio fuels. The findings strongly suggest that water vapor is one of the prime catalysts involved, but do not neglect the catalytic roles of iron oxide, alumina, various metallic oxides in the refractories as well as, perhaps, other substances which are unknown.

Corrosion Due to SO_3

A most serious result is attributable to the presence of SO_3. In flue gases it very markedly elevates the dew point of the flue gases from a normal temperature of 130-140°F, in the absence of SO_3, to as much as 375°F, according to the amount of SO_3. If dew point thus occurs, there is sulfuric corrosion to a greater or lesser degree. (See Table A-23.)

A further point in reference to burning of sulfur is in the inevitable SO_2 produced and the promulgation of air pollution laws which limit the grade level SO_2 content of air to 0.1 ppm or less. If sulfur is present in the fuel, and since the laws must be obeyed, there is no recourse other than a stack height suitable for proper diffusion of the SO_2 before the stack gases return to grade by action and in the down-wind direction. Stack height adequate for draft is no longer the key factor since height must be established for proper diffusion through the Sutton-Lowery or Pearson-Bosanquet formulations (*Air Pollution Handbook,* McGraw Hill) or other acceptable procedures.

Published speeds of flame propagation have been of small moment for many years in burner design. Speed of flame propagation relates to a state of flash back in premix burners or to a condition when flame moves countercurrently to the direction of gas movement, resulting in internal burning and possible destruction of the burner. Experience teaches that burner design rather than flame speed is the critical factor, since flash back can and does occur when gas-air movement exceeds 20 ft./sec. compared to the less than 3 ft./sec. given by published data. As further contradiction, published rates for flame propagation in hydrogen-air mixtures are 16 Ft./sec. maximum and burner experience has confirmed many times that flash back frequently occurs at 250 ft./sec. in the burners.

As a general rule, it may be said that with mixtures of detonable gases such as hydrogen, acetylene, ethylene oxide and others with typical methane-based hydrocarbons there is increasing danger of flash back in normal burner operation. This factor must concern the operator of premix burners which are not designed for such fuels, but if the premix burners are designed for the detonative fuel mixture there need be little concern. These burners typically fire fuels which are 90% H_2 and 10% CH_4. Burners designed on the raw-gas basis will accept any fuel without danger of flash back.

In the typical process plant where there are many sources of fuels, and where in all probability the analyses and characteristics of the individual fuels will vary widely, there is a potential for difficulty with burner operation and control. This difficulty is due to the manner in which the fuels are delivered to the burners. Often the various fuels are piped to a so-called mixdrum which does, indeed, bring the fuels to a common point from which they can be distributed but which fails to produce a mixture to any appreciable degree. Failure of the fuels to mix within the drum sets up a condition in which, at any particular moment, there is no assurance of reasonably fixed calorific values. Under such conditions the calorific value of fuel gases can vary from close to the lowest value admitted to the mix drum to close to the highest value, and burners, designed for a mean value, are constantly operating in deviation from design conditions and are constantly producing widely vary-

ing heat release. Operation is needlessly difficult, controls hunt for stabilization, and process upsets occur to a greater or lesser degree.

Because of the fuel changes discussed, there is change in the flash back tendency of burners; but once flash back has occurred in an operating burner later changes in fuel will not necessarily correct the condition of flash back. Unless this condition is corrected, there will be damage to the burner. This is an operating hazard that can become quite serious. In general, the flash back tendency can be said to vary according to the ratio of the upper explosive limit to the lower explosive limit. This ratio for methane, the reference fuel, is 3.00 (15%-5%), and with methane the flash back tendency is considered as 1.00. With propane the ratio is greater and it has a greater tendency to produce flash back. It is interesting that with hydrogen, acetylene, ethylene oxide, carbon disulfide, ether and others the ratio and the flash back tendency are so great that standard labyrinthine flame arrestors are of no value whatsoever. The only substitute is a properly designed water seal where a solid water barrier breaks the flame front. (Refer to Table 2-2.)

Flash back occurs as a minor explosion which, according to the nature of the fuel, can be a gentle "thoop" or violent "crack" as if from a high-power rifle. The latter is well within the range of detonation. There is a significant difference between an explosion and detonation because while the former results from an extremely rapid rise in pressure due to progressive burning of the fuel mass, the latter is due to instantaneous burning of the entire fuel mass to produce a supersonic detonation wave of, at times, tremendous energy, as with dynamite. While detonation in gas-air mixtures does not approach the violence of dynamite, it can still be quite serious if there is no immediate area for relief of the energy. Fortunately, such an area is available in typical burners so burner detonation in flash back will seldom do any real damage although it can be very frightening. As mentioned, detonative tendency becomes significant as the ratio of higher explosive limits to lower explosive limits increases, and again the ratio for methane as $15/5 = 3.00$ can be considered as unity.

Gas-Air Mixture Explosion Hazards

Various fuels have various characteristics and knowledge of these can be useful, but here again, there is small agreement as to the specific ratios. Interpretation of Table 2-2 is based on flash back probability of methane with its U/L ratio of 3.00 and unity as to its flash back tendency. Ethane with its ratio of 4.02 is 1.34 times as likely to flash back. Propane at 5.25 is 1.75 times more flash back prone and ethylene at 10.04 is 3.33 times as flash back prone. These data are based on pure gases, as shown. When hydrogen is mixed with methane as fuel, there is a great moderation of the "infinite" factor to more than 4.00, and mixtures of 90% H_2 with 10% CH_4 can be successfully burned in properly designed premix burners. A more significant conclusion from the table refers to flame arrestors and whether they will serve their purpose of stopping flame. Where the flash back probability is infinite, the labyrinthine arrestor has no value and for other gases where the U/L ratio reaches or exceeds 11.00, the arrestor becomes a well-designed water seal for complete safety in all conditions. It is not presently known why the cooling effect of the labyrinthine arrestor effectively quenches the flame front in some gases and not in others but it is known that the water barrier of the water seal does serve the purpose unless there is active passage of gas through the liquid at the time the flame front arrives. If this is the case, there is no water barrier; thus, the flame front will continue past the water seal. There has been a provision that the water seal must be properly designed if it is to serve its purpose. In this respect, the gas must pass through the water as a series of bubbles with each bubble separated by a definite water barrier. Such seal drums are commercially available. These well-proven devices have a further advantage in that there is not the least pressure surging either upstream or downstream of the seal in any state of gas flow.

Any Oxygen Can Be Dangerous

There are many cases where detonable or explosive gases, in a molal ratio of mixture which is below or above the explosive or detonable limits, are passed to an area of potential ignition without flame arrestor protection because it is felt that since the molal ratio is outside the flammable or explosive range there can be no serious results. Indeed this is the case if the gases are in a homogenous mixture as they reach the ignition source; but if the mixture is not homogeneous (because of oxygen-gas striation) there can be a very serious explosion or detonation. A guide here could well be that if there is any oxygen in gases such as hydrogen, acetylene, ethylene oxide, carbon disulfide or ethers, it is dangerous and protective measures are demanded. In acetylene synthesis (because acetylene tends to be pyrophoric) there must be great care in the handling. Acetylene can readily set up a highly exothermic reaction as $2 \text{-} C_2H_2 = CH_4 + 3C$.

This reaction in pipes conducting acetylene can cause the pipe to become red hot almost instantly causing the pipe to fail, to distort badly and to oxidize badly. This reaction occurs in the absence of oxygen and is exothermic because of the methane formed.

There was earlier mention of heats of dissociation for CO_2 and H_2O as factors in the determination of theoretical or ultimate flame temperature. While the heat loss due to these dissociations is insignificant at 2,500°F, it becomes increasingly important as the temperature rises to account for some surprisingly low ultimate temperatures where cursory examination would indicate a much higher temperature due to stoichiometric fuel burning. If we set up a hypothetical condition in which methane as a single pound-mol is burned with dry air and consider that in methane there are 12.01 lbs. of carbon at 14,100 Btu/lb. and 4.032 lbs. of hydrogen at a lower heating value of 51,500 Btu/lb., we burn 379.54 cu. ft. of methane which has a lower heating value, as published widely, at 910 Btu/cu. ft. as determined by calorimeter burning.

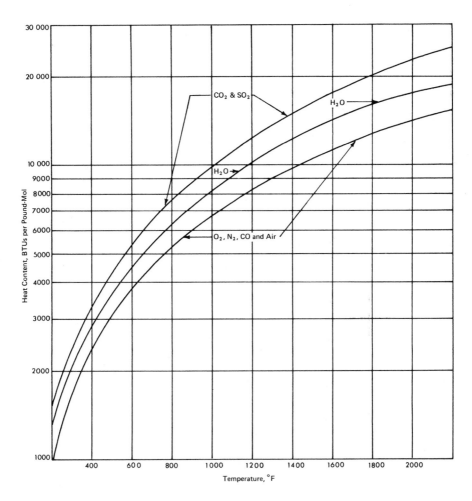

Figure 9-4. Sensible heat content of gases (above 60°F) divide pound-mol heat content by molecular weight to get heat content per pound.

Therefore, the total heat release on a volumetric basis is 379.54 (910) = 345,381 Btu/mol of CH_4. But on a weight basis we have:

Carbon	12.01	(14,100)	= 169,341 Btu
Hydrogen	4.032	(51,500)	= 207,648 Btu
			376,989 Btu

It is evident that in the calorific value difference as shown there are some 31,608 Btu unaccounted for if the volume and weight calorific

values are correct which, according to literature reference, they are. With dry air, the reaction of 1 mol of methane with dry air would be

$$CH_4 + 2O_2 + 7.57N_2 = CO_2 + 2H_2O + 7.57N_2$$

Molal heat contents of the products based on a temperature of 4,100°F, totals 379,740 Btu, which is quite close to the weight value of 376,989 Btu. (See Figure 9-4.) If there were no heat unaccounted for, 4,100°F would be the approximate flame temperature for methane. But there is unaccounted for heat according to the volume basis. Molal heat content at 3,700°F is 339,500 Btu, which is again quite close to the volumetric heat production. From this we can conclude that a temperature close to 3,700°F is the flame temperature for methane. However, both the 4,100 and the 3,700 figures are probably high because at this temperature there would be great synthesis of NOx in endothermic reactions and probable theoretical temperatures in each case are nearer to 4,050°F and 3,650°F and absolute precision here is impossible to within 50°F.

As a matter of fact and because of CO_2-H_2O dissociation at above 2,500°F, it is virtually impossible to secure flame temperature higher than 3,100°F with air and gas temperatures of 100°F.

Gross and Net Heating Values

The student will find that for fuels containing hydrogen there will always be two heating values for the fuel, with one value as the gross or higher heating value and the other as the net or lower heating value. The higher heating value can be considered as that for the actual release of heat while the lower heating value can be considered as the useful portion of the actual heat released. As the hydrogen content of the fuel burns, water is produced and water as a vapor requires latent heat which does not become available until the water is condensed. Since stack temperatures are always above the dew point, the latent heat quantity exits unrecovered from the stack, carrying with it the sensible heat required to elevate its temperature to that of the stack gases. Also, the lower heating value may be considered as the sensible heat potentially recoverable per unit volume or per unit weight. The lower heating value simply subtracts the latent heat demand from the total heat produced.

Fuels containing no hydrogen such as CO, C, S, COS and others have single quoted heating values. As examples and for CO, the calorific value is stated as 321 Btu/cu. ft. For hydrogen, the HHV is also 321 Btu/cu. ft., but the LHV is quoted as 273

Btu/cu. ft. To save mathematical gymnastics, it is common in process work to use lower heating values for heat demand and heat release, but if this is not clearly spelled out, a serious error can exist.

The use of preheated air as the source of oxygen for fuel burners is a matter which is much debated among men studying process conditions. Such debate is usually in reference to fuel economy. Less expensive operation is desired and the effects that may result on the process function are sometimes disregarded. Therefore, it is the intent here to evaluate some potential process effects, excluding economics, which is discussed in the chapter on efficiency.

If air flowing to the burners is heated, the sensible heat added to the air in turn adds to the sensible heat from the fuel to produce a certain elevation of flame/furnace temperature as proposed. However, this effect is all too frequently a disappointment unless the air pressure drop across the burners is considerably greater than with colder air because of air expansion at higher temperatures. Because of this less oxygen per cubic foot of air and slower burning of fuel create problems of greater or lesser magnitude. If, through greater pressure drop and incremental turbulence due to the greater pressure drop, the speed of burning can be held to a reasonable value, there is less potential for process upset. This is a matter for careful study and discussion with the burner manufacturer.

There is often an effort to predict incremental radiant heat transfer resulting from the predicted increase in flame/furnace temperature; but many years of experience show that this is quite disappointing. While there will be a certain increase in radiant transfer, the increase seldom justifies prediction. The deviation from prediction is puzzling because there is a firm basis in the Steffan-Boltzmann extrapolation, which should be correct. There are certain reasons for the deviation not the least of which is the velocity of discharge from the burner alteration and its effects on heat transfer contours to the tubes or surfaces of the heater. What may have been an excellent heat transfer contour with the low velocity of cold air. Burning speed and rate may alter to a degree, which completely alters heat transfer to cancel much of the higher temperature advantage. While there may be an increase in radiant heat delivery there is no certainty that the increase will be in the order of calculations leading to adoption of preheated air. Neither is there a certainty of less than anticipated improvement. Such an alteration in firing as the use of preheated air and a higher pressure-drop for the air supply is a somewhat "cut and try" procedure.

Surface Combustion

A function referred to loosely as surface combustion as a means for either initiation of burning in a gas-air mixture, as with a platinum sponge or by surface catalysis, is a phenomenon which merits consideration in process firing. It is common knowledge that a platinum sponge entered to a zone in which there is a suitable gas-air mixture will ignite the mixture and, as a matter of fact, much more rapidly and effectively in a hydrogen-air mixture than in a hydrocarbon-air mixture. It is also common knowledge that causing a fuel-air mixture to flow along and in contact with a surface will significantly speed the burning reactions, presumably through some effect of oxygen-fuel adsorption at the surface and, to all effects and purposes, without specific regard to the nature of the surface except that some surfaces such as platinum, iron oxide (ferric) and nickel oxide are better in speeding reactions. This is generally in keeping with catalytic agents in that some are better than others and there is reason to presume that alumina is reasonably good as such an agent. Alumina is a prime component of refractories. Therefore, the catalytic agent is characteristically present in the walls and surfaces of a typical furnace.

But, and as has been pointed out, for the catalyst to promote and speed burning the gas-air mixture must sweep over and in contact with the surface, which is far from the case in the typical process heater where the burning fuel-air mixture moves at right angles to the refractory surfaces. Therefore, according to surface combustion theory, the effect of surface acceleration of burn-

ing cannot occur. However, the effect of acceleration is often noted in a hot furnace because of the accelerative effect of the high temperature as is nicely confirmed through reference to Arrhenius's equations (pages 4-6, Fourth Edition, Perry's *Chemical Engineers' Handbook,* McGraw-Hill) in delineation of the acceleration of the velocity of chemical reactions by temperature increment. However, the burners for gas fuel commonly used for pyrolysis heaters for primary reforming (steam-hydrocarbon) or for olefins production do direct the gas-air mixture against refractory surfaces in avoidance of forward flame travel and here surface catalysis is undoubtedly significant. Operators of steam generating equipment are familiar with the full-of-flame appearance of the generator furnace at cold start conditions, but the same operators also know that as the generator furnace heats, flames for specific heat release shorten rapidly and at final operating temperature there will be little visible flame. This condition of progressive acceleration of burning as the furnace heats cannot be due to any surface catalysis effect yet it is present and easily subject to confirmation.

Temperature Effect on Reaction Velocities

In the course of daily engineering work the equations of Arrhenius are seldom useful because of the difficulty in getting data for energies of activation which are required. A relatively simple and research-proven procedure which is reasonably accurate for determining temperature increase to obtain a required condition of reaction is based on the teaching of Arrhenius (*Chemical Engineers' Handbook,* Perry, 3rd Edition, McGraw-Hill) in which it is pointed out that if absolute temperature is increased from 520°F to 538°F the reaction velocity doubles. The ratio of 538/520 = 1.03461, which can be rounded to 1.035 with tiny error.

Thus, if a reaction is not satisfactorily completed at an observed temperature in °F the temperature required for completion can be estimated as follows:

$$(T_1 + 460) \times [(0.035 \times N) + 1] - 460 = T_2$$

where:

T_1 = Initial observed temperature, °F
T_2 = Temperature for increased reaction, °F
N = Reaction rate increase

If, as an example, an observed temperature at 1,200°F is not driving the reaction satisfactorily and the reaction velocities must be trebled ($N = 3$) the calculation would be:

$$(1,200 + 460) \times [(0.035 \times 3) + 1]$$
$$- 460 = 1,374.3°F.$$

Combustion Aids

Senior members of the process fraternity will recall that in the '20s and early '30s, a very necessary structure called a Dutch Oven was part of all process heaters where it was necessary to burn the fuels of that era. The structures were necessary because of less than preferred performance of burners, also typical of that era, several years prior to the time when design research made rapid burning of fuels possible. Without the Dutch Oven, the furnace would be full of wildly rolling flame, but with it, the burning was speeded, and it was possible to fire reasonably well. The Dutch Oven was a refractory-lined structure of many shapes and dimensions in which there existed a quite high temperature level. The high temperature so speeded the combustion reactions that suitable firing was possible, but here again the effect was due to incremental temperature level rather than any surface effect because of the relatively great mass of burning fuel and the relatively minor refractory surface area. (See Table 9-1.)

Difficulty with Sulfur Compounds

In the typical process plant, where the raw materials for process are laden to some degree with sulfur, there is a great problem of what to do with sulfur-laden product residual materials where the products may be as small quantities of H_2S, mercaptans, organic sulfides, COS and others. These products are typically mixed with steam. Some form of burning is the obvious solution but here there are factors which need careful consideration. First, the waste product stream must be either a liquid or a gas—not both. The disposal problem is much more difficult and expensive if the stream is a liquid. Therefore, the stream should be in the gaseous phase. For this there must be no condensation or dew point between the point of origin and the point of disposal. Such a requirement is solved through insulation and steam tracing of the waste products line with 15 psig exhaust steam if the tracing is operated under condensing conditions through terminal discharge and a suitable steam trap and not directly to atmosphere.

Since the normal pressure for such waste streams is measured in ounces, a 215°F discharge temperature for disposal is usually satisfactory; but here we encounter another problem. The gas is usually quite corrosive at higher temperature levels and usually contains only minor mol-percentages of the offensive waste in steam. Because the gases must be discharged to a furnace, at a relatively high temperature level, and (accordingly) the discharge device is subjected to high temperature exposure, the discharge device should be made of heat and sulfur resistant steel (any of the 400 series steels (Fe + Cr), 304 (18-8) or 309 (25-12) but not of 310 (25-20). Corrosion can thus be inhibited but the problem of greatly diluted fuel (waste matter) in an inert stream of steam requires that the manner of discharge cause very rapid diffusion to the high temperature zone in which there is an ample supply of oxygen as excess air for the source of high temperature. Such waste gas streams, properly discharged and diffused, normally require ample time and temperature to assure burning of the nauseous or toxic waste products. Assured burning is demanded for the mercaptans or the organic sulfides because when there is 0.001 ppm or less in air, there can be a pronounced unpleasant odor!

Air Pollution

Because of air pollution factors which have reached a demanding condition it has been neces-

Table 9-1
Reaction Rate vs Temperature Level

Data of the presentation have been used in research/practice seldom to deviate more than plus-or-minus 5% and are usually quite accurate. Accurate data for reaction temperature are difficult to obtain in practice.

The following procedure is based on a known state of reaction based on an absolute temperature Ta (Rankine or Kelvin) as observed:

2 x Reaction Rate	= Ta x 1.0346
4 x Reaction Rate	= Ta x 1.0704
8 x Reaction Rate	= Ta x 1.1074
16 x Reaction Rate	= Ta x 1.1457
32 x Reaction Rate	= Ta x 1.1853
64 x Reaction Rate	= Ta x 1.2263
128 x Reaction Rate	= Ta x 1.2687
256 x Reaction Rate	= Ta x 1.3126

NOTE: Interpolation will supply intervening Temperature/Rate data.

Table 9-2
Odor-Nuisance Levels of Chemicals

Chemical	ppm	Odor
H_2S	0.00047	Rotten eggy
Ethyl mercaptan	0.001	Earthy, sulfidy
Phenol	0.047	medicinal
Styrene	0.047	Rubbery
Methyl mercaptan	0.0021	Sulfidy, pungent
Dimethyl amine	0.047	Fishy
Mono-methyl amine	0.021	Fishy, pungent
Para-cresol	0.001	Tar-like, pungent

Note: From the *Journal of the Air Pollution Control Association.*

sary to evaluate conditions of complete combustion because of the relative inaccuracy of the instruments used for combustion control. Typically, the hand-carried Orsat is used, but it is notoriously a source of misinformation because of errors in its operation, reagent exhaustion and sampling as well as sample temperature change in the course of analysis. Greater analytical sophistication is possible through use of instrument-type analyzers. Many analytical errors can be avoided through their use but in very careful operation the best accuracy is limited to 0.1%. If, for example, there is 0.1% of CO in flue gases there is loss of fuel which can be interesting, but there is no serious air pollution resulting even though as much as 1,000 ppm of CO are present because diffusion will produce satisfactory dilution at grade after emergence from the stack.

But if the combustible should be trimethylamine, which has a fishy odor, there would be great difficulty because only 0.00021 ppm of this product in the air will deliver a distinct fishy odor to a reasonably sensitive nose and diffusion from

1,000 ppm would be impossible in the case of the average stack height. Other chemicals which can be sources of difficulty and the air concentrations which can produce odor-nuisance are given in Table 9-2. Odor nuisance due to such small concentrations will demand solution, but diffusion from the stack to grade cannot provide solution without very great stack height, which presents problems of feasibility, cost and area limitation for maximum stack height. The solution largely lies in provision of greater temperature level as burning progresses along with adequate excess air in the burning zone which translates to greater fuel cost in many cases. The term *adequate excess air* must be established as the odor conditions vary, but the minimum O_2 in a sample taken directly from the furnace and not from the stack is 1%, with 2-6% preferred. At times the greater temperature due to excess air reduction (if this is possible) solves the problem with no fuel increase. In the O_2 range of which we speak excess air is essentially $O_2/0.209$. However, at times it is necessary to adopt other burning procedures if the time-temperature conditions of an existing facility through fundamental design error cannot abate the odor nuisance. The study of combustion kinetics has progressed more in the past five years than in all prior history because air pollution problems demand solution.

Bibliography

Alloy Steel Division. *Enduro Stainless Steels* (Massilon, Ohio: Republic Steel Corporation, 1951).

American Gas Association. *Gaseous Fuels*. Edited by Louis Shnidman (Eastman, P.A.: Mack Printing Company, 1948).

Clarke, Loyal, and Davidson, R. *Manual for Process Engineering Calculations* (New York: McGraw-Hill Book Company, Inc., 1962).

Grant, Julius. *Hackh's Chemical Dictionary*, 4th ed. (New York: McGraw-Hill Book Company, Inc., 1969).

Griswold, John. *Fuels, Combustion and Furnaces* (New York: McGraw-Hill Book Company, Inc., 1946).

Haslam, Robert T., and Russell, Robert P. *Fuels and their Combustion* (New York: McGraw-Hill Book Company, Inc., 1926).

Keenan, Joseph H., and Kaye, Joseph. *Gas Tables* (New York: John Wiley and Sons, Inc., 1948).

Keenan, Joseph H., and Keyes, F.G. *Thermodynamic Properties of Steam* (New York: John Wiley and Sons, Inc., 1936).

Kent, R.T., Editor, *Mechanical Engineers' Handbook* (New York: John Wiley and Sons, Inc., 1950). Part I; Design and Production. Edited by C. Carmichael. Part 2: Power. Edited by J.K. Salisbury.

Kern, Donald Q. *Process Heat Transfer* (New York: McGraw-Hill Book Company, Inc., 1950).

Lange, Norbert A. *Handbook of Chemistry*, 10th ed. (New York: McGraw-Hill Book Company, Inc., 1967).

Lewis, Bernard, and Von Elbe, Guenther. *Combustion, Flames and Explosions of Gases*, 2nd ed. (Campbell, Calif.: Academy Press, Inc., 1961).

Lewis, Bernard, et al. *Fourth International Symposium on Combustion* (Baltimore, Md.: Williams and Wilkins Company, 1953).

Marks, Lionel S., and Baumeister, Theodore. *Marks' Mechanical Engineers' Handbook* 4th and 6th ed. (New York: McGraw-Hill Book Company, Inc.).

Maxwell, J.B. *Data Book on Hydrocarbons* (New York: Van Nostrand Reinhold Co., 1950).

McAdams, William H. *Heat Transmission*, 3rd ed. (New York: McGraw-Hill Book Company, Inc., 1954).

Nelson, Wilbur L. *Petroleum Refinery Engineering*, 4th ed. (New York: McGraw-Hill Book Company, Inc., 1958).

NGSMA Engineering Data Book (Tulsa, Okla.: Natural Gasoline Supply Men's Association. 1946, 1957, 1966).

Pacific Coast Gas Association. *Gas Engineers' Handbook* (New York: McGraw-Hill Book Company, Inc., 1934).

Perry, John H., et al. *Chemical Engineers' Handbook*, 4th ed. (New York: McGraw-Hill Book Company, Inc., 1963).

Peterson, Arnold P., and Gross, Ervin E., Jr. *Handbook of Noise Measurement* (West Concord, Mass.: General Radio Company, 1967).

Reid, Robert C., and Sherwood, T.K. *Properties of Gases and Liquids*, 2nd ed. (New York: McGraw-Hill Book Company, Inc. 1966).

Stainless Steel Handbook (Pittsburgh, Pa.: Allegheny Ludlum Steel Corp., 1951).

Steam: Its Generation and Use (New York: Babcock and Wilcox Co., 1955).

Trinks, W. *Industrial Furnaces*, Volume 1 (New York: John Wiley and Sons, Inc.).

Walker, W.H., and Associates. *Principles of Chemical Engineering* (New York: McGraw-Hill Book Company Inc., 1937).

Weast, Robert C., Editor-in-Chief. *Handbook of Chemistry and Physics*, 42nd and 47th ed. (Cleveland Ohio: The Chemical Rubber Co., 1960, 1966).

Glossary

Absolute pressure Total pressure which is equal to gage pressure plus atmospheric pressure, which varies with altitude. Atmospheric pressure at sea level is 14.696 psi.

Absolute temperature On the Fahrenheit scale, this is the temperature as indicated by any means plus 459.72 (460). On the Centigrade scale, this is the temperature as indicated by any means plus 273.18.

Air-fuel ratio The ratio of air weight or volume to fuel weight or volume. This ratio will vary as the fuels vary and according to the quantity of excess air required.

API gravity Empirical scale for measuring the density of liquid petroleum products with the unit defined as the Degree API. Calculation for API gravity is as follows:

141.5/Specific Gravity − 131.5 = API gravity

141.5/(131.5 + API Gravity) = specific gravity

Ash Inorganic residue remaining after burning of fuels and usually as the oxide or carbonate of Na, Ca, Mg, Si, V or Fe.

Asphalts Normally solid or semi-solid bitumenous substances which occur in nature or as products of refinery operation as residual material. Also referred to as tars.

ASTM American Society for Testing Materials to provide standards for various materials and substances typical of engineering practice.

Avogadro's Hypothesis Equal volumes of all gases under identical conditions of temperature and pressure contain equal numbers of molecules.

Barrel The standard unit of liquid measure for the petroleum industry; 42 U.S. gallons or 35 Imperial gallons, also 9,702 cu. in. or 5.614 cu. ft.

Boiling point Temperature at which the vapor pressure of a liquid is equal to the pressure bearing on its surface.

Boyle's Law The volume of any gas varies inversely as the absolute pressure provided the temperature remains constant. Also known as Mariotte's Law.

British thermal unit (Btu) The quantity of heat required to raise the temperature of 1 lb. of water $1°F$ at or near its point of maximum density ($39.10°F$). The Btu is equal to 0.252 kilogram-calorie.

Calorific value A measure of the heating value of fuel stated in btu/lb. or in btu/cu. ft.

Centigrade (Celcius) Temperature scale typical of the metric system based on $0°$ as the freezing point of water and $100°$ as the boiling point of water.

Centipoise A reference factor for viscosity which is

0.01 poise or centistokes times the specific gravity at a specific temperature.

Centistoke A reference factor for viscosity equal to 0.01 stoke.

Cold test Refers to pour point for a liquid or the lowest temperature at which the liquid can be poured. A low cold test indicates a liquid which can be poured at low temperature.

Corrosion Any condition of undesired chemical attack which is considered detrimental to apparatus, piping, metallic structures or the like.

Critical velocity In gases, this is the speed of sound in the particular gas or mixture of gases. The governing factors are the absolute temperature, the molecular weight and the ratio of specific heats.

Dalton's Law of Partial Pressures The total pressure of a mixture of gases is equal to the sum of the partial pressures of the individual gases which are present. The partial pressure of any particular gas is equal to its mol-percentage times the total pressure of the mixture.

Density The mass of any substance per unit volume at any specific temperature or, in the case of gases, any specific pressure.

Dew point The condition of pressure and temperature at which the liquefaction of a vapor begins.

Distillate The product of a distillation process.

Distillation A process of heating a liquid to its boiling point then condensing the vapor formed in boiling.

Doctor test A standard procedure for determining whether undesirable sulfur compounds are present in petroleum distillates. A "sweet" compound does not contain the undesirable sulfur compounds and a "sour" one does contain them.

Emulsion A mechanical mixture of two liquids such as oil and water which do not naturally occur in the mixed phases.

Engler viscosity A viscosity which is obtained by dividing the outflow time in seconds for 200 cc of the liquid being tested by the time in seconds for the outflow of 200 cc of water at 68° F (20° C) when using an Engler viscosimeter.

Fahrenheit A temperature scale which is based on 32° as the freezing point of water and 212° as the boiling point of water when the water is pure and at 14.696 psi absolute pressure.

Fire point The lowest temperature at which an oil vaporizes rapidly enough to burn for at least 5 sec. when a small bead of flame is passed over the oil.

Fixed carbon The percentage of a combustible material which cannot be vaporized at 1,742° F (950° C).

Flash point The lowest temperature at which there is enough vapor evolution from the surface of the oil being tested to make a small flash when a small bead of flame is passed over the oil.

Fluid A substance such as a gas or a liquid which yields readily to any force which tends to change or alter its shape. Fluids, as such, possess no definite shape or form and uniformly fill any space to which they are introduced.

Formula weight (Molecular weight) The sum of the atomic weights of the components of a molecule expressed in the English system as a number of pounds equal to the formula weight of 1 pound-mol.

Freezing point The temperature at which a liquid solidifies.

Gallon (Imperial) A volume of water which weighs 10 lbs. at 68° F. Equal to approximately 276.96 cu. in. or approximately 0.16 cu. ft.

Gallon (U.S.) A unit of volume equal to 231 cu. in. A gallon of water at 60° F weighs 8.337 lbs. and is approximately equal to 0.134 cu. ft.

Gas An aeriform fluid having neither shape nor volume since volume is proportional to both pressure and temperature; gas has all the characteristics of a fluid with the added property of being compressible or expandable to a very great degree.

Gravity Used in the sense of specific gravity to indicate the ratio of the weight of a specific volume of a substance to the weight of an equal volume of water. (*See* API gravity.) Otherwise, gravity is the attraction of the earth for bodies expressed as weight.

Heat A measurable state of molecular excitation which is produced by friction, by expression of atomic energy or by the burning of fuels.

Heat of combustion-gross or higher heating value The total heat produced in the burning of a fuel.

Heat of combustion-net or lower heating value The total heat evolved in the burning of a fuel less the latent heat of vaporization for any water which may be formed in the process of combustion. Literally, the useful heat produced as the fuel is burned unless the temperature of the combustion products is driven below the dew point for recovery of the latent heat.

Humidity Relative humidity is the ratio of the quantity of vapor actually present to the quantity of vapor which could be present at any specific temperature level. Absolute humidity is the amount of vapor actually present and expressed either in its expansive force or in its weight per unit volume.

Hydrocarbon A chemical compound containing carbon and hydrogen.

Hygroscopic Readily absorbing and becoming coated with as well as retaining moisture but not to such degree as to convert a solid to a solution in water.

Initial boiling point (IBP) The temperature at which, in laboratory distillation, the first drop of distillate falls from the condenser.

Inorganic Usually refers to metals or their compounds with inorganic acids or oxygen; In the broad sense denotes absence of carbon.

IP Institute of Petroleum, the British counterpart of API.

Kinematic viscosity The ratio of the absolute viscosity of a liquid to its specific gravity at the temperature level at which the viscosity is measured.

Kinetic energy The capacity for performing work or the energy which a body has by virtue of its movement, expressed as mass times velocity squared divided by two.

Kinetic theory of gases The theory that all gases are made up of spherical molecules which above absolute zero are in constant motion and that the distance between the molecules is relatively large in proportion to their size. Molecules constantly change their direction of movement because of perfectly elastic collision with other molecules. Temperature is due to average kinetic energy of the molecules. Pressure is due to the constant bombardment of the containing vessel by the molecules as they move.

Latent heat Heat which when added to a mass causes a change in physical state of the mass but does not alter the temperature of the mass such as evaporation of water or melting of ice or metal.

Liquid A fluid characterized by free movement of the constituent molecules among themselves but without the tendency to separate from one-another. Liquids yield readily to pressure and have all the characteristics of fluids. Liquids are compressible only to an extremely small degree.

Liter A metric unit of capacity or volume equal to 61.022 cu. in.

Melting point The temperature at which the liquid and solid phases of a material are in equilibrium.

Metal A substance which typically shows metallic luster and is a conductor of heat and electricity. It is opaque and is malleable or ductile to varying degrees; it may be fused.

Mineral Any element or compound occurring in nature; usually inorganic substances of definite chemical composition and crystal structure.

Mol (Mole) A weight of a substance numerically equal to its molecular weight.

Molecule When atoms are bonded together they form a molecule. In the case of an element or of a compound a molecule is the smallest unit which retains the chemical characteristics of the substance.

Olefin Any open-chain hydrocarbon containing one double bond. Diolefins contain two double bonds.

Organic Hydrocarbons and their derivatives or essentially all carbon compounds whether of natural or synthetic origin.

Pensky-Martens Test A closed cup test for the flash point of oils.

Perfect gas A gas which obeys the $PV = nRT$ postulation or its internal energy, E, is a function of temperature alone.

pH An arbitrary means for indicating the state of acidity, neutrality or alkalinity of a solution. The exact significance is still debated. A pH of 7.00 indicates neutrality. Departure in the upward direction indicates alkalinity and departure in the downward direction indicates acidity.

Phenol Usually referred to as carbolic acid (C_6H_5 OH) but also any one of a series of aromatic compounds which has the OH group attached.

Pour point The lowest temperature at which an oil can be poured or will flow under specified test conditions.

Redwood viscosity A British standard which is the number of seconds required for 50 cc of an oil or liquid to pass through a standard Redwood viscosimeter.

Residual oil Bottoms product from distillation of oil which can be fuel oil or a charge stock for vacuum operation, or for delayed coking.

Saybolt Furol Viscosity (*SSF*) The normal viscosity standard for the more viscous oils and approximately 1/10th viscosity by the Saybolt Universal method.

Saybolt Universal Viscosity (*SSU*) The time in seconds for 60 cc of fluid to flow through the capillary tube of a Saybolt Universal Viscosimeter.

Specific gravity The ratio of the weight of a given volume of a material to an equal volume of pure water at the same temperature.

Specific heat The quantity of heat required to elevate the temperature of a unit weight of a substance one degree. In the English system expressed as Btu/lb.

Spontaneous ignition temperature (*auto-ignition temperature*) The temperature at which a fuel ignites of its own accord in the presence of oxygen.

Stoke The unit of kinematic viscosity. Also used in some areas of industry to denote the addition of fuel to a furnace, usually in reference to solid fuels.

Thermal value (*heat of combustion*) In the English system the number of Btu per pound or cubic foot which are released in the burning of fuel.

Thermal conductivity The quantity of heat passing through a standard plate in a unit time with a temperature differential of one degree between the faces of the plate. A standard measure of the ability to conduct heat.

Ton (*Long*) A weight equal to 2,240 lbs.

Ton (*Metric*) A weight equal to 1,000 kilograms or 2,205 lbs.

Ton (*U.S. Standard*) A weight equal to 2,000 lbs.

Vapor density The weight of a unit volume of a vapor at stated temperature and pressure.

Vapor pressure The pressure exerted by a vapor when a state of equilibrium has been reached between a material and the vapor produced by the material at specific temperature. When the vapor pressure exceeds the pressure of the atmosphere over a liquid, it is said to be boiling.

Viscosimeter Apparatus with which the viscosity of a fluid is determined.

Viscosity A property of liquids which causes them to resist change in shape because of internal molecular friction and as measured in a capillary tube which is standard; literally, the resistance to flow at standard conditions.

Appendix

Table A-1
Equivalents

Acre	43,560.	square feet
Acre	4,047.	square meters
Acre	160.	square rods
Acre	0.4047	hectare
Acre-foot	7,758.	barrels
Atmosphere	33.94	feet of water
Atmosphere	29.92	inches of mercury
Atmosphere	760.0	millimeters of mercury
Atmosphere	14.70	pounds per square inch
Barrel	5.6146	cubic feet
Barrel	42.0	gallons
Barrel per hour	0.0936	cubic foot per minute
Barrel per hour	0.700	gallon per minute
Barrel per hour	2.695	cubic inches per second
Barrel per day	0.02917	gallon per minute
British thermal unit	0.2520	kilogram calorie
British thermal unit	0.2928	watt-hour
B.T.U. per minute	0.02356	horse power
Centimeter	0.3937	inch
Centimeter of mercury	0.1934	pound per square inch
Chain	66.00	feet
Chain	4.00	rods
Cubic centimeter	0.06102	cubic inch
Cubic foot	0.1781	barrel
Cubic foot	7.4805	gallons (U.S.)
Cubic foot	0.02832	cubic meter
Cubic foot per minute	10.686	barrels per hour
Cubic foot per minute	28.800	cubic inches per second
Cubic foot per minute	7.481	gallons per minute
Cubic inch	16.387	cubic centimeters

Table A-1 (continued)
Equivalents

Cubic meter	6.2897	barrels
Cubic meter	35.314	cubic feet
Cubic meter	1.308	cubic yards
Cubic yard	4.8089	barrels
Cubic yard	46,656.	cubic inches
Cubic yard	0.7646	cubic meter
Foot	30.48	centimeters
Foot	0.3048	meter
Foot of water @ 60°F.	0.4331	pound per square inch
Foot per second	0.68182	mile per hour
Gallon (U.S.)	8.337	pounds of water @ 60°F.
Gallon (U.S.)	0.02381	barrel
Gallon (U.S.)	0.1337	cubic foot
Gallon (U.S.)	231.000	cubic inches
Gallon (U.S.)	3.785	liters
Gallon (U.S.)	0.8327	gallon (Imperial)
Gallon per minute	1.429	barrels per hour
Gallon per minute	0.1337	cubic foot per minute
Gallon per minute	34.286	barrels per day
Gram	15.432	grains
Gram	0.03527	ounce
Horse power	42.44	B.T.U.'s per minute
Horse power	33,000.	foot-pounds per minute
Horse power	550.	foot-pounds per second
Horse power	1.014	horse power (metric)
Horse power	0.7457	kilowatt
Horse power hour	2,547.	British thermal units
Inch	2.540	centimeters
Inch of mercury	1.134	feet of water
Inch of mercury	0.4912	pound per square inch
Inch of water @ 60°F.	0.0361	pound per square inch
Kilogram	2.2046	pounds
Kilogram Calorie	3.968	British thermal units
Kilogram per square cm.	14.223	pounds per square inch

(Table A-1 continued on next page)

Table A-1 (continued)
Equivalents

Kilometer	3,281.	feet
Kilometer	0.6214	mile
Kilowatt	1.341	horse power
Link (Surveyor's)	7.92	inches
Liter	0.2642	gallon
Liter	1.0567	quarts
Meter	3.281	feet
Meter	39.37	inches
Mile	5,280.	feet
Mile	1.6093	kilometers
Mile per Hour	1.4667	feet per second
Ounce (Avoirdupois)	437.5	grains
Ounce (Avoirdupois)	28.3495	grams
Pound	7,000.	grains
Pound	0.4536	kilogram
Pound per square inch	2.309	feet of water @ 60°F.
Pound per square inch	2.0353	inches of mercury
Pound per square inch	51.697	millimeters of mercury
Pound per square inch	0.0703	kilogram per sq. cent.
Quart (Liquid)	0.946	liter
Rod	16.5	feet
Rod	25.0	links
Square centimeter	0.1550	square inch
Square foot	0.0929	square meter
Square inch	6.452	square centimeters
Square kilometer	0.3861	square mile
Square meter	10.76	square feet
Square mile	2.590	square kilometers

Table A-1 (continued)
Equivalents

Temp. Centigrade	5/9	(Temp. Fahr. -32)
Temp. Fahrenheit	9/5	(Temp. Cent. $+32$)
Temp. Absolute C.		Temp. $^\circ$C $+273$
Temp. Absolute F.		Temp. $^\circ$F $+460$
Ton (Long)	2,240.	pounds
Ton (Metric)	2,205.	pounds
Ton (Short or Net)	2,000.	pounds
Ton (Metric)	1.102	tons (short or net)
Ton (Metric)	1,000.	kilograms
Ton (Metric)	6.297	barrels of water @ 60°F.
Ton (Metric)	7.454	barrels (36° API)
Ton (Short or Net)	0.907	ton (metric)
Watt-hour	3.415	British thermal units
Yard	0.9144	meter

NAUTICAL MEASUREMENTS

Nautical Mile	6,080.	feet
Fathom	6.	feet
Cable Length	120.	fathoms
Knot of Speed	1.	nautical mile per hour

Table A-2
Equivalent Measures of the Metric System

METRIC		UNITED STATES	
Length			
1 meter	= 39.370 inches	1 inch	= .0254 meters
	= 3.281 ft.	1 foot	= .3048 meters
	= 1.093 yd.	1 yard	= .9144 meters
Surface			
1 sq. centimeter	= .155 sq. inches	1 sq. inch	= 6.45 sq. centimeters
1 sq. meter	= 10.764 sq. feet	1 sq. foot	= .092 sq. meters
	= 1.196 sq. yards	1 sq. yard	= .836 sq. meters
1 sq. kilometer	= .386 sq. miles	1 sq. mile	= 2.590 sq. kilometers
1 hectare	= 2.471 acres	1 acre	= .405 hectare

(Table A-2 continued on next page)

Table A-2 (continued)
Equivalent Measures of the Metric System

Volume

1 cubic centimeter	= .061 cu. inches	1 cubic inch	= 16.387 cubic centimeters
1 cubic meter	= 35.314 cu. feet	1 cubic foot	= .028 cubic meters
	= 1.308 cu. yards	1 cubic yard	= .764 cubic meters
1 stere	= .275 cords (wood)	1 cord (wood)	= 3.624 steres

Capacity

1 liter	= 1.056 liquid quarts	1 liquid quart	= .946 liters
	= .908 dry quarts	1 dry quart	= 1.11 liters
	= .264 U.S. gallons	1 U.S. gallon	= 3.785 liters
1 hectoliter	= 2.837 U.S. bushels	1 U.S. bushels	= .352 hectoliters

Weight

1 gram	= .032 troy ounces	1 grain	= .0648 grams
	= .0352 av. ounces	1 troy ounce	= 31.103 grams
	= 15.432 grams	1 av. ounce	= 28.35 grams
1 kilogram	= 2.2046 av. pounds	1 pound	= .4536 kilograms
1 metric ton	= 2,204.62 av. pounds	1 short ton	= .907 metric tons
1 carat	= 3.08 av. grains	1 carat	= 200. milligrams

Note: The basic units in the metric system are the meter, the unit of length, and the kilogram, the unit of mass. The liter, a measure of capacity, is the volume of a kilogram of water at the temperature 4°C. All other units in the system are multiples or decimal subdivisions of these. All units are closely related. For instance, 1 liter equals 1 cubic decimeter and 1 liter of water weighs 1 kilogram. The multiples and subdivisions of each unit is ten. Thus:

ten millimeters = one centimeter	ten meters = one decameter
ten centimeters = one decimeter	ten decameter = one hectometer
ten decimeters = one meter	ten hectometers = one kilometer
	ten kilometers = one myriameter

The same scale applies to the other units as: ten liters = one decaliter and ten decigrams = one gram. The multiples of the units use Greek prefixes while the subdivisions use the Latin; thus, deca = 10; hecto = 100; Kilo = 1000; myria = 10,000; deci = 1/10; centi = 1/100; milli = 1/1,000.

Taking into consideration the above explanation, most measures can be easily calculated from metric to US Standards and vice versa through the use of these tables.

Table A-3
Weights and Measures (US)

Dry measure: 2 pints = 1 quart; 8 quarts = 1 peck; 4 pecks = 1 bushel; 105 quarts = 1 standard barrel.

Liquid measure: 8 fluid drams = 1 fluid ounce; 4 fluid ounces = 1 gill; 4 gills = 1 pint liquid; 2 pints liquid = 1 quart liquid; 4 quarts liquid = 1 gallon; 31½ gallons = 1 barrel; 2 barrels = 1 hogshead.

Linear measure: 12 inches = 1 foot; 3 feet = 1 yard; 5½ yards = 1 rod; 40 rods = 1 furlong; 8 furlongs = 1 statute mile; 6080.20 feet = 1 nautical mile.

Some special linear measures: 1000 mils = 1 inch; 72 points = 1 inch; 4 inches = 1 hand; 7.92 inches = 1 surveyor's link; 9 inches = 1 span; 6 feet = 1 fathom; 40 yards = 1 bolt (cloth); 10 chains = 1 furlong.

Square measure: 144 square inches = 1 square foot; 9 square feet = 1 square yard; 30¼ square yards = 1 square rod; 160 square rods = 1 acre; 160 acres = 1 quarter section; 640 acres = 1 square mile; 36 square miles = 1 township.

Cubic measure: 1728 cubic inches = 1 cubic foot; 27 cubic feet = 1 cubic yard; 128 cubic feet = 1 cord; A "board foot," used in lumber measurements, is a volume equivalent to that of a board 1 foot by 1 foot by 1 inch, or 144 cubic inches.

Miscellaneous measures: 3 inches = 1 palm; 4 inches = 1 hand; 6 inches = 1 span; 18 inches = 1 cubit; 21.8 inches = 1 Bible cubit; 2½ feet = 1 military pace.

Circular measure: 60 seconds = 1 minute; 60 minutes = 1 degree; 30 degrees = 1 sign; 90 degrees = 1 quadrant; 4 quadrants = 1 circle; 360 degrees = 1 circle.

Paper measure: For small papers the old measure is still in use: 24 sheets = 1 quire; 20 quires = 1 ream (480 sheets). For papers put up in cases, bundles, or frames the following measure is now used; 25 sheets = 1 quire; 20 quires = 1 standard ream (500) sheets.

Mariner's measure: 6 feet = 1 fathom; 120 fathoms = 1 cable length; 7½ cable lengths = 1 mile.

Apothecaries' fluid measure: 60 minims = 1 fluid dram; 8 fluid drams = 1 fluid ounce; 16 fluid ounces = 1 liquid pint; 8 liquid pints = 1 gallon.

Apothecaries' weight: 20 grains = 1 scruple; 3 scruples = 1 dram; 8 drams = 1 ounce; 12 ounces = 1 pound.

Avoirdupois weight: 27 1/32 grains = 1 dram; 16 drams = 1 ounce; 16 ounces = 1 pound; 100 pounds = 1 short hundredweight; 112 pounds = 1 long hundredweight; 2000 pounds = 1 short ton; 2240 pounds = 1 long ton.

Troy weight: 24 grains = 1 pennyweight; 20 pennyweights = 1 ounce; 12 ounces = 1 pound (Troy). Carat* (for precious stones) 1200 milligrams.

Miscellaneous unit measurements: 196 pounds of flour = 1 barrel; 200 pounds of beef or pork = 1 barrel; 135 pounds of potatoes or apples = 1 barrel; 280 pounds of salt = 1 barrel; 400 pounds of molasses = 1 barrel; 200 pounds of sugar = 1 barrel; 240 pounds of lime = 1 barrel; 100 pounds of fish = 1 quintal; 100 pounds of nails = 1 keg; 56 pounds of butter = 1 firkin; 5 pounds of spices = 1 can; 1100 pounds of rice = 1 tierce. In measuring iron, lead, etc., 14 pounds = 1 stone; 21½ stones = 1 pig.

---

*The carat was formerly an ambiguous term having many values in various countries. Karat fineness of gold = 1/24 (by weight) gold. For example, 24 karats fine = pure gold; 18 karats fine = 18/24 pure gold.

Table A-4
Temperature Conversion Chart
Centigrade—Fahrenheit

°C		°F	°C		°F	°C		°F	°C		°F
−73.3	−100	−148.0	2.8	37	98.6	33.3	92	197.6	293	560	1040
−67.8	−90	−130.0	3.3	38	100.4	33.9	93	199.4	299	570	1058
−62.2	−80	−112.0	3.9	39	102.2	34.4	94	201.2	304'	580	1076
−59.4	−75	−103.0	4.4	40	104.0	35.0	95	203.0	310	590	1094
−56.7	−70	−94.0	5.0	41	105.8	35.6	96	204.8	316	600	1112
−53.9	−65	−85.0	5.6	42	107.6	36.1	97	206.6	321	610	1130
−51.1	−60	−76.0	6.1	43	109.4	36.7	98	208.4	327	620	1148
−48.3	−55	−67.0	6.7	44	111.2	37.2	99	210.2	332	630	1166
−45.6	−50	−58.0	7.2	45	113.0	37.8	100	212.0	338	640	1184
−42.8	−45	−49.0	7.8	46	114.8	43	110	230	343	650	1202
−40.0	−40	−40.0	8.3	47	116.6	49	120	248	349	660	1220
−37.2	−35	−31.0	8.9	48	118.4	54	130	266	354	670	1238
−34.4	−30	−22.0	9.4	49	120.2	60	140	284	360	680	1256
−31.7	−25	−13.0	10.0	50	122.0	66	150	302	366	690	1274
−28.9	−20	−4.0	10.6	51	123.8	71	160	320	371	700	1292
−26.1	−15	5.0	11.1	52	125.6	77	170	338	377	710	1310
−23.3	−10	14.0	11.7	53	127.4	82	180	356	382	720	1328
−20.6	−5	23.0	12.2	54	129.2	88	190	374	388	730	1346
−17.8	0	32.0	12.8	55	131.0	93	200	392	393	740	1364
−17.2	1	33.8	13.3	56	132.8	99	210	410	399	750	1382
−16.7	2	35.6	13.9	57	134.6	100	212	414	404	760	1400
−16.1	3	37.4	14.4	58	136.4	104	220	428	410	770	1418
−15.6	4	39.2	15.0	59	138.2	110	230	446	416	780	1436
−15.0	5	41.0	15.6	60	140.0	116	240	464	421	790	1454
−14.4	6	42.8	16.1	61	141.8	121	250	482	427	800	1472
−13.9	7	44.6	16.7	62	143.6	127	260	500	432	810	1490
−13.3	8	46.4	17.2	63	145.4	132	270	518	438	820	1508
−12.8	9	48.2	17.8	64	147.2	138	280	536	443	830	1526
−12.2	10	50.0	18.3	65	149.0	143	290	554	449	840	1544
−11.7	11	51.8	18.9	66	150.8	149	300	572	454	850	1562
−11.1	12	53.6	19.4	67	152.6	154	310	590	460	860	1580
−10.6	13	55.4	20.0	68	154.4	160	320	608	466	870	1598
−10.0	14	57.2	20.6	69	156.2	166	330	626	471	880	1616
−9.4	15	59.0	21.1	70	158.0	171	340	644	477	890	1634
−8.9	16	60.8	21.7	71	159.8	177	350	662	482	900	1652
−8.3	17	62.6	22.2	72	161.6	182	360	680	488	910	1670
−7.8	18	64.4	22.8	73	163.4	188	370	698	493	920	1688
−7.2	19	66.2	23.3	74	165.2	193	380	716	499	930	1706
−6.7	20	68.0	23.9	75	167.0	199	390	734	504	940	1724
−6.1	21	69.8	24.4	76	168.8	204	400	752	510	950	1742
−5.6	22	71.6	25.0	77	170.6	210	410	770	516	960	1760
−5.0	23	73.4	25.6	78	172.4	216	420	788	521	970	1778
−4.4	24	75.2	26.1	79	174.2	221	430	806	527	980	1796
−3.9	25	77.0	26.7	80	176.0	227	440	824	532	990	1814
−3.3	26	78.8	27.2	81	177.8	232	450	842	538	1000	1832
−2.8	27	80.6	27.8	82	179.6	238	460	860	566	1050	1922
−2.2	28	82.4	28.3	83	181.4	243	470	878	593	1100	2012
−1.7	29	84.2	28.9	84	183.2	249	480	896	621	1150	2102
−1.1	30	86.0	29.4	85	185.0	254	490	914	649	1200	2192
−0.6	31	87.8	30.0	86	186.8	260	500	932	677	1250	2282
0.0	32	89.6	30.6	87	188.6	266	510	950	704	1300	2372
0.6	33	91.4	31.1	88	190.4	271	520	968	732	1350	2462
1.1	34	93.2	31.7	89	192.2	277	530	986	760	1400	2552
1.7	35	95.0	32.2	90	194.0	282	540	1004	788	1450	2642
2.2	36	96.8	32.8	91	195.8	288	550	1022	816	1500	2732

Table A-5
Volume and Weight of Water at Various Temperatures

°F	Relative Volume*	cu. ft./lb.	F°	Relative Volume	cu. ft./lb.
32	1.000176	62.42	290	1.0830	57.65
39.2	1.000000	62.43	300	1.0890	57.33
40	1.000004	62.43	310	1.0953	57.00
50	1.00027	62.42	320	1.1019	56.66
60	1.00096	62.37	330	1.1088	56.30
70	1.00201	62.30	340	1.1160	55.94
80	1.00338	62.22	350	1.1235	55.57
90	1.00504	62.11	360	1.1313	55.18
100	1.00698	62.00	370	1.1396	54.78
110	1.00915	61.86	380	1.1483	54.36
120	1.01157	61.71	390	1.1573	53.94
130	1.01420	61.55	400	1.167	53.5
140	1.01705	61.38	410	1.177	53.0
150	1.02011	61.20	420	1.187	52.6
160	1.02337	61.00	430	1.197	52.2
170	1.02682	60.80	440	1.208	51.7
180	1.03047	60.58	450	1.220	51.2
190	1.03431	60.36	460	1.232	50.7
200	1.03835	60.12	470	1.244	50.2
210	1.04256	59.88	480	1.256	49.7
212	1.04343	59.83	490	1.269	49.2
220	1.0469	59.63	500	1.283	48.7
230	1.0515	59.37	510	1.297	48.1
240	1.0562	59.11	520	1.312	47.6
250	1.0611	58.83	530	1.329	47.0
260	1.0662	58.55	540	1.35	46.3
270	1.0715	58.26	550	1.37	45.6
280	1.0771	57.96	560	1.39	44.9

*Water at 39.2° = 1.

Table A-6
Effect of Altitude in Reducing the Boiling Point of Water

Altitude Feet	Barometer at 32°F Inches	Boiling Point °F	Atmospheric Pressure, psi	Altitude Feet	Barometer at 32° Inches	Boiling Point °F	Atmospheric Pressure, psi
0	29.92	212	14.70	8,000	22.38	198	10.98
500	29.43	211	14.46	8,500	21.96	197	10.78
1,000	28.93	210	14.21	9,000	21.55	196	10.58
1,500	28.44	209	13.97	9,500	21.15	195	10.38
2,000	27.94	209	13.72	10,000	20.75	194	10.19
2,500	27.44	208	13.48	10,500	20.36	193	10.00
3,000	16.94	207	13.23	11,000	19.98	192	9.81
3,500	26.44	206	12.99	11,500	19.60	191	9.63
4,000	25.95	205	12.75	12,000	19.24	191	9.45
4,500	25.47	204	12.52	12,500	18.88	190	9.27
5,000	25.01	203	12.29	13,000	18.52	189	9.09
5,500	24.55	202	12.06	13,500	18.17	188	8.92
6,000	24.09	201	11.83	14,000	17.82	187	8.75
6,500	23.65	200	11.61	14,500	17.47	186	8.58
7,000	23.22	199	11.39	15,000	17.12	185	8.41
7,500	22.80	199	11.18	15,500	16.77	184	8.24

Table A-7
Specific Heat of Water at Various Temperatures

Temperature °C	°F	Specific Heat	Temperature °C	°F	Specific Heat
0	32	1.0106	55	131	0.9994
5	41	1.0065	60	140	0.9999
10	50	1.0031	65	149	1.0005
15	59	1.0009	70	158	1.0012
20	68	1.0000	75	167	1.0020
25	77	0.9992	80	176	1.0029
30	86	0.9988	85	185	1.0038
35	95	0.9986	90	194	1.0048
40	104	0.9986	95	203	1.0059
45	113	0.9987	100	212	1.0070
50	122	0.9990	—	—	—

Table A-8
Properties of Saturated Steam

Absolute Pressure, psi	°F	Specific Volume, cu. ft./lb.	Density, lb./cu. ft.	Heat of liquid above 32°F	Latent heat of evapo- ration	Total heat of steam above 32°F	Internal energy (Btu), evapo- ration	Entropy	
								Water	Evaporator
14.7	212.00	26.79	0.03732	180.0	970.4	1,150.4	897.6	0.3118	1.4447
15	213.00	26.27	0.03806	181.0	969.7	1,150.7	896.8	0.3133	1.4416
20	228.00	20.08	0.04980	196.1	960.0	1,156.2	885.8	0.3355	1.3965
25	240.1	16.30	0.0614	208.4	952.0	1,160.4	876.8	0.3532	1.3604
30	250.3	13.74	0.0728	218.8	945.1	1,163.9	869.0	0.3680	1.3311
35	259.3	11.89	0.0841	227.9	938.9	1,168.8	862.1	0.3808	1.3060
40	267.3	10.49	0.0953	236.1	933.3	1,169.4	855.9	0.3920	1.2841
45	274.5	9.39	0.1065	243.4	928.2	1,171.6	850.3	0.4021	1.2644
50	281.0	8.51	0.1175	250.1	923.5	1,173.6	845.0	0.4113	1.2468
55	287.1	7.78	0.1285	256.3	919.0	1,175.4	840.2	0.4196	1.2309
60	292.7	7.17	0.1394	262.1	914.9	1,177.0	835.6	0.4272	1.2160
65	298.0	6.65	0.1503	267.5	911.0	1,178.5	831.4	0.4344	1.2024
70	302.9	6.20	0.1612	272.6	907.2	1,179.8	827.3	0.4411	1.1896
75	307.6	5.81	0.1721	277.4	903.7	1,181.1	823.5	0.4474	1.1778
80	312.0	5.47	0.1829	282.0	900.3	1,182.3	819.8	0.4535	1.1665
85	316.3	5.16	0.1937	286.3	897.1	1,183.4	816.3	0.4590	1.1561
90	320.3	4.89	0.2044	290.5	893.9	1,184.4	813.0	0.4644	1.1461
95	324.1	4.65	0.2151	294.5	890.9	1,185.4	809.7	0.4694	1.1367
100	327.8	4.429	0.2258	298.3	888.0	1,186.3	806.6	0.4743	1.1277
105	331.4	4.230	0.2365	302.0	885.2	1,187.2	803.6	0.4789	1.1191
110	334.8	4.047	0.2472	305.5	882.5	1,188.0	800.7	0.4834	1.1108
115	338.1	3.880	0.2577	309.0	879.8	1,188.8	797.9	0.4877	1.1030
120	341.3	3.726	0.2683	312.3	877.2	1,189.6	795.2	0.4919	1.0954
125	344.4	3.583	0.2791	315.5	874.7	1,190.3	792.6	0.4959	1.0880
130	347.4	3,452	0.2897	318.6	872.3	1,191.0	790.0	0.4998	1.0809
135	350.3	3.331	0.3002	321.7	869.9	1,191.6	787.5	0.5035	1.0742
140	353.1	3.219	0.3107	324.6	867.6	1,192.2	785.0	0.5072	1.0675
145	355.8	3.112	0.3213	327.4	865.4	1,192.8	782.7	0.5107	1.0621
150	358.5	3.012	0.3320	330.2	863.2	1,193.4	780.4	0.5142	1.0550
155	361.0	2.920	0.3425	332.9	861.0	1,194.0	778.1	0.5175	1.0489
160	363.6	2.834	0.3529	335.6	858.8	1,194.5	775.8	0.5208	1.0431
165	366.0	2.753	0.3633	338.2	856.8	1,195.0	773.6	0.5239	1.0376

(Table A-8 continued on next page)

Table A-8 (continued)
Properties of Saturated Steam

Absolute pressure, psi	°F	Specific Volume, cu. ft./lb.	Density, lb./cu. ft.	Heat of liquid above 32°F	Latent heat of evaporation	Total heat of steam above 32°F	Internal energy (Btu), evaporation	Enthropy Water	Enthropy Evaporation
170	368.5	2.675	0.3738	340.7	854.7	1,195.4	771.5	0.5269	1.0321
175	370.8	1.602	0.3843	343.2	852.7	1,195.9	769.4	0.5299	1.0268
180	373.1	2.533	0.3948	345.6	850.8	1,196.4	767.4	0.5328	1.0215
185	375.4	2.468	0.4052	348.0	848.4	1,196.8	765.4	0.5356	1.0164
190	377.6	2.406	0.4157	350.4	846.9	1,197.3	763.4	0.5384	1.0114
195	379.8	2.346	0.4262	352.7	845.0	1,197.7	761.4	0.5410	1.0066
200	381.9	2.290	0.437	354.9	843.2	1,198.1	759.5	0.5437	1.0019
205	384.0	2.237	0.447	357.1	841.4	1,198.5	757.6	0.5463	0.9973
210	386.0	2.187	0.457	359.2	839.6	1,198.8	755.8	0.5488	0.9928
215	388.0	2.138	0.468	361.4	837.9	1,199.2	754.0	0.5513	0.9885
220	389.9	2.091	0.478	363.4	836.2	1,199.6	752.3	0.5538	0.9841
225	391.9	2.046	0.489	365.5	834.4	1,199.9	750.5	0.5562	0.9799
230	393.8	2.004	0.499	367.5	832.1	1,200.2	748.8	0.5586	0.9758
235	395.6	1.964	0.509	369.4	831.1	1,200.6	747.0	0.5610	0.9717
240	397.4	1.924	0.520	371.4	829.5	1,200.9	745.4	0.5633	0.9676
245	399.3	1.887	0.530	373.3	827.9	1,201.2	743.7	0.5655	0.9638
250	401.1	1.850	0.541	375.2	826.3	1,201.5	742.0	0.5676	0.9600
260	404.1	1.782	0.561	378.9	823.1	1,202.1	738.9	0.5719	0.9525
270	407.9	1.718	0.582	382.5	820.1	1,202.6	735.8	0.5760	0.9454
280	411.2	1.658	0.603	386.1	817.1	1,203.1	732.7	0.5800	0.9385
290	414.4	1.602	0.624	389.4	814.2	1,203.6	729.7	0.5840	0.9316
300	417.5	1.551	0.645	392.7	811.3	1,204.1	726.8	0.5878	0.9251
310	420.5	1.502	0.666	395.9	808.5	1,204.5	724.0	0.5915	0.9187
320	423.4	1.456	0.687	399.1	805.8	1,204.9	721.2	0.5951	0.9125
330	426.3	1.413	0.708	402.2	803.1	1,205.3	718.5	0.5986	0.9065
340	429.1	1.372	0.729	405.3	800.4	1,205.7	715.9	0.6020	0.9006
350	431.9	1.334	0.750	408.2	797.8	1,206.1	713.3	0.6053	0.8949
360	434.6	1.298	0.770	411.2	795.3	1,206.4	710.7	0.6085	0.8894
370	437.2	1.264	0.791	414.0	792.8	1,206.8	708.2	0.6116	0.8840
380	439.8	1.231	0.812	416.8	790.3	1,207.1	705.7	0.6147	0.8788
390	442.3	1.200	0.833	419.5	787.9	1,207.4	703.3	0.6178	0.8737
400	444.8	1.17	0.86	422.0	786.0	1,208.0	701.0	0.621	0.868
450	456.5	1.04	0.96	435.0	774.0	1,209.0	690.0	0.635	0.844
500	467.3	0.93	1.08	448.0	762.0	1,210.0	678.0	0.648	0.822
550	477.3	0.83	1.20	459.0	751.0	1,210.0	668.0	0.659	0.803
600	486.6	0.76	1.32	469.0	741.0	1,210.0	658.0	0.670	0.783

Table A-9
API Gravity Tables and Weight Factors

API Gravity	Specific Gravity	Lbs./U.S. Gal.	US Gals./Lb.	API Gravity	Specific Gravity	Lbs./US Gal.	US Gals./Lb.
0	1.0760	8.962	0.1116	51	0.7753	6.455	0.1549
1	1.0679	8.895	0.1124	52	0.7711	6.420	0.1558
2	1.0599	8.828	0.1133	53	0.7669	6.385	0.1566
3	1.0520	8.762	0.1141	54	0.7628	6.350	0.1575
4	1.0443	8.698	0.1150	55	0.7587	6.316	0.1583
5	1.0366	8.634	0.1158				
				56	0.7547	6.283	0.1592
6	1.0291	8.571	0.1167	57	0.7507	6.249	0.1600
7	1.0217	8.509	0.1175	58	0.7467	6.216	0.1609
8	1.0143	8.448	0.1184	59	0.7428	6.184	0.1617
9	1.0071	8.388	0.1192	60	0.7389	6.151	0.1626
10	1.0000	8.328	0.1201				
				61	0.7351	6.119	0.1634
11	0.9930	8.270	0.1209	62	0.7313	6.087	0.1643
12	0.9861	8.212	0.1218	63	0.7275	6.056	0.1651
13	0.9792	8.155	0.1226	64	0.7238	6.025	0.1660
14	0.9725	8.099	0.1235	65	0.7201	5.994	0.1668
15	0.9659	8.044	0.1243				
				66	0.7165	5.964	0.1677
16	0.9593	7.989	0.1252	67	0.7128	5.934	0.1685
17	0.9529	7.935	0.1260	68	0.7093	5.904	0.1694
18	0.9465	7.882	0.1269	69	0.7057	5.874	0.1702
19	0.9402	7.830	0.1277	70	0.7022	5.845	0.1711
20	0.9340	7.778	0.1286				
				71	0.6988	5.817	0.1719
21	0.9279	7.727	0.1294	72	0.6953	5.788	0.1728
22	0.9218	7.676	0.1303	73	0.6919	5.759	0.1736
23	0.9159	7.627	0.1311	74	0.6886	5.731	0.1745
24	0.9100	7.578	0.1320	75	0.6852	5.703	0.1753
25	0.9042	7.529	0.1328				
				76	0.6819	5.676	0.1762
26	0.8984	7.481	0.1337	77	0.6787	5.649	0.1770
27	0.8927	7.434	0.1345	78	0.6754	5.622	0.1779
28	0.8871	7.387	0.1354	79	0.6722	5.595	0.1787
29	0.8816	7.341	0.1362	80	0.6690	5.568	0.1796
30	0.8762	7.296	0.1371				
				81	0.6659	5.542	0.1804
31	0.8708	7.251	0.1379	82	0.6628	5.516	0.1813
32	0.8654	7.206	0.1388	83	0.6597	5.491	0.1821
33	0.8602	7.163	0.1396	84	0.6566	5.465	0.1830
34	0.8550	7.119	0.1405	85	0.6536	5.440	0.1838
35	0.8498	7.076	0.1413				
				86	0.6506	5.415	0.1847
36	0.8448	7.034	0.1422	87	0.6476	5.390	0.1855
37	0.8398	6.993	0.1430	88	0.6446	5.365	0.1864
38	0.8348	6.951	0.1439	89	0.6417	5.341	0.1872
39	0.8299	6.910	0.1447	90	0.6388	5.316	0.1881
40	0.8251	6.870	0.1456				
				91	0.6360	5.293	0.1889
41	0.8203	6.830	0.1464	92	0.6331	5.269	0.1898
42	0.8155	6.790	0.1473	93	0.6303	5.246	0.1906
43	0.8109	6.752	0.1481	94	0.6275	5.222	0.1915
44	0.8063	6.713	0.1490	95	0.6247	5.199	0.1924
45	0.8017	6.675	0.1498				
				96	0.6220	5.176	0.1932
46	0.7972	6.637	0.1507	97	0.6193	5.154	0.1940
47	0.7927	6.600	0.1515	98	0.6166	5.131	0.1949
48	0.7883	6.563	0.1524	99	0.6139	5.109	0.1957
49	0.7839	6.526	0.1532	100	0.6112	5.086	0.1966
50	0.7796	6.490	0.1541				

Table A-10
Paraffin Hydrocarbons

Name	Formula	H/C Ratio, Wt.	Melting Point, °F
Methane	CH_4	0.33	----
Ethane	C_2H_6	0.25	----
Propane	C_3H_8	0.22	----
Butane	C_4H_{10}	0.208	----
Pentane	C_5H_{12}	0.20	
Hexane	C_6H_{14}	0.194	
Heptane	C_7H_{16}	0.19	
Octane	C_8H_{18}	0.187	
Nonane	C_9H_{20}	0.185	
Decane	$C_{10}H_{22}$	0.183	
Undecane	$C_{11}H_{24}$	0.181	
Duodecane	$C_{12}H_{26}$	0.180	10.4
Tridecane	$C_{13}H_{28}$	0.179	21.2
Tetradecane	$C_{14}H_{30}$	0.178	41.0
Pentadecane	$C_{15}H_{32}$	0.1777	50.0
Hexadecane	$C_{16}H_{34}$	0.1770	64.5
Heptadecane	$C_{17}H_{36}$	0.1764	71.6
Octadecane	$C_{18}H_{38}$	0.1759	82.4
Nondecane	$C_{19}H_{40}$	0.1754	89.6
Eicosane	$C_{20}H_{42}$	0.1750	98.9
Tricosane	$C_{23}H_{48}$	0.1739	118.4
Pentacosane	$C_{25}H_{52}$	0.1733	129.2
Nonocosane	$C_{29}H_{60}$	0.1724	145.4
Duotriacontane	$C_{32}H_{66}$	0.1718	158.0
Pentatriacontane	$C_{35}H_{72}$	0.1714	167.0

Table A-11
Diolefin Hydrocarbons

Name	Formula	H/C Ratio, Wt.	Boiling Point, °F
Allene (Propyne)	C_3H_4	0.1111	10.3
Butadiene	C_4H_6	0.1250	24.1
Isoprene	C_5H_8	0.1333	95.4
Trimethyl Butadiene	C_7H_{12}	0.1428	

Table A-12
Aromatic Hydrocarbons

Name	Formula	H/C Ratio, Wt.	Boiling Point, °F
Benzene	C_6H_6	0.0833	176.2
Toluene	C_7H_8	0.952	230.9
mXylene	C_8H_{10}	0.1041	282.2
oXylene	C_8H_{10}	0.1041	291.2
pXylene	C_8H_{10}	0.1041	281.1
Mesitylene	C_9H_{12}	0.1111	329.1
Dibenzyl	$C_{14}H_{14}$	0.0833	545.2
Triphenylmethane	$C_{19}H_{16}$	0.0701	677.3

Table A-13
Naphthene (Cyclic) Hydrocarbons

Name	Formula	H/C Ratio, Wt.	Boiling Point, °F
Cyclopropane	C_3H_6	0.1666	−27.0
Cyclobutane	C_4H_8	0.1666	54.7
Cyclopentane	C_5H_{10}	0.1666	120.7
M-Cyclopentane	C_6H_{12}	0.1666	161.4
E-Cyclopentane	C_7H_{14}	0.1666	218.1
Cyclohexane	C_6H_{12}	0.1666	177.3
M-Cyclohexane	C_7H_{14}	0.1666	213.6

Table A-14
Olefin Hydrocarbons

Name	Formula	H/C Ratio, Wt.	Melting Point, °F
Ethylene	C_2H_4	0.166	−272.9
Propylene	C_3H_6	0.166	−300.8
Butylene	C_4H_8	0.166	−202.0
Amylene	C_5H_{10}	0.166	−191.2
Hexylene	C_6H_{12}	0.166	−145.3
Heptylene	C_7H_{14}	0.166	
Octylene	C_8H_{16}	0.166	
Nonylene	C_9H_{18}	0.166	
Decylene	$C_{10}H_{20}$	0.166	
Pentadecylene	$C_{15}H_{30}$	0.166	46.4
Eicosylene	$C_{20}H_{40}$	0.166	83.3
Melene	$C_{30}H_{60}$	0.166	143.5

Table A-15
Acetylene Hydrocarbons

Name	Formula	H/C Ratio, Wt.	Boiling Point, °F
Acetylene	C_2H_2	0.0833	−118.5
Allylene	C_3H_4	0.1111	−10.3
Crotonylene	C_4H_6	0.1250	80.6
Valerylene	C_5H_8	0.1333	131.0
Isopropyl Acetylene	C_5H_8	0.1333	158.0
Butyl Acetylene	C_6H_{10}	0.1388	181.4
Heptyne	C_7H_{12}	0.1428	219.2

Table A-16
Stainless Steel Characteristics

Type	Cr.	Ni.	Scaling Temp. Long Term	Scaling Temp. Intermediate	Free-Sulfur Res.
301	17	7	1,700	1,600	F
302	18	8	1,700	1,600	F
304-S	18	8	1,700	1,600	F
305	18	8	1,700	1,600	F
302-B	18	8	1,800	1,650	F
303	18	8	1,700	1,400	F
316	18	8	1,700	1,600	F
317	18	8	1,700	1,600	F
321	18	8	1,700	1,600	F
347	18	8	1,700	1,600	F
308	20	10	1,700	1,600	F
309	25	12	2,000	1,800	E
310	25	20	2,100	1,900	P
314	25	20	2,100	1,900	P
403	12	—	1,300	1,500	E
405	12	—	1,300	1,500	E
410	12	—	1,300	1,500	E
414	12	2	1,250	1,400	F+
416	12	—	1,250	1,400	E
418	12	—	1,300	1,500	E
420	12	—	1,200	1,400	E
440	17	—	1,400	1,500	E
442	21	—	1,800	1,900	E
446	28	—	2,000	2,150	E

Note: A frequently disregarded factor in the choice of heat-resisting steel is that of resistance to attack of elemental sulfur in the form of H_2S, Mercaptans, Organic Sulfides, Carbonyl Sulfide (COS) and others where dissociation of these compounds occurs. Oxides of sulfur at temperatures above the dew point are no more harmful than oxides of carbon. Note that in the type 400 steels, when the Ni content is less than 1%, the Ni is not shown.

Table A-17
Temperature Estimation From Color

°F	Color
990	Barely discernible red
1,050	Blood red
1,175	Dark cherry red
1,250	Medium cherry red
1,375	Cherry red
1,550	Bright cherry red
1,650	Red-orange
1,725	Orange
1,825	Yellow
1,975	Light yellow
2,200	White

Note: These data provide the basis for temperature measurement in the use of the color-comparison optical pyrometer. Careful observation of color at measured temperature provides a basis for estimating temperature of an observed point in the absence of instrument checks which, after experience, can be within 50 to 100°F of the actual temperature.

Table A-18
Fusion Temperatures for ASTM Pyrometric Cones Used for Establishing PCE (Pyrometric Cone Equivalent) Characteristics of Refractories for Heat Resistance

Cone Number	Fusion Temperature, °F	Cone Number	Fusion Temperature, °F
15	2,615	30	3,002
16	2,669	31	3,056
17	2,687	32	3,092
18	2,714	32.5	3,131
19	2,768	33	3,173
20	2,786	34	3,200
23	2,876	35	3,245
26	2,903	36	3,290
27	2,921	37	3,308
28	2,939	38	3,335
29	2,984		

Table A-19
Explosive Limits in Fuel-Air Mixture

Data for explosive limits in fuel-air mixture which are typically given as % of fuel in air tend to be confusing as O_2 percentage limits become limiting as, for example, in mixture of fuel with CO_2 and O_2 or H_2O and O_2. These data as presented will be correct for *completely homogeneous* mixtures but such a state of mixture is rare rather than typical as is shown in that the Safety Departments of some major companies define 2% O_2 as hazardous and there is reason to believe that *any* O_2 in detonative gases such as H_2, C_2H_2, CS_2 and others is dangerous. Note that the O_2 is critical in any mixture of gases.

CH_4 -	5.00% - 15.00%		CO -	12.50% - 74.20%
O_2 -	19.90% - 17.80%		O_2 -	18.33% - 5.40%
N_2 -	75.10% - 67.20%		N_2 -	69.17% - 20.40%
C_2H_6 -	3.10% - 12.45%		H_2S -	4.30% - 45.50%
O_2 -	20.30% - 18.34%		O_2 -	20.05% - 11.42%
N_2 -	76.60% - 69.21%		N_2 -	75.65% - 43.08%
C_3H_8 -	2.10% - 10.10%		CS_2 -	1.25% - 50.00%
O_2 -	20.51% - 18.83%		O_2 -	20.69% - 10.47%
N_2 -	77.39% - 71.07%		N_2 -	78.06% - 39.53%
Butane -	1.86% - 8.41%		NH_3 -	15.50% - 26.60%
O_2 -	20.56% - 19.18%		O_2 -	17.70% - 15.37%
N_2 -	77.58% - 72.41%		N_2 -	66.80% - 58.03%
Pentane -	1.40% - 7.80%		Naphtha -	1.10% - 6.00%
O_2 -	20.65% - 19.31%		O_2 -	20.72% - 19.69%
N_2 -	77.95% - 72.89%		N_2 -	78.18% - 74.31%
Hexane -	1.25% - 6.90%		Gasoline -	1.50% - 7.40%
O_2 -	20.68% - 19.50%		O_2 -	20.63% - 19.40%
N_2 -	78.07% - 73.60%		N_2 -	77.87% - 73.20%
Acetylene -	2.50% - 80.00%		Benzene -	1.35% - 6.75%
O_2 -	20.42% - 4.19%		O_2 -	20.66% - 19.25%
N_2 -	77.08% - 15.81%		N_2 -	77.99% - 74.00%
Ethylene -	2.75% - 28.60%		HCN -	5.60% - 40.00%
O_2 -	20.37% - 14.96%		O_2 -	19.77% - 12.57%
N_2 -	76.88% - 56.44%		N_2 -	74.63% - 47.43%
Propylene -	2.00% - 11.10%		Butadiene -	2.00% - 11.00%
O_2 -	20.53% - 18.62%		O_2 -	20.53% - 18.64%
N_2 -	77.47% - 70.28%		N_2 -	77.47% - 70.36%
Hydrogen -	4.00% - 74.20%			
O_2 -	20.11% - 7.50%			
N_2 -	75.89% - 18.30%			

Note: Explosive limits data (UEL − LEL) taken from *Gaseous Fuels,* L. Shnidman, American Gas Association. These data are widely accepted as valid.

Table A-20
Drill Sizes and Areas

Inch Dia.	MTD* Size	Dia. Inches	Area Sq. In.	Inch Dia.	MTD* Size	Dia. Inches	Area Sq. In.
	80	.0135	.000143		32	.116	.0106
	79	.0145	.000165		31	.120	.0113
1/64	..	.0156	.00019	1/8	..	.125	.0123
	78	.016	.00020		30	.1285	.0130
	77	.018	.00025		29	.136	.0145
	76	.020	.00031		28	.1405	.0155
	75	.021	.00035	9/64	..	.1406	.0156
	74	.0225	.00040		27	.144	.0163
	73	.024	.00045		26	.147	.0174
	72	.025	.00049		25	.1495	.0175
	71	.026	.00053		24	.152	.0181
	70	.028	.00062		23	.154	.0186
	69	.0292	.00067	5/32	..	.1562	.0192
	68	.030	.00075		22	.157	.0193
1/32	..	.0312	.00076		21	.1495	.0175
	67	.032	.00080		20	.161	.0203
	66	.033	.00086		19	.166	.0216
	65	.035	.00096		18	.1695	.0226
	64	.036	.00102	11/64	..	.1719	.0232
	63	.037	.00108		17	.175	.0235
	62	.038	.00113		16	.177	.0246
	61	.039	.00119		15	.180	.0254
	60	.040	.00126		14	.182	.0260
	59	.041	.00132		13	.185	.0269
	58	.042	.00138	3/16	..	.1875	.0276
	57	.043	.00145		12	.189	.02805
	56	.0465	.00170		11	.191	.02865
3/64	..	.0469	.00173		10	.1935	.0294
	55	.0520	.00210		9	.196	.0302
	54	.0550	.0023		8	.199	.0311
	53	.0595	.0028		7	.201	.0316
1/16	..	.0625	.0031	13/64	..	.2031	.0324
	52	.0635	.0032		6	.204	.0327
	51	.0670	.0035		5	.2055	.0332
	50	.070	.0038		4	.209	.0343
	49	.073	.0042		3	.213	.0356
	48	.076	.0043	7/32	..	.2187	.0376
5/64	..	.0781	.0048		2	.221	.0384
	47	.0785	.0049		1	.228	.0409
	46	.081	.0051		A	.234	.0430
	45	.082	.0053	15/64	..	.2343	.0431
	44	.086	.0058		B	.238	.0444
	43	.089	.0062		C	.242	.0460
	42	.0935	.0069		D	.246	.0475
3/32	..	.0937	.0069	1/4	E	.250	.0491
	41	.096	.0072		F	.257	.0519
	40	.098	.0075		G	.261	.0535
	39	.0995	.0078	17/64	..	.2656	.0554
	38	.1015	.0081		H	.266	.0556
	37	.104	.0085		I	.272	.0580
	36	.1065	.0090		J	.277	.0601
7/64	..	.1093	.0094		K	.281	.0620
	35	.110	.0095	9/32	..	.2812	.0621
	34	.111	.0097		L	.290	.0660
	33	.113	.0100		M	.295	.0683

Table A-20 (continued)
Drill Sizes and Areas

Inch Dia.	MTD* Size	Dia. Inches	Area Sq. In.	Inch Dia.	MTD* Size	Dia. Inches	Area Sq. In.
19/64	. .	.2968	.0692	1/2	. .	.5000	.1963
	N	.302	.0716	33/64	. .	.5156	.2088
5/16	. .	.3125	.0767	17/32	. .	.5312	.2217
	O	.316	.0784	35/64	. .	.5468	.2349
	P	.323	.0820	9/16	. .	.5625	.2485
31/64	. .	.3281	.0846	37/64	. .	.5781	.2625
	Q	.332	.0866	19/32	. .	.5937	.2769
11/32	R	.339	.0901	39/64	. .	.6093	.2916
	. .	.3437	.0928	5/8	. .	.625	.3068
	S	.348	.0950	41/64	. .	.6506	.3223
	T	.358	.1005	21/32	. .	.6562	.3382
23/64	. .	.3593	.1014	43/64	. .	.6718	.3545
	U	.368	.1063	11/16	. .	.6875	.3712
3/8	. .	.375	.1104	45/64	. .	.7031	.3883
	V	.377	.1116	23/32	. .	.7187	.4057
	W	.386	.1170	47/64	. .	.7343	.4236
25/64	. .	.3906	.1198	3/4	. .	.750	.4418
	X	.397	.1236	49/64	. .	.7656	.4604
	Y	.404	.1278	25/32	. .	.7812	.4794
13/32	. .	.4062	.1296	51/64	. .	.7968	.4987
	Z	.413	.1340	13/16	. .	.8125	.5185
7/16	. .	.4375	.1503	53/64	. .	.8281	.5386
39/64	. .	.4531	.1613	27/32	. .	.8337	.5591
17/32	. .	.4687	.1726	55/64	. .	.8593	.5800
31/64	. .	.4843	.1843	7/8	. .	.875	.6013

*MTD = Morse Taper Drill

Table A-21
Dry Air Velocity and Flow Due to Pressure Drop Weight of Air 760/60 76.33 #M

Pressure Drop Inches Water	Velocity (Ft./Min.)	Cu. Ft. FlowPh./ Sq. Ft.	Pressure Drop Inches Water	Velocity (Ft./Min.)	Cu. Ft. FlowPh./ Sq. Ft.
.025	632	38,000	3.25	7,220	430,000
.03	695	41,700	3.50	7,492	450,000
.04	803	48,100	3.75	7,756	465,000
.05	896	53,760	4.00	8,010	480,000
.08	1,135	68,100	4.25	8,256	490,000
.10	1,266	75,550	4.50	8,496	509,000
.15	1,520	90,750	4.75	8,729	525,000
.20	1,791	107,000	5.00	8,943	535,000
.25	2,003	120,000	5.50	9,392	560,000
.3	2,193	131,000	6.00	9,810	587,000
.4	2,533	151,000	6.50	10,210	610,000
.5	2,832	170,000	7.00	10,595	623,000
.6	3,102	186,000	7.5	10,968	651,000
.7	3,351	200,000	8.0	11,328	677,000
.8	3,582	215,000	9.0	12,015	718,000
.9	3,800	228,000	10.0	12,665	755,000
1.00	4,005	241,000	11.0	13,282	790,000
1.25	4,478	268,000	12.0	13,875	825,000
1.50	4,905	293,000	13.0	14,440	862,000
1.75	5,298	315,000	14.0	14,985	895,000
2.00	5,664	339,000	15.0	15,510	925,000
2.25	6,007	360,000	16.0	16,020	957,000
2.50	6,332	378,000	17.0	16,513	982,000
2.75	6,641	400,000	18.0	16,990	1,015,000
3.00	6,937	415,000	19.0	17,456	1,037,000
			20.0	17,910	1,065,000

Table A-22
Air for Fuels Combustion

If ambient temperature and humidity can be high for a significant portion of operating time, air calculation should be based on 10.88 cu ft/cu ft of methane. But high conditions of temperature and humidity are typically rare, and it is common, for normal conditions, to use 10 cu ft air/cu ft CH₄ in calculation. However, such calculation is for theoretical air and makes no provision for excess air. Typical excess air for calculation is 25% which is not necessarily an operating excess air. Therefore, theoretical air is multiplied by a factor of 1.25 for air supply.

Calorific value of CH_4 is substantially 1,000 Btu/cu ft Higher (Gross) Heating Value (HHV) or 910 Btu/cu ft Lower (Net) Heating Value (LHV). Because of temperature and humidity variation, precise calculation of air demand for fuels burning is possible for only a fixed set of temperature-humidity conditions which, in operation, is not possible. Calculation of air demand for fuels burning must take temperature-humidity conditions into account to be sure of enough air (oxygen) in all conditions of operation.

HHV Basis - (Q/1000) x 10 x 1.25 - Air Demand at 25% Excess Air, CFH
LHV Basis - (Q/910) x 10 x 1.25 - Air Demand at 25% Excess Air CFH
Q - Total Heat Release, BTU/HR.

Procedure as outlined is satisfactory for any typical gaseous or liquid fuel and will always deliver enough air (which is vitally important). If error exists, it will be on the plus side.

Table A-23
Effect of SO₃ on the Dew-Points of Gases Containing Various Mol-Percentages of H₂O Vapor

Mol-Percent H₂O & Dew-Point	Dew-Point Temperature Increase When PPM of SO₃ are Present in the Gases											
	PPM	Dew-Point	PPM	Dew-Point	PPM	Dew-Point	PPM	Dew-Point	PPM	Dew-Point	PPM	Dew-Point
2.6% - 70F												
5.2% - 92F	2	78F	5	114F	10	146F	20	174F	50	210F	100	238F
7.9% - 108F	2	100F	5	136F	10	168F	20	196F	50	228F	100	252F
10.5% - 116F	2	115F	5	148F	10	178F	20	204F	50	236F	100	264F
13.1% - 124F	2	124F	5	156F	10	186F	20	212F	50	244F	100	272F
15.8% - 130F	2	132F	5	164F	10	194F	20	220F	50	252F	100	277F
18.4% - 137F	2	138F	5	178F	10	198F	20	224F	50	254F	100	280F
21.0% - 142F	2	145F	5	179F	10	200F	20	227F	50	257F	100	284F
23.7% - 146F	2	149F	5	183F	10	204F	20	229F	50	261F	100	287F
26.3% - 150F	2	154F	5	190F	10	209F	20	231F	50	265F	100	290F
29.0% - 155F	2	159F	5	196F	10	214F	20	234F	50	268F	100	293F
31.5% - 158F	2	163F	5	202F	10	218F	20	237F	50	272F	100	296F
36.8% - 161F	2	166F	5	207F	10	222F	20	240F	50	275F	100	299F
47.3% - 175F	2	169F	5	212F	10	227F	20	244F	50	280F	100	303F
59.2% - 186F	2	185F	5	220F	10	235F	20	250F	50	289F	100	310F
75.0% - 197F	2	197F	5	230F	10	243F	20	259F	50	299F	100	321F
	2	209F	5	242F	10	252F	20	269F	50	310F	100	333F

PPM	Dew-Point	PPM	Dew-Point	PPM	Dew-Point	PPM	Dew-Point	PPM	Dew-Point	PPM	Dew-Point	PPM	Dew-Point	PPM	Dew-Point
200	266F	200	317F	500	306F	500	355F	1000	338F	1000	373F	2000	366F	2000	399F
200	234F	200	320F	500	316F	500	358F	1000	348F	1000	376F	2000	372F	2000	402F
200	292F	200	323F	500	324F	500	361F	1000	352F	1000	379F	2000	378F	2000	404F
200	300F	200	326F	500	328F	500	364F	1000	356F	1000	382F	2000	383F	2000	406F
200	306F	200	330F	500	336F	500	369F	1000	364F	1000	386F	2000	388F	2000	406F
200	308F	200	339F	500	342F	500	376F	1000	365F	1000	395F	2000	390F	2000	422F
200	312F	200	348F	500	348F	500	385F	1000	368F	1000	416F	2000	394F	2000	438F
200	314F	200	359F	500	351F	500	397F	1000	370F	1000	429F	2000	396F	2000	457F

Note: Because in normal fuels burning at 25% excess air the mol-percent of water-vapor ranges from a high of 15.3% to a low of 10.5%; because of inaccuracy in SO₃ measurement in which as little as 30% or as much as 90% of the SO₃ actually present in combustion gases may be measured; because of the significant effect of relative humidity on SO₃ production (Ph.D. thesis, Richard Martin, Univ. of Tulsa) and because of the abrupt cooling effect of air-leakage into combustion gases, any weight-percent of sulphur or mol-percent of sulphur in excess of 0.75% in fuel is cause for concern since dew-point of SO₃ immediately produces sulfuric corrosion hazard.

Index